**Peacock's**

# Elementary Microtechnique

# Peacock's Elementary Microtechnique

## Fourth edition

**Revised by Savile Bradbury, M.A., D.Phil.**

University Lecturer in Human Anatomy
and
Fellow of Pembroke College, Oxford

Distributed in the United States by
CRANE, RUSSAK & COMPANY, INC.
52 Vanderbilt Avenue
New York, New York 10017

*First published 1935*
by Edward Arnold (Publishers) Ltd.,
25 Hill Street,
London WIX 8LL

*Second Edition* 1940
*Reprinted* 1943, 1947, 1950, 1955
*Third Edition* 1966
*Fourth Edition* 1973

ISBN: 0 7131 2368 0



Text set in 10/11pt. IBM Univers, printed by photolithography, and bound in Great Britain at The Pitman Press, Bath

# Preface to the third edition

The kindly reception accorded to the first two editions of 'Elementary Microtechnique' appears to have justified my belief that students might be helped in their work if they had an opportunity of learning rather more about the reasons underlying the various microtechnical processes than the average laboratory instruction-sheet could possibly afford space to give.

Because I felt that the third edition should remain in 'a handy, laboratory-bench, form' I have found it difficult to prevent its growing too large and thus defeating its purpose. Since 1940 a number of new techniques, some in their experimental stage when the 2nd edition was published, have been perfected. Where I have felt that these were of use to, and within the compass of, the Sixth Form, Training College and First-year University Students for whom the book was, and is, primarily intended, I have included them. On the other hand, most of the old methods have proved their worth and it has not been an easy matter either to select or to reject. There seems to be no particular merit in including something new, simply because it is new, unless it has some worthwhile advantage over an old and tried method.

I have, of course, included the Feulgen cytological techniques and I have incorporated some notes on embedding by the collodion, freezing, gelatin and resin methods. As some education authorities are now acting a little more generously in the matter of laboratory allowances, I have included some notes on phase-contrast microscopy. At the same time, although I have excluded sundry of the former hints on home-made visual aids, I have retained some of the 'do-it-yourself' recipes.

Acting on the suggestions and profiting by the experience of many readers of the previous editions who were, in the main, of the opinion that 'the motorist should be a better motorist if he knows how his motor-car works', I have retained, in a much revised form, the chapters on 'The Microscope and its Use' and 'Protoplasm and the Cell'.

The chapter on 'Microtechnical Processes—Principles and Techniques' has been revised, enlarged, and, as far as possible, arranged in the order in which a student is likely to make his first acquaintance with the processes.

The chapter on 'Methods for Specific Purposes' has undergone the greatest change. Not only has it been much enlarged but, again in response to several suggestions, it has been re-arranged to include the subject-matter of the former chapters on 'Sources of Material' and 'Preservation of Material'. It is hoped that the re-arrangement will obviate cross-referencing by the reader.

The chapter on 'Formulae and Hints' has also been much enlarged as have the Bibliography and the Index.

In the Preface to the First Edition I wrote: . . . it is clear that I owe debts of gratitude to very many people . . .' During the preparation of the Third Edition my circle of indebtedness has grown wider and space would almost fail me to record all the help I have received.

I cannot adequately thank my friends and former colleagues A. R. Brooks, B.Sc., G. S. Brown, M.A., R. E. Gibbs, B.Sc., J. Goddard, A.T.D., Captain L. Hix, B.Sc., R.N. (Retd.), A. J. Mee, O.B.E., M.A., B.Sc., H.M.I., and J. B. Wiseman, B.Sc. (who has been a tower of strength, a well of information, and an unfailing source of inspiration all the way through the process of revision); my brother, A. C. Peacock, B.A., A.R.I.C., (who has also helped with the proofs); and my children, Mrs. U. H. Fraser, B.Sc., Major J. D. C. Peacock, M.A., R.E.M.E., and N. C. Peacock, M.A. All these have helped me with expert technical advice in their various fields.

Perhaps a one-time Headmaster may be excused for experiencing a sense of pleasure, not unmixed with a little pride, when he sees former pupils making their ways useful in the world. But when those same former pupils, now highly qualified and occupying positions of responsibility, are still more than willing to help him now, as they did in the past, his pleasure and his pride are, quite properly, enhanced. I hope, therefore, that G. M. Barrett, M.D., F.R.S.M., R. W. Bateman, B.Sc., J. E. Cousens, M.A., J. Gay, Ph.D., Professor J. G. Hawkes, Sc.D., Mary Jones, B.Sc., A. F. Posnette, Sc.D., D. Shaw Esq., E. J. Winter, Ph.D., and F. N. Wright, M.A., will accept my thanks for their generous and willing help.

Indeed, to all who have helped I wish to express my gratitude, not only for the help they have so willingly and freely given me, but also for the quite overwhelming kindliness with which my requests have been received. This is something that has to be experienced to be believed and I find it impossible to express the sense of joy – for that is the only word that can adequately convey my meaning – that their co-operation or, as one correspondent put it, 'that free interchange between the science teaching fraternity', has given me. My thanks are none the less sincere by being limited to a footnote acknowledgment on the appropriate page, and I hope none has been overlooked.

With added emphasis I quote once more from the Preface to the First Edition: 'No expression of gratitude would be complete without including my publishers, who have shown so much patience and helpfulness in dealing with my suggestions and corrections . . . Finally, I wish to thank my wife for her unfailing help, encouragement and patience throughout', and, may I add, her tolerance and understanding.

H.A.P.

Beavan's Hill,
August 1965

# Preface to the fourth edition

In the preparation of this new edition I have tried as far as possible to maintain the character of the book as laid down by its author. Experience has shown that a reference book intended for use in the laboratory benefits from the inclusion of some of the basic principles which lie behind the practical methods. Some new material has been added, particularly in Chapter 3 in the light of recent advances in our knowledge of cell structure. In order to maintain the book at a reasonable length some minor deletions have been made in Chapter 7. In an effort to facilitate the use of this book in the laboratory, the index has been divided into two sections. The first lists organisms, techniques and the names of substances of interest in microtechnique; the second part is an index of chemicals, dyes and their chief synonyms.

In this revision I have received help from many sources, too numerous to mention by name; I would like however to thank Dr. J. R. Baker, F.R.S., Emeritus Reader in Cytology in the University of Oxford. Our present day micro-techniques owe much to his work, and I am especially grateful to him for his help and advice in recent years.

Microtechnique must benefit greatly from the rapid dissemination of the experience of those who practise in this field; I hope that this new edition of one of the established manuals in this field may be of some further service in this. Any suggestions for improvement and the pointing out of errors and omissions would be welcomed by the publishers and myself.

*Oxford, 1972* S.B.

# Contents

# Abbreviations and symbols, etc.

| | |
|---|---|
| **1, 2,** etc. | successive stages of the same process |
| (i), (ii), etc. | alternative methods, or methods for different processes |
| (*a*), (*b*), etc. | alternative methods, or methods for different processes |
| alc. | alcohol (-ic solution) |
| approx. | approximate(ly) |
| aq. | aqueous solution (aq. dest. = distilled water) |
| A.R. | Analytical (quality) Reagent |
| B.P. | British Pharmacopeia |
| b.p. | boiling point |
| °C | degree(s) Celsius* |
| cf. | compare |
| C.I. | Colour Index (The abbreviation precedes the preferred designation and usage-number allocated to dyes in Part I of the 1956 Colour Index of the Society of Dyers and Colourists.) |
| C.I.No. | Colour Index Number (The abbreviation precedes the five-figure constitution-number allocated to dyes in Part II of the 1956 Colour Index of the Society of Dyers and Colourists.) |
| cm | centimetre(s) |
| conc. | concentrated |
| d | day(s) |
| *d* | diameter |
| dil. | dilute |
| dM | decimolar concentration |
| esp. | especially |
| f(f). | and following page(s) |
| g | gramme(s) |
| h | hour(s) |
| kg | kilogramme(s) |
| l | litre(s) |
| M | molar concentration |
| m | metre(s); and milli (x $10^{-3}$) |
| μm | micrometre† (or micron†) (= 0.001 mm) |
| min | minute(s) (time) |
| ml | millilitre(s) |
| mm | millimetre(s) |
| mμm | milli-micrometre(s) |
| m.p. | melting point |
| N | normal concentration |
| N.A. | numerical aperture of a lens |
| O.P. | over proof |
| p(p). | page(s) |
| pH | hydrogen ion exponent |
| s | second(s) (of time) |
| satd. | saturated solution |
| satis. | sufficient to make a saturated solution |
| S/C | source(s) and/or, method(s) of culture, of material |
| soln. | solution |
| sp. gr. | specific gravity |
| w.s. | water-soluble |
| w/v | weight per volume |
| Y | yellowish |
| → | result of treatment |

* Formerly called 'centigrade', which term was abandoned by the Conférence Générale des Poids et Mesures in 1948.
† The abbreviation 'μm' and the name 'micrometre' are to be preferred to the abbreviation 'μ' and the name 'micron'.

# 1 How to use the book

A good craftsman knows how his tools work; how best to use them; the properties of the materials with and in which he is working; and how to get the best out of those materials in so far as he is able.

The microtechnician's chief tool is the microscope. The materials in which he is working are animal and vegetable tissues. The materials he uses are various chemical reagents and stains.

Therefore:

1 Read Chapter 2 to familiarize yourself with the mechanism, manipulation and care of the microscope. A good many students, unless instructed otherwise, fail to get the best out of their instrument simply because they do not know how to do so.

2 Read Chapter 3 concerning the nature of protoplasm and the cell. Just as the budding wood-worker can ruin a piece of wood by trying to plane it against the grain, simply because he is not aware that there is such a thing as 'grain', so the budding microtechnician can ruin his preparations if he knows nothing of the material in which he is working.

3 Read those parts of Chapter 4 that deal with the *principles* underlying the various microtechnical processes you will be using. For the sake of convenience the processes have been arranged, as far as possible, in the order in which they will be used in one of the very common methods with which you will later become familiar.
Leave the reading of those parts of Chapter 4 that deal with the various *techniques* until you come to the time when you need to use any particular one. In course of time most of the techniques will become, as it were, 'second nature', but the underlying principles must never be forgotten. In other words, remember not only *what* you are doing at any given time, but also *why* you are doing it.

4 Work through the standard methods given in Chapter 5 systematically. Do not pass on to a new method until you have thoroughly mastered the old and can produce a microscopical preparation worthy of you. Before starting any process, refresh your memory both about the underlying principles and about the actual technique(s) by rereading the relevant section(s) of Chapter 4. Above all, have patience and perseverance, and take the greatest care in carrying out the various processes. Careless work brings its own rewards. They will not be to your liking.

5 Before using any particular stain, familiarize yourself with its components, find out exactly what the stain is intended for, and what results you may expect. You will find details about stains in Chapter 7, which is arranged in alphabetical order. Different components in a stain may necessitate a variation in technique.
The nomenclature of stains is somewhat confused. The preamble to Chapter 7 explains the nomenclature that has been used in this book.

6 If you are in doubt about the suitability of any of the routine methods given in Chapter 5 for the particular tissue you are going to use, refer to Chapter 6 – 'Methods for Specific Material'. In it you will find variations of the routine methods.
If still in doubt, use your common-sense. You will probably find that a routine method will do quite well, with adjustments to suit your particular material or circumstances. And you can console yourself with the knowledge that much microtechnical work is done by rule-of-thumb. If you have taken the trouble to use the book in the way suggested you will have sufficient confidence to go forward.
Where appropriate, there are also given, under the various alphabetically-arranged headings in Chapter 6, sources and/or methods of culture of the given material and methods for its preservation.

7 Provided you work accurately, it is usually cheaper to make up your own reagents if you are using any large quantity. Chapter 7, which is arranged alphabetically, includes various formulae, together with some suggestions and hints that may help you from time to time.

8 As time goes on and you become more interested in the subject, you will find it profitable to refer to the books listed in the Bibliography.

9. Throughout this book the *abbreviations* shown on p. ix have been used.

# 2

# The compound optical microscope and its use

## 2.1 COMPONENT PARTS OF THE MICROSCOPE

The component parts of the microscope are shown in Fig. 2.1.

The main body of the instrument is known as the *stand* which consists of a *base* or *foot*, to which is attached a *limb*. Generally, the limb is made inclinable relative to the foot by means of a *hinge-joint* for ease of manipulation.

Some instruments have a source of illumination, with or without a transformer for voltage control, built into the base.

Unless a built-in lamp is provided, the limb carries at its lower end a *mirror* for reflecting light from the external light-source towards the object. The mirror is mounted in a gymbal so that the position of the mirror may be adjusted in accordance with the light-source. The mirror usually has two surfaces, one *plane*, the other *concave*.

Above the mirror (or the built-in light-source) is the *condenser-housing* designed to carry a (*sub-stage*) *condenser* (an integral system of lenses) for concentrating the light reflected by the mirror. The condenser-housing may be moved up and down by means of a rack-and-pinion adjustment. In some instruments, but not in all, by means of another adjustment it may also be centred, i.e. so adjusted as to ensure that its optical axis lies along the optical axes of the eye-piece and the objective (see below) which, together, form the optical axis of the microscope.

At its lower end, immediately below the condenser, the condenser-housing is fitted with a (*sub-stage*) *iris-diaphragm* for varying the width of the beam of light entering the condenser and reaching the object.

The condenser-housing may also be fitted with a movable *ring* to hold *filters* — discs of coloured glass. Filters are of use in reducing eye strain (e.g. a blue filter will reduce the glare from white light) and in improving contrast in stained objects (e.g. a green filter will improve the contrast in an object stained red).

The condenser-housing ring may also be used to carry *patch-stops* — discs of metal used in dark-ground illumination (see para. 2.3, p. 8) and para. 2.5, p. 16).

Above the condenser-housing is the *stage* which has, at its centre, a circular aperture for the passage of light. The upper lens of the condenser protrudes into the base of this aperture. If, by means of rack-and-pinion mechanisms, the stage can be moved from side to side, and/or from back to front, it is described as a *mechanical stage*. This is a useful refinement for making fine adjustments in the position of an object.

Mechanical stages may be fitted with vernier scales for relocating the position of an object by noting the vernier readings; to relocate the object, the slide is replaced on the stage and verniers set to the values noted previously.

Inserted in holes in the stage are *stage-clips* for clamping in position the glass slide carrying the object to be examined.

For work involving the maintenance of the object at a temperature higher than room-temperature an electrically-heated *warm-stage* may be fitted.

At its upper end the limb carries a *body-tube* within which there may be a *draw-tube*. These tubes are finished with matt-black on the inside to prevent random reflections. The draw-tube may have a scale of millimetres engraved on it; alternatively, a ring may be engraved around the tube at the correct tube length (usually 160 mm, see p. 8 ).

The *ocular* or *eye-piece* slides into the upper end of the body-tube, or into the draw-tube if this be fitted. The ocular is a fitting carrying a lens or, more usually, two lenses, namely, the *eye-lens* nearer the eye, and the *field-lens* nearer the object. Within the ocular, at the focal plane of the eye lens, is fixed the metal annulus or *field-diaphragm*. [Fig. 2.2b].

It must be explained here that, because of the physical properties of the glass used in their construction and because of their own characteristics, simple lenses may have certain faults. For example, they may suffer from *chromatic aberration* caused by light of different wave-lengths (and hence of different colours) being focused at different points along the axis of the lens.

*Achromatic lenses* have this fault corrected in so far as concerns red and green light. Such lenses also have another fault, namely, *spherical aberration* which is corrected, only in so far as green light is concerned. Spherical aberration results from rays of light which pass through areas near the edges of the lens being focused at points nearer the lens than those rays which pass through the centre of the lens.

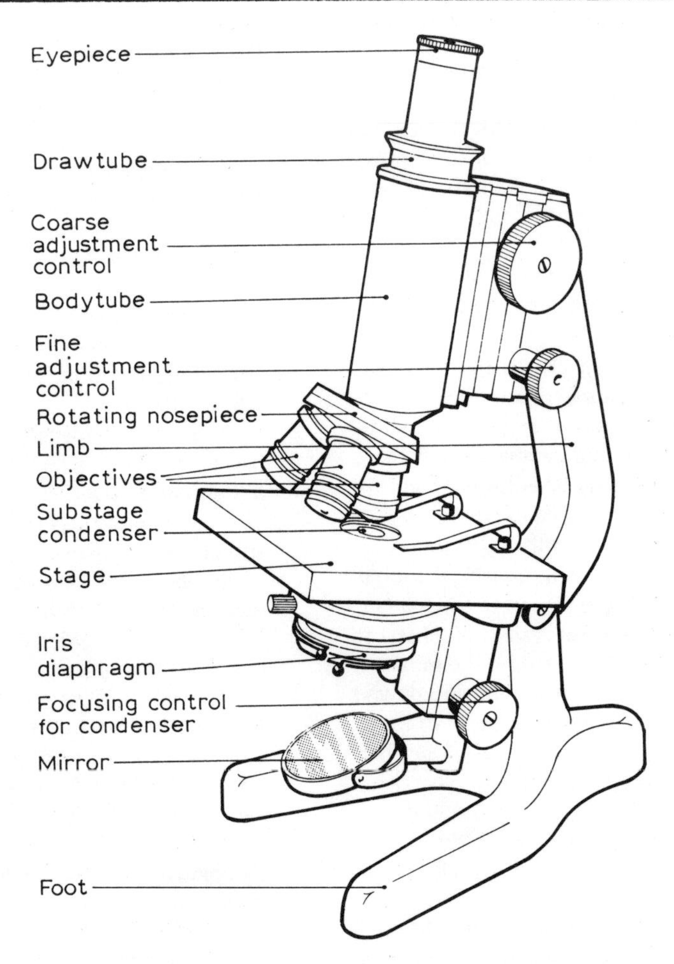


Fig. 2.1 The compound optical microscope.

Eye-pieces in common use, however, are not usually corrected optically. This is because the eye-piece is so constructed that the relative positions of the eye-lens and the field-lens result in a tendency for the chromatic aberration of one lens to cancel out that of the other.

*Compensating eye-pieces* are eye-pieces optically corrected for use in conjunction with apochromatic and fluorite objectives (see below). Such eye-pieces may sometimes be recognized by the mark 'COMP' on the metal ring into which the eye-lens is fitted. This particular combination of eye-piece and objective is not likely to come within the scope of elementary work.

A *pointer eye-piece* contains an adjustable pointer by means of which the exact position of an object can be demonstrated by teacher to pupil and vice-versa.

Eye-pieces are designated by their magnifying power which is stamped on the ring of metal holding the eye-lens.

At the lower end of the body-tube is the *nose-piece* into which is screwed a fitting which carries the *achromatic objective.*

The *objective* [Fig. 2.2a p. 5] is an integral system of lenses forming a compound lens of very short focal length and giving a real, enlarged image of the object. Objectives may be of the *'dry'* type, or of the *'immersion'* type.

When a 'dry' objective is in use there is an air-space between the lower lens of the objective and the surface of the *cover-glass* or *cover-slip*, a disc or rectangle of very thin glass which protects the object on the slide. Light passing from the object through the cover-slip undergoes refraction on passing through the air in this space before it reaches the objective. As a result, the *resolving power* of the objective, particularly if it is of high power, is impaired. To overcome this difficulty immersion objectives are used.

Very high power objectives are designed to be used with a layer of cedar-wood or other oil (*oil-immersion* type), or of a water (*water-immersion* type) placed between the bottom of the objective

Fig. 2.2 (a) Flatfield objectives of varying initial magnifications. The external appearance of each lens in shown above whilst below it is sectioned to show the optical elements. Note the complexity of construction of the 100 X planapochromatic oil immersion lens. (E. Leitz (Instruments) Ltd.)

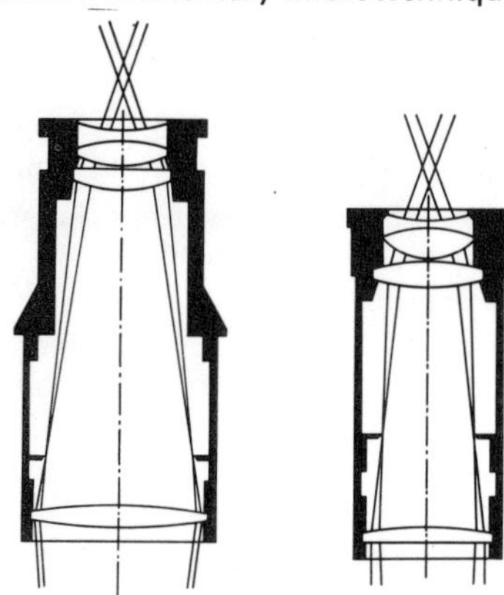

Fig. 2.2 (b) Sectional diagrams showing ray paths through two types of modern eye-piece. (E. Leitz (Instruments) Ltd.)

and the top of the cover-slip. The immersion media have refractive indices approximating to that of glass. As a result, the light from the object does not suffer refraction as it passes from cover-slip to objective and the image is brighter and suffers less from optical aberrations. Oil-immersion objectives are marked 'OIL', or 'OEL', or 'H.I.' (*homogeneous immersion*). Water-immersion objectives are marked 'W.I.', or 'Was'. Immersion objectives should never be used 'dry'.

*Apochromatic objectives* are both more highly corrected and considerably more expensive than achromatic objectives. They correct chromatic aberration not only for red and green light but also for blue light. They also correct spherical aberration for two colours. Such objectives are marked 'Apo'.

*Fluorite* or *semi-apochromatic objectives* contain some optical components made of the mineral fluorite and their corrections are intermediate between those of achromats and apochromats.

A troublesome defect of many high power objectives is that there is a considerable curvature of the field; this is particularly noticeable when the objective is in use for photomicrography. For this application *flat-field objectives* are now much used.

Objectives were formerly and, indeed, are often still designated by their focal length. This may be expressed either in British or in metric units, e.g. $\frac{2}{3}$ in., $\frac{1}{6}$ in., etc., equivalent, respectively, to 16 mm, 4 mm, etc. The modern practice, however, is to designate objectives by their *primary magnification*, e.g. 'x 10' (see para. 2.4, p. 10). Whichever designation is used it will be found engraved upon the objective mount, as also will be the numerical aperture (N.A.) (see p. 8).

Objectives with focal lengths about 16 mm or more are sometimes referred to as *low-power* (LP), while those with focal lengths of 4 mm or less are sometimes referred to as *high-power* (HP).

To enable different objectives to be used with the minimum of trouble the nose-piece may be designed to carry more than one objective, and to rotate. The *rotating nose-piece*, or *turret*, may be *double, triple*, or *quadruple* according to whether it carries, respectively, two, three, or four different objectives. Provided the different objectives are parfocal,* once an object has been focused with one objective it will be found to be approximately in focus when other objectives are revolved into position.

## 2.2 THE COMPOUND MICROSCOPE AS AN OPTICAL INSTRUMENT

We can see, and distinguish between, objects around us because they reflect light of varying intensity and colour. If a piece of glass is immersed in a mixture of chloral hydrate and glycerol the glass is indistinguishable from the liquid. This is because the glass and the liquid have the *same* refractive index and hence we receive light of the *same* intensity and colour from both. Thus, in an unstained or uncoloured tissue we can distinguish different parts only if they have *different* refractive indices resulting in our receiving light of *different* intensity from the different parts.

When two rays of light from the same source pass through media of different refractive indices, the ray which passes through the medium of higher refractive index is retarded relative to that which passes through the medium of lower refractive index. Assuming that no absorption of light takes place, the two rays, on emerging from the two media, although still of the same amplitude (intensity) will be 'out-of-step' (out-of-phase) and thus, when combined, will interfere with each other. It is this *interference* which produces the microscopical image. All optical microscopes depend for their operation on interference effects.

* i.e., with the lengths of the objective barrels so arranged that, in relation to each other, the objective lenses are automatically at the correct position from the object.

To enable two separate objects to be resolved (i.e. to enable two separate images to be seen in the microscope) the distance between the two objects must not be less than about half the wave-length of the light used. If the distance is less than this, the two images will merge. This minimum distance is about one-third of a micrometre (approx. 0.3 μm) and is called the *resolving power* of the microscope. (See also 'Numerical Aperture', p. 8.)

It would therefore seem that the smallest object that can be seen with a compound optical microscope is about 0.3 μm in size and that no amount of magnification can possibly reveal any more detail nor in any way assist *resolution*, i.e. the ability to produce two separate images and allow discrimination between two separate objects.

In point of fact, the minimum size of object that can be seen with the average 'student's microscope' (with magnification x400) is about 0.5 μm; with a good-quality microscope it is about 0.3 μm; and with a 'research type' microscope (with 2 mm oil-immersion lens and magnification x 1200) it is about 0.2 μm.

**The Functions of the Essential Optical Elements of the Compound Microscope***

A simple 'magnifying glass' has only a limited power of magnification. The maximum magnification such a lens will give is about x20.

The compound microscope enables much more resolution and magnification to be obtained. This it does by the use of two lenses (or combinations of lenses) known, respectively, as the objective and the ocular, arranged as shown in Fig. 2.3 (p. 8).

The objective (O) is a plano-convex lens combination of very short focal length ($f_1$).

The object under examination (AB) is placed just outside the focal plane ($F_1$) of the objective which produces a 'real', inverted, magnified image (B′A′) of the object, just within the focal plane ($F_2$) of the ocular (E).

The ocular is a bi-convex lens combination of focal length ($f_2$) greater than that of the objective.

The ocular acts as an ordinary 'magnifying glass' and produces a virtual, inverted, and further enlarged image (B″A″) of the object.

As the eye cannot satisfactorily focus on to any object nearer than about 25.5 cm, it focuses on to the final, much enlarged, image (B″A″) at the optimum distance for distinct vision (known as the 'near point'), or at a point still farther from the eye.

The size of the image (B′A′) in relation to that of the object (AB) is in direct proportion to the relative distances between the object and the objective, and between the objective and the image (B′A′).

* I am indebted to Captain L. Hix, B.Sc., R.N. (Retd.) for suggestions in the preparation of these notes and of Fig. 2.3.

## 2.3 THE EFFICIENT USE OF A MICROSCOPE

In addition to the proper functioning of its various parts, the efficient use of a microscope depends on a number of factors.

### The Illumination of the Object

Unless the object under examination be properly illuminated the objective cannot do its work effectively. Illumination may be accomplished in several ways.

*Illumination by transmitted light*

Transmitted light is used when the rays of light are directed through the transparent parts of the object by a suitable mirror.

The purpose of a *plane mirror* (P) (Fig. 2.5) is to reflect light from any given source (S) towards the object (AB).

The purpose of a *concave mirror* (C) (Fig. 2.4) is to *concentrate* the reflected light on the object. This is occasionally used when the microscope is not fitted with a sub-stage condenser and the objective is of very low power.

The *sub-stage condenser* (N) (Fig. 2.5), used in conjunction with the *plane* mirror (P), is also used for concentrating the light.

The use of the *sub-stage iris diaphragm* (D), (Fig. 2.5) which governs the aperture of the cone of illuminating light rays, is sometimes an aid to resolution, i.e. structure differentiation when the object is transparent. It is also helpful in matching the aperture of the illuminating system to the numerical aperture of the particular objective in use, so permitting the latter to give its optimal image quality.

*Illumination by reflected light*

Reflected light is used when the light is directed and, if desired, concentrated by a plano-convex lens, from above on to the object which is placed on a dark or light ground according to its nature. This is a useful method for opaque objects (Fig. 2.6).

*Dark-ground (oblique) illumination*

Dark-ground illumination is used when no direct light enters the microscope objective and the object is made visible by the diffraction of light rays around it, just as the particles of dust are seen in a ray of sunlight in a darkened room. The method is useful for the examination of Protozoa, diatoms and bacteria. Some suggestions for its use are given on p. 16.

**The Numerical Aperture of the Objective**

The *numerical aperture* (N.A.) of the objective is a most important optical concept because on it depends the ability of the objective to *resolve* or differentiate structure. *The higher the N.A., the greater the resolution.*

For general work, sufficient resolution will be obtained from a 4 mm ($\frac{1}{6}$ in.) objective having N.A. 0.70. The N.A. will usually be found stamped on the objective mount either with or without the letters 'N.A.'.

The N.A. is found by multiplying the refractive index of the medium between the objective and the object by the sine of half the angular aperture of the objective. The *angular aperture* of a lens is the maximum angle of the cone of light from the object accepted by the lens.

**Tube-length**

Tube-length is the distance between the upper end of the objective and the upper end of the eye-piece.

An old microscope can almost be dated by the fact that its tube-length will be 25.4 cm – the optimum distance for distinct vision. It has long since been recognized, however, that 25.4 cm is in no way a critical distance in microscopic work and

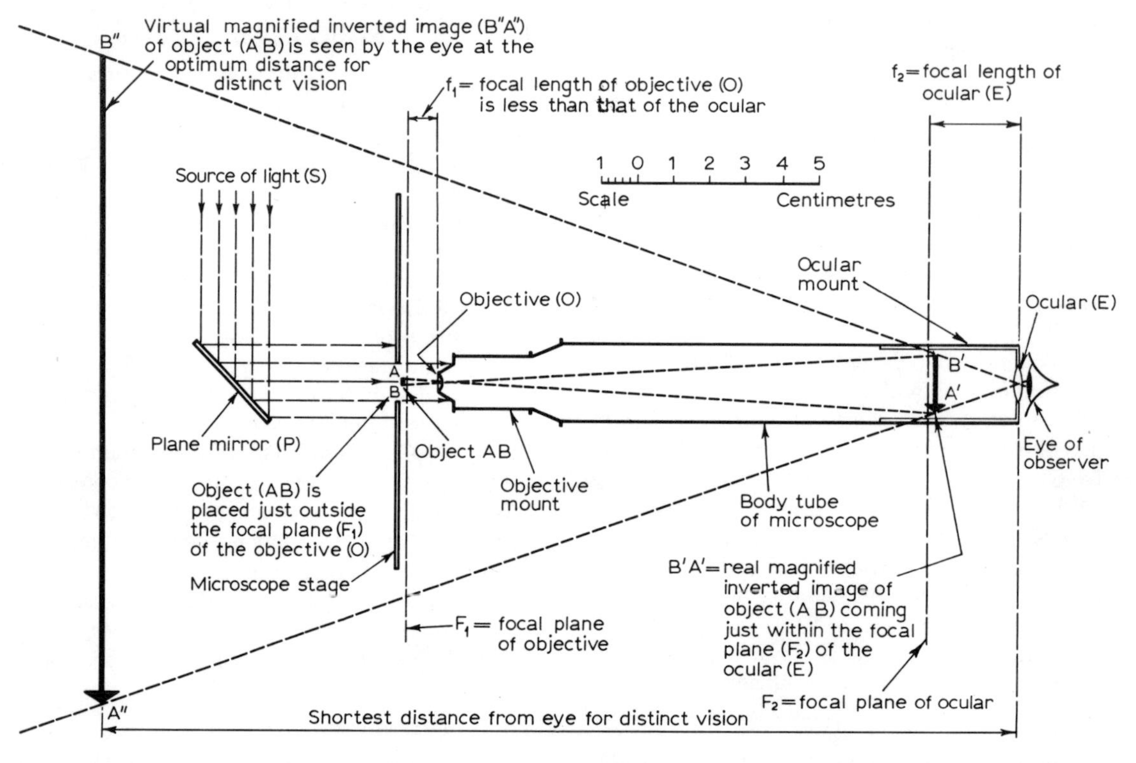


Fig. 2.3 Diagrammatic arrangement of microscope objective and ocular to illustrate positions of real and virtual images of the object. (For explanation, see text p. 7.)

modern instruments are made with their tube-lengths standardized at 160 mm – a distance that ensures comfortable operation. Better-class instruments have an engraved adjustable draw-tube so

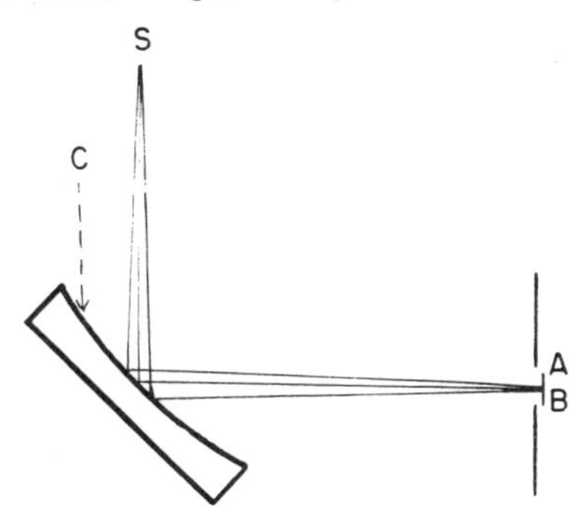


Fig. 2.4* Use of concave mirror.

that the microscope may be used, for example, with Leitz objectives which are corrected for a tube-length of 170 mm. Generally speaking, the objectives likely to be used by students are those corrected for use with a tube-length of 160 mm, though this figure will vary with the thickness of the cover-slip in use. Remember that *an error in tube length* (caused, for example, by failure to

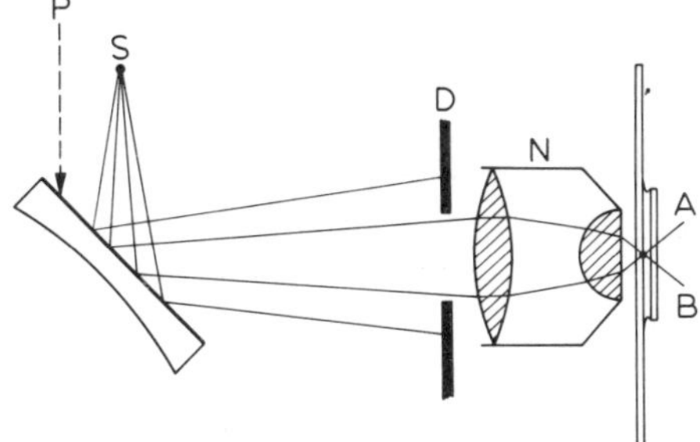


Fig. 2.5* Use of plane mirror and substage condenser.

adjust the draw tube or to house an eye-piece correctly) *results in decreased definition* (see below).

The tube-length will usually be found engraved upon the objective.

**Working Distance**

Working distance is the distance between the object and the lower end of the objective. It is desirable that the objective should have as long a working distance as possible. Objectives of 4 mm are now obtainable with a working distance of 1.0 mm.

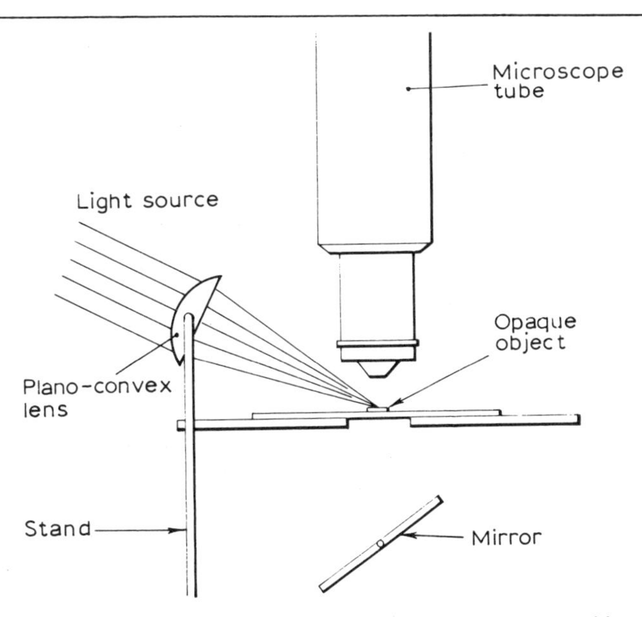


Fig. 2.6 Use of a plano-convex lens to focus light onto an opaque object.

* In Figs. 2.4, 2.5, and 2.8 the mirror and object are shown in the same relative positions as they occupy in Fig. 2.3. It will be understood that in actual practice the beam of light from the mirror will be projected *upwards* to the object lying above, unless the microscope has been laid horizontally for micro-projection (para. 2.7).

### Cover-slip Thickness

A cover-slip of correct thickness should be used, but without the maker's catalogue for guidance this dimension may not be known. In general, a cover-slip of thickness 0.17 mm or 0.18 mm will be correct. If the cover-slip is thicker than 0.18 mm, decrease the tube-length; if thinner than 0.18 mm, increase the tube-length.

Remember that *increase of the thickness of the layer of mountant above the object is equivalent to increase of cover-slip thickness.*

## 2.4 MAGNIFICATION

When an object is viewed through a microscope its size is apparently increased; the degree of magnification is expressed in *diameters.*

### Formula for finding Magnification

*Magnification by the objective*

This is known as the *primary magnification*. It is equal to

$$\frac{l}{f}'$$

where $l$ = tube-length, i.e. the distance between the upper end of the objective and the upper end of the eye-piece; and $f$ = the focal length of the objective, as marked on it.

*Total magnification by objective and eye-piece*

Total magnification is found by multiplying the primary magnification of the objective by the magnification of the eye-piece.

$$\textit{Total magnification} = \frac{l}{f} \times e,$$

where $e$ = the magnification of the eye-piece; $f$ = the focal length of the objective; $l$ = the tube-length of the microscope.

*Magnifications frequently used in elementary work:*

| | |
|---|---|
| For dissection . . . . . . . | x20 |
| " low power work . . . | x60 to x80 |
| " high power work . . . | x240 to x320 |

### Comparison of Size of Image with Actual Size of Object

For the sake of comparison the degree of magnification of an object may be considered relative to the apparent size of a similar object held 25 cm from the eye, i.e. at the *'near-point'*, which is the least possible distance compatible with distinct vision.

For example, an object of diameter 0.1 mm viewed through a microscope fitted with a x6 eye-piece and a 4 mm objective (a combination giving a total magnification of 240 diameters) will appear as large as a similar object of diameter 24.0 mm (i.e. 0.1 mm x 240) seen at a distance of 25 cm from the eye.

### Microscopic Measurement

*Units of microscopic measurement*

There are two units of measurement used in microscopy, viz. the *micrometre* (formerly called the 'micron') and the *nanometre.**

The *micrometre* ($\mu$m) = $10^{-6}$ m = 1/1000 mm = 0.001 mm.

This unit is used when working with the optical microscope.

The *nanometre* (nm) = $10^{-9}$ m = 1/1 000 000 mm = 0.000 001 mm.

This unit is only used when working with the electron microscope and is outside the scope of this book.

### Method of Measurement of the Object

Measurement of an object by means of a microscope involves the use of a *stage micrometer* and an *eye-piece micrometer* of which there are various types for various purposes. The following description of the simplest forms will serve to illustrate the principles underlying their use.

The *stage micrometer* consists of a glass slide of the usual dimensions (7.5 cm x 2.5 cm) with a linear millimetre scale engraved upon it. The scale has one hundred 0.01 mm (10 $\mu$m) divisions, every ten divisions being marked by extended lines. The engraved portion is protected by a cover slip.

* The Ångstrom Unit (Å) is still much used by electron microscopists; 1 Å = $\frac{1}{10\,000\,000}$ mm or 0.0001 $\mu$m.

When in use the slide is held in position on the microscope stage in the usual way and used to calibrate the value of the divisions of the eye-piece scale.

The *eye-piece micrometer* or *eye-piece scale* consists of a glass disc usually 21 mm in diameter. On it is engraved a linear scale with one hundred equal divisions, every tenth division being numbered and indicated by a longer line. This scale may be 1 cm long, or less. In any case the size of the divisions is arbitrary. The engraved portion is protected by another glass disc. In use the eye-piece scale or *graticule* rests on the field-stop (field-diaphragm) of the eye-piece.

*Calibration of the eye-piece scale or graticule*

The eye-piece graticule must be calibrated at a given tube-length for each combination of ocular and objective. If any one factor is changed the graticule must be re-calibrated.

To calibrate the eye-piece graticule the stage-micrometer is secured on the stage and brought into focus. It is then moved about until the initial division mark on it coincides with the initial division mark on the eye-piece graticule. A count is taken along both scales until a point is reached where a division mark on the stage-micrometer scale coincides with a division mark on the eye-piece graticule. Then, as each division on the stage-micrometer scale = 10 $\mu$m,

Value in micrometres of *one* division on graticule scale

$$= \frac{\text{Number of divisions on stage-micrometer scale} \times 10}{\text{Number of divisions on eye-piece graticule}}$$

Bearing in mind the limits of the resolving power of the light microscope, it is almost meaningless to express microscopic measurements in terms of anything less than an integer of micrometres. Even if the best possible refinements are used, measurements should not be expressed in fractions smaller than 0.5 $\mu$m.

A card showing the calibration factors for the eye-piece graticule for each objective in use with any particular instrument should be kept secure in each microscope case. Objectives intended for use with one instrument should not be interchanged with those intended for use with another.

**Table of approximate total magnifications***

| Objective | | Eye-piece | | | | | | |
|---|---|---|---|---|---|---|---|---|
| Focal Length $= f$ | Primary Magnification $= \frac{l}{f}$ | Magnification = e (diameters) | | | | | | |
| | | x4 | x5 | **x6** | **x8** | x10 | x12 | x15 |
| 50 mm or 2″ | x3.2 | 13 | 16 | 19 | 26 | 32 | 38 | 48 |
| 25 mm or 1″ | x6.4 | 26 | 32 | 38 | 51 | 64 | 76 | 96 |
| **16 mm or $\frac{2}{3}$″** | x10 | 40 | 50 | **60** | **80** | 100 | 120 | 150 |
| 8 mm or $\frac{1}{3}$″ | x20 | 80 | 100 | 120 | 160 | 200 | 240 | 300 |
| 6 mm or $\frac{1}{4}$″ | x26.6 | 106 | 133 | 160 | 213 | 266 | 319 | 399 |
| **4 mm or $\frac{1}{6}$″** | x40 | 160 | 200 | **240** | **320** | 400 | 480 | 600 |
| 3 mm or $\frac{1}{8}$″ | x53.5 | 212 | 265 | 318 | 424 | 530 | 636 | 795 |
| 2 mm or $\frac{1}{12}$″ | x80 | 320 | 400 | 480 | 640 | 800 | 960 | 1 200 |
| Tube-length $= l$ = 160 mm (assumed) | | Approximate total magnification in Diameters $= \frac{l}{f} \times e$ | | | | | | |

Heavy type indicates lens combinations frequently used in elementary work

* Adapted from Martin and Johnson's *Practical Microscopy*, by permission of the publishers, Messrs. Blackie, London.

*Micrometer eye-piece*

It will be remembered that the field-stop is fixed at the point where the foci of the eye-lens and the field-lens coincide. As the eye-piece graticule rests on the field-stop it may be out of focus when viewed through the eye-lens. To overcome this difficulty, special *micrometer eye-pieces* are made in which the eye-lens is easily adjustable to bring the eye-piece scale into focus.

*Filar micrometer eye-piece*

The filar micrometer eye-piece has a hair mounted in an adjustable housing so that the hair can be moved from one side to the other across the field of view. The distance moved by the hair is shown on a scale calibrated in relation to the number of revolutions of the adjusting screw.

More elaborate types of micrometer eye-piece are available, some involving an optical doubling of the image of the object. Manipulation of the calibrated screw allows the two images to be first superimposed and then just separated so that they appear to touch each other; this allows a direct reading of the diameter of the object to be obtained. For details of this type of eye-piece a reference work on microscopy should be consulted.

*Mechanical stage*

If the object to be measured overlaps the ends of the eye-piece scale, it must obviously be moved if its whole length has to be measured. This is easily done by means of the mechanical stage which can be moved up and down and from side to side. The distance the object is moved is measured on vernier scales fitted alongside the stage.

When the object is moved by the mechanical stage, it is necessary to have some point of reference from which measurements can be made. This is best provided by cross-hairs fitted in the ocular or the objective.

It will be appreciated that the mechanical stage is also useful for making fine adjustments in, or relocating, the position of objects and for systematically searching a preparation e.g. a stained blood film.

## 2.5 THE MICROSCOPE IN USE

### Care of the Microscope

*Repairs*

It is good practice never to tamper with a microscope or its accessories. If, for example, the stage or the inclinable limb show any signs of wobble; if the mirror gymbal is slack – allowing the mirror to move out of position; if the mirror will not centre properly; if the objective or the condenser cannot be properly aligned; if there is any 'sloppiness' in the coarse adjustment; if, on leaving an object correctly focused under high power for a few minutes, it is found that the object has slipped out of focus – showing that the fine adjustment is 'sloppy'; remember always that these errors are best corrected by the expert in such work – the scientific instrument maker. The 'handy amateur' may easily do damage more costly to repair than the original defect.

*Storage*

When not in regular use the microscope should be kept in the case provided for it, with the lid properly shut to keep out dust. The case should be kept in a fume-free atmosphere. If an objective is kept in the working position when the microscope is stored, an eye-piece should also be kept in position to prevent dust settling on the back lens of the objective. If the back lens does pick up dust, remove it with a camel-hair brush.

If the microscope is in use but has to be left out of its case for some time it should be covered with a cover of ample size and suitable shape made from polythene sheet. Failing a special cover, a polythene bag of the type used for household purposes is a useful make-shift.

*Cleaning*

It is impossible to see well with dirty, dusty, or scratched lenses, but these must never be cleaned with a duster or handkerchief as scratched lenses will certainly result. Instead, use a lens-tissue, applied with a rotary motion, after first breathing on the lens. Lens-tissues are obtainable from dealers in photographic materials and there should be a small stock, kept in a dust-free box, allocated to each microscope case. If the dirt is difficult to remove, or the lens has acquired a greasy deposit, or if (through what can only be described as sheer carelessness) some Canada balsam has found its way on to the lens, wipe it off very gently with a lens-tissue bearing *a trace only* of benzene or xylene. *Excess benzene or xylene will dissolve the lens cement.* Polish off immediately, but gently, with a dry lens-tissue. A lens-tissue should also be used for wiping immersion fluid from immersion objectives. Never keep a once-used lens-tissue, however clean it looks, 'for use next time', and *never* use alcohol for cleaning lenses. It softens the cement used in their manufacture.

Make sure that the stage is kept clean, but do *not* use the lens-tissue for this purpose. Instead, use a piece of clean, *lint-free* material such as linen.

### Choice of Lens Combinations

The higher the magnification of the lens and the larger its numerical aperture, the more curved is the field. The lower the magnification, the flatter is the field.

As a guide to the beginner, the following combinations* of objectives and eye-pieces may be taken as suitable for the purposes indicated. Those in brackets are desirable additions. *See page 11 for the magnifications obtained from various combinations.*

It is a common failing to examine preparations under too high a power; much more information can be gained about the general arrangement and relationships of the parts of the specimen if a very *low* power is used. Only then, if more detailed study is required, is it necessary to change to the higher powers of the instrument.

### Adjustments to the Microscope

Apart from major adjustments in the nature of repairs – which should always be left to an expert – there are various minor adjustments which must be made if the best results are to be obtained. A routine sequence of adjustments is suggested on pages 15 and 16.

### Adjustment of Illumination

However good the mechanical and optical features of a microscope may be, successful results can be obtained only if illumination of the object is correctly adjusted; the very first rule to remember is: use the *concave* side of the mirror *without* the condenser; use the *plane* side of the mirror *with* the condenser.

#### *Adjustment of transmitted light*

Make sure that the sub-stage iris diaphragm, if fitted, is fully open. Remove the eye-piece. Insert a low-power objective. Adjust the mirror so that the

| Botany, Zoology, and General Biology | Objective | Eye-piece |
|---|---|---|
| Wing of fly; scale of fish; sting of bee; fruits of dandelion, clematis, and birch | 50 mm | x6 [x8] |
| Rotifera | 50 mm | [x6], x8, [x10] |
| Circulation in tadpole tail; water flea; scales of small fish | 25 mm [16 mm] | x6 |
| Foraminifera | 50 mm, 25 mm | [x6], x8, [x10] |
| Chaetae of earthworm; barbules of feather; hairs on fruits of dandelion, etc. | 4 mm | x8 |
| Control of staining | 16 mm, 4 mm | x6 |
| Epidermis of leaf; pollen grains; blood corpuscles; unicellular animals from hay infusions | 4 mm | x8, x10 |
| Animal and plant histology | [25 mm] 16 mm, 4 mm | [x6], x8, x10 |
| Spermatozoa of earthworm; blood corpuscles; yeast; *Pleurococcus*; bacteria (appear as specks) | 2 mm | x10 |
| Bacteriology; haematology; pathology; serology | 16 mm, 4 mm, 2 mm | [x6], x8, x10 |

*Note:* The low-power (50 mm to 16 mm) and the medium-power (4 mm) objectives are, with occasional exceptions, of the 'dry' type, i.e. there is a film of air between top of cover-slip and bottom of objective.

* In part after Shann, *First Lessons in Practical Biology*, Bell, London.

back-lens of the objective is *fully and evenly filled with light*. Replace the eye-piece. *Regard this procedure as routine, however expert you may feel you are.* Some microscopes are fitted with built-in electric illumination either at mains voltage or at a voltage reduced through a built-in or separate transformer. If the instrument is not so fitted, use a 60 watt pearl bulb mounted in a simple metal housing. Details of a suitable housing, designed by Dr. J. R. Baker are given in Fig. 2.7.

There are occasions when it may be advantageous to reduce the intensity of illumination from a low-voltage electric bulb and for this purpose a variable resistance should be wired in series with the lamp. Resistances for this purpose may be obtained from laboratory suppliers or from retailers in London who specialize in the sale of Government surplus equipment. For 60 watt pearl bulbs the most satisfactory method of controlling the intensity of the light is by the use of one or more neutral density filters which are placed in the light path.

The light source should be arranged so that it is about 20 cm in front of, and on the same level as, the mirror.

If no diaphragm is fitted it is best to start with the plane side of the mirror. *When the condenser is in position, the plane side of the mirror must be used.* For a statement of the routine sequence of adjustments, see pages 15 and 16.

### *Adjustment of reflected light*

For the illumination of opaque objects from above, light is focused on to the object from an oblique angle. This is accomplished by means of a plano-convex lens, i.e. a 'bull's eye'. The lens is mounted on a stand provided with a ball-and-socket joint so that it may be adjusted to any desired angle between illuminant and object. (See Fig. 2.6, p. 9.)

Whether the plane or the convex side of the lens is turned towards the object will depend to some degree on the particular lens and on the source of light. The author's experience has been that both in artificial light and in daylight a better result has been obtained by turning the *plane* side towards the object. This may be because the source of light is coming from an extended surface and, when the plane side of the lens is turned towards the object, both surfaces of the lens take part in producing deviation.

In the absence of a plano-convex lens a simple substitute is a round-bottomed flask filled with water. The flask, clamped by its neck to a retort stand and with its base supported on a ring, is placed in line with and mid-way between the source of light and the microscope stage, about 15 cm distant from each. The lamp-bulb should be about 25 cm and the base of the flask about 6 cm from the bench top, but these distances must be adjusted to suit the microscope.

Illumination is increased if a piece of thin white card is placed underneath the slide carrying the object. Cut a piece of postcard 13 cm x 2.5 cm, and make slight transverse folds 2.5 cm from each end. The centre portion of 8 cm will carry a slide and the 2.5 cm portions at the ends will form 'handles'. When examining white or pale objects, replace the white card by a black one; or place a piece of black paper between white card and slide.*

* Adapted from ***The Structure and Development of the Fungi***, Gwynne-Vaughan and Barnes, University Press, Cambridge.

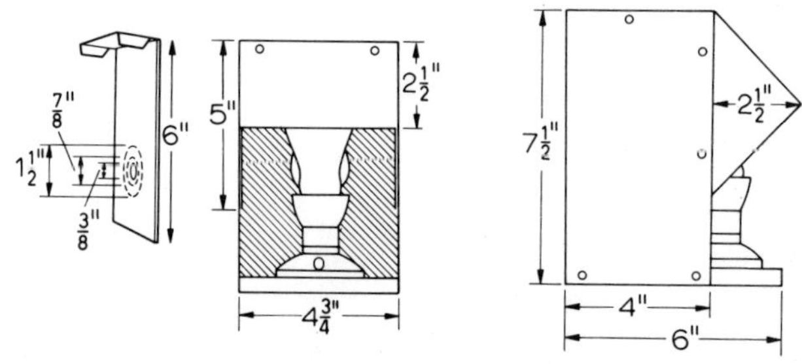


Fig. 2.7 A simple metal lamp house designed for use with an opal bulb. (*Times Ed. Suppl.* 31 Oct. 1969.) The attachable field stop (shown on the left) may be constructed with three different sizes of hole, depending on the focal length of the objective which it is intended to use.

When very small opaque objects are being examined with high-power lenses having short working distances, the source of light must necessarily be almost on a level with the microscope stage, and the light must be re-focused on to the object by some form of parabolic reflector. Work of this kind is not likely to be done by the elementary student; those interested should refer to some advanced book on microscopy for details of the apparatus and technique involved.

*Adjustment of dark-ground illumination*

As the use of dark-ground illumination involves a special technique, instructions for the adjustment of the illumination are given separately on pages 16 and 17.

**Adjustment of Object**

Remember that *all* microscope lenses have a curved field and that the focus is absolutely sharp only in the centre of the field.

Place the slide, object upwards, on the stage and secure it by means of the stage clips. The slide should be adjusted so that the object is directly underneath the low-power objective already in position. This adjustment is more easily made if the eye-piece is first removed. The presence of the object in the field of view will be recognized by the decrease in illumination and by the appearance of colour if the object be coloured. The eye-piece, if previously removed, should now be replaced.

**Adjustment of Focus**

*Adjustment of low-power objective, without condenser*

Looking sideways at the instrument, bring the *low-power* objective down, fairly close to the object, by means of the coarse focusing device. Now look down the microscope in the usual way with one eye (whichever is found to be the more convenient) and, *keeping the other eye open,* bring the object into focus by racking *upwards*, i.e. by using the coarse focusing device to draw the objective away from the object. This lessens the risk of hitting the cover-slip and of ruining the object and objective by crashing the objective on the slide. Using low-power, the focus obtained with the coarse adjustment will probably be sufficiently sharp.

The low-power (LP) gives a general view and may be used for searching. *It is a good habit always to use the* LP *first.*

*Adjustment of high-power objective, without sub-stage condenser*

The high-power (HP) gives a detailed view of a very limited area of the object. Before the HP is used this limited area must be brought into the centre of the field under the LP.

Great care must be exercised in focusing the 4 mm, and higher-power, objectives. This is best accomplished by using the fine adjustment to bring the objective so close to the cover-slip that, when the eye is placed on a level with the stage, the objective appears almost to touch its reflection in the cover-slip. The objective may now be drawn *away* from the stage by means of the fine adjustment, and the object will come into focus.

Most modern microscopes, when fitted with rotating nose-pieces, are so designed that, provided the objectives are parfocal, once the object has been focused through one objective it is almost in focus when another objective is brought into position. But remember that an extra thick cover-slip or a ring of cement may project so high as to catch the base of a high-power objective as it is swung into position. When this is likely to occur the objective must be racked up beforehand.

*Keep both your eyes open, move gently, and never use any force.*

*Adjustment of high-power objective, with sub-stage condenser*

NOTE: As the best results with a high-power objective will not be obtained without the use of a sub-stage condenser, *the following sequence of processes should be used as a standard procedure before embarking on microscopic work.*

1. Place the lamp-holder, fitted with a 60 watt bulb, directly in front of the microscope, about 20 cm away from it and with the lamp-housing aperture on about the same level as the microscope mirror. If the lamp is not housed behind a blue-glass screen, place a daylight-blue filter in the sub-stage ring.
2. See that the sub-stage iris is fully open.

3 Rotate the nose-piece until the low-power (16 mm) objective is in the working position, i.e. in line with the body-tube.
4 Remove the eye-piece.
5 Keep the eye about 15 cm above the end of the body-tube. Adjust the mirror (*plane* side) until the back-lens of the objective is completely and evenly filled with light.
6 Replace the eye-piece.
7 Place a microscopic slide of a well-stained section on the stage and see that it is fixed securely.
8 Bring the sub-stage condenser to the top of its travel.
9 Using the coarse adjustment, bring the object into focus.
10 If the condenser is fitted with a sub-stage centring device, the sub-stage iris-diaphragm should now be closed to a pin-hole and the condenser racked down until an image of the aperture of the iris appears in the field of view. If this aperture does not now appear in the *centre* of the field, the centring screws must be adjusted until it does so.
11 Re-open the sub-stage iris-diaphragm fully.
12 Hold the point of a sharpened pencil against the lamp bulb surface until its shadow is seen in the field of view.
13 Adjust the height of the condenser until the tip of the pencil is seen clearly superimposed on the object. If the grain of the glass or the lettering on the bulb becomes visible, a further *slight* movement of the condenser will cause it to disappear.
14 Remove the eye-piece.
15 Keep the eye about 15 cm above the end of the body-tube. Close the sub-stage iris-diaphragm until about three-quarters of the back-lens of the objective is evenly illuminated. When the condenser is correctly adjusted the outline and details of the object should appear sharp. Take care *not* to alter the position of the mirror.
16 Replace the eye-piece. The microscope is now ready for use with LP.

*To change to high-power*

Do *not* touch the condenser, and do *not* touch the mirror.

1 Rotate the nose-piece to bring a high-power objective into position. In doing this take care that the objective does not foul, for example, the stage clips, a thick cover-slip, or a thick ring of cement round the cover-slip.
2 A slight movement of the *fine* adjustment should bring the object into sharp focus.
3 Remove the eyepiece.
4 Keep the eye about 15 cm above the end of the body-tube and open the sub-stage iris diaphragm until about two-thirds of the back lens of the objective appears evenly illuminated.
5 Replace the eye-piece.

*Adjustment of oil-immersion objective*

NOTE: *The procedure suggested in this paragraph should be adopted only after following the sequence of operations detailed above.*

First centre the object under a medium-power objective as indicated in the previous section. Change over to a 3 mm or 2 mm objective. Now place one drop of immersion oil, or one drop of 'golden syrup' diluted with its own volume of water, either on the cover-slip, dead central over the object, or on the objective. (It is better to use 'golden syrup' for preparations which might be damaged by the use of xylene when the immersion oil is being cleaned off.) Next lower the objective with the usual, or even greater care. Great care really is necessary (especially in moving the slide), and the thinnest cover-slips must be used. It is usually essential to open the iris diaphragm to its maximum extent.

After use, the oil is carefully removed from the objective and slide by means of a lens-tissue bearing a *mere trace* of benzene or xylene. Finish off with a clean lens-tissue. 'Golden syrup' is removed by water.

**Use of Dark-Ground Illumination**

The technique of dark-ground illumination is not difficult to acquire, but it should not be attempted until the student has become thoroughly acquainted with the use of the microscope with transmitted light.

*Equipment required*

A sub-stage condenser with a numerical aperture about 1.0. (The N.A. will be found marked on the mount.) A sub-stage diaphragm with stop-carrier.

A set of patch-stops ranging in diameter from about 2.3 cm to 0.75 cm. These may be made from celluloid or polythene discs (cut to fit the stop-carrier) by painting on them circular patches of Brunswick black with a final coat of matt-black. A 16 mm objective with N.A. about 0.28, and a 6 mm objective with N.A. less than 0.6. Eye-pieces x8 and x10.

*Preliminary focusing*

Arrange a fairly small diaphragm aperture and, with a twisting motion (unless there be a device for focusing the sub-stage condenser, when the normal mechanism will be used), lower the condenser (N, Fig. 2.8) so that its upper end is a little below the base of the slide. Focus the object (AB) under the 16 mm objective (the position of the condenser may require adjustment) and arrange the light *dead central* in the field. Use as bright a light as close as possible to the plane side of the mirror (P). If the white light is irritating, insert a daylight-blue glass on the stop carrier.

*Obtaining the dark-ground*

Insert a moderately small patch-stop (T) in the stop carrier (first removing the coloured glass if this was inserted). Open the diaphragm as wide as possible, taking care not to move the position of lamp, mirror, or objective. Carefully move the condenser upwards until it is almost touching the base of the slide. The object will now be illuminated

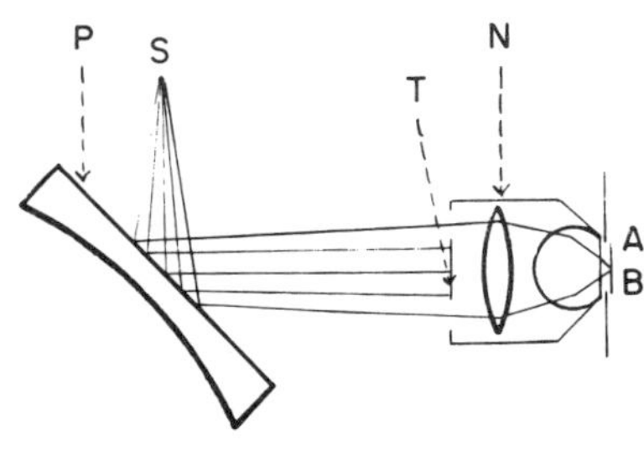


Fig. 2.8* Use of patch stop (T) and condenser (N) for low power dark-ground illumination.

only by rays of light which are so oblique that the direct light cannot enter the objective. The image is formed by the light diffracted by the object, and is of a brightly illuminated object on a dark background. By the use of larger patch stops, a dark ground effect may be obtained with lenses of up to 0.6 N.A. For lenses with a greater aperture than this, a special reflecting condenser, which must be in oil immersion contact with the underside of the slide, is required.

*Additional practical points*

The lower the power of the objective, the smaller is the patch-stop required.

The higher the power of the objective, the bigger is the patch-stop required.

Too small a patch-stop gives an indistinct field, and too big a patch-stop gives no contrast.

Eye-pieces of too low power result in the field being incompletely darkened.

Different eye-pieces require different sizes of patch-stops.

Chromatic aberration (the image being surrounded by coloured fringes) and spherical aberration (the image being indistinct) cannot be avoided with thick objects. Clarity will be greatest at the centre of the field.

The best combinations of objectives, eye-pieces, patch-stops and condenser positions will be found by experiment.

If the only high-power objective available has too high a N.A. (for example, a 4 mm objective often has N.A. 0.85), remove the objective, and reduce its numerical aperture by placing on top of it a metal washer (suitably blackened), such as is used on electric terminals, and replace the objective. The correct size of washer must be determined by experiment.

Slides and cover-slips must be clean and thin, or definition will be poor. No. $1\frac{1}{2}$ cover-slips (0.17 mm thick) should be used if they are obtainable; otherwise use No. 1 thickness.

*Material suitable for practice*

Scrape the inside lining of your cheek lightly with a wooden tongue-depressor and smear onto a clean, thin slide. Add a small drop of 0.95% saline and cover.

## 2.6 DRAWING FROM THE MICROSCOPE

Having made his sections, the wise student will make a drawing of what he sees. It is not inappropriate to quote here the remark that an examining

* See footnote to Figs. 2.4 and 2.5, page 9.

professor once made to the author: *'A very large proportion of the drawings made by examinees when they first arrive at the University are, frankly, abominable.'* The remedy for this sad state of affairs is obvious. Apart from its being extremely unscientific, it is foolish, to say the least, to fail to make careful, accurate drawings of what *you* see.

There are two very simple, but very sound, rules for drawing from the microscope. They are:

(i) *Draw what you see; not what you think you ought to see, and not what the text-book diagram shows.*

Always remember that the best text-book diagrams have been produced, or should have been produced, as the result of very many, very patient observations of the object. They are, as it were, a formalized, composite, picture. Very rarely does a single observation through a microscope reveal all that may be seen in different circumstances. Indeed, such a revelation is so rare an event that the observer may find himself exclaiming, 'It's absolutely diagrammatic!'. The examiner rightly regards such occasions with some suspicion and, consequently, much prefers you to draw what *you* see, provided you draw it carefully and accurately. It is surprising how many students seem, at first, to be content to make careless drawings unless they are reminded that, above all things, the scientist must be accurate in his observations.

(ii) *Remember that you are examining a three-dimensional body.*

All too often students' observations seem to be restricted to a careless, partial examination of transverse sections and the study of two-dimensional diagrams and photographs. For example, a section of a much-convoluted plasma-membrane may appear as a jumble of broken lines, hollow circles, ellipses, and so on, all of varying sizes and extending in various directions, depending on just where the line of section lies. If this is the final picture that is retained in the observer's eye it is both incomplete and inaccurate. A more accurate impression will be obtained by racking the focus back and forth to bring different levels of the section into view. However many sections of different sorts the student may cut, the exercise is quite valueless if he or she fails to build up, however gradually, a picture of the organ and the organism *as a solid object.*

As an example of examiners' requirements the following is a question set recently in an Advanced Level Biology paper:

> "Stain and mount a transverse and a longitudinal section of the stem provided. Using the 'Plasticine' provided create accurate models of the shape of (*a*) a pith or medulla cell, (*b*) a sclerenchyma fibre element."*

Candidates were provided with a micrometer eyepiece and a lump of 'Plasticine'. They were not required to make representations of details of internal structure of the cell or of the fibre element, but it is obvious that without very careful serial sectioning in various planes, followed by careful examination of the sections, they would be quite unlikely to be able to satisfy the examiners' minimum requirements. When serial drawings are made of different levels in the section, a better, but as yet incomplete, picture will begin to form in the observer's mind.

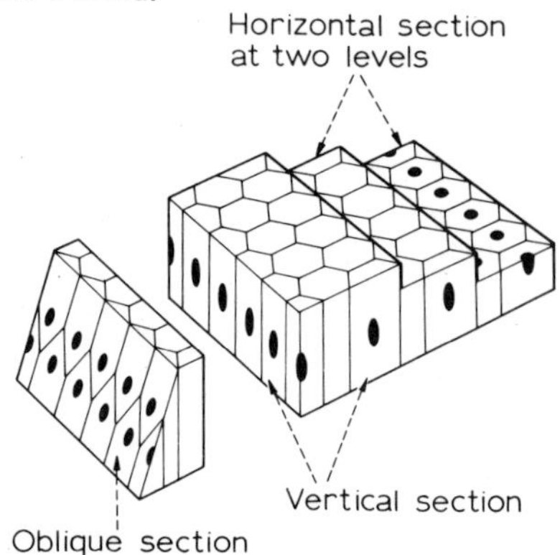


Fig. 2.9 A diagram of the appearances given when a sheet of simple columnar epithelium is sectioned in various planes. Note how an oblique section may give the false impression of two layers of cells. (Redrawn from Hewer, *Histology for Medical Students,* 9th edn., Heinemann Medical Books Ltd.)

Diagrams should purposely be made very simple in order to convey the three-dimensional idea. Detail tends to confuse the matter until the student has acquired the art of making mental pictures; but acquire this art he must if he wishes fully to understand the structure of the plants and animals he is studying. Very often this is just a matter of using simple methods and his brain to interpret simple things.

* Reproduced by permission of the Oxford and Cambridge Schools Examinations Board.

Only after careful observation of longitudinal, tangential and radial, as well as of transverse sections, as far as this is practicable, will the three-dimensional nature of the object become apparent, and its structure obviously bear some relation to its functions. Figure 2.9 illustrates these points.

**Making the Drawing**

Reference was made in a previous paragraph to looking into the microscope with one eye and keeping the other eye open. The 'other eye' may very well be used for looking at the sheet of drawing paper, placed to one side of the microscope. To do this there is no necessity to develop a squint, nor need the eye become tired. To look from microscope to paper and back to microscope, all that is necessary is to change the direction of the line of vision, or of the head itself, very slightly. Constant reference back to the microscope is a necessity when making a drawing and this is more likely to be achieved if it is done without a major change of position every time. Some little practice will soon overcome preliminary awkwardness.

A bright spot of light focused on the eye is harmful and, unless the illumination is adjusted carefully, prolonged observation may result in some eye strain. When using the microscope, therefore, not only should both eyes be kept open but the illumination should be adjusted to allow comfortable viewing, provided that the light intensity is sufficient to reveal all that there is to be seen. Particular use should be made of the sub-stage iris-diaphragm when viewing water-mounted or living specimens in order to improve the contrast of the image. Neutral density screens are best for controlling the intensity of illumination.

An important point to bear in mind is that cells must *never* be drawn as 'holes', for they rarely are holes. All cells have a limiting boundary, sometimes thin and sometimes thick, and careful drawing, for example by the use of thinner or thicker pencil lines, can serve to indicate this fact. Again, groups of cells must *never* be shown as a jumble of 'holes'. Careful observation will indicate that not only have the individual cells their individual boundaries but that adjacent boundaries are interconnected in some quite specific manner according to the nature of the cells.

Drawings under low-power should show the outline and the main features of the object drawn to the same scale as they appear in the microscope. The scale of magnification should be indicated alongside the drawing and the name of the object should be stated. Thus: '. . . . . . . . as seen under LP' 'x . . . . . . . .'

Drawings under high-power should show only representative areas of the field of view, never the whole of it, and, needless to say, the different kinds of cells should be clearly labelled. It is useful sometimes to make a connected series of drawings under HP from a number of areas, either scattered among or taken along one or more axes, of the LP view. The corresponding part of the LP drawing should always have the exact point of the HP observation neatly indicated upon it.

The student is sometimes at a loss to know how big to draw cells seen under high-power. It is usually best to draw the object to represent the magnification as given by the microscope, and to state that magnification on the drawing. There are occasions, for example when a connected series of drawings under high-power is required, as in plant anatomy, when the largest individual cells should be drawn as large as postage stamps, i.e. about 2.0 cm x 2.5 cm (with the approximate magnification stated) and the rest to scale. The drawing should be titled appropriately as suggested above.

**The Camera Lucida**

This is a simple optical device for enabling the observer to make reasonably accurate outline drawings, of correct scale and proportion, of objects seen under the microscope. The *camera lucida* should never be used for drawing detail. This must be filled in by eye, whether under low-power or high-power.

In its simplest form the *camera lucida* consists of two components, namely, a small reflecting prism and a plane mirror. The prism, which has a small unsilvered area in the centre of its silvered surface, is fixed immediately above the eye-piece. The mirror is attached to the eye-piece in such a manner that it can be inclined at an angle of 45° both to the prism and to the surface of the bench at one side of the microscope.

To use the *camera lucida* a sheet of drawing paper is placed on the bench under the mirror. Presupposing the intensity of illumination of the object and of the paper are exactly balanced, and the mirror inclined at the precisely correct angle to the paper, the observer, with his pencil-point on the paper and his eye looking into the microscope, will see an image, not only of the object, but also of the pencil-point and paper. All that remains is to trace on the paper the outline of the object as the pencil is made to follow it in the field of view This requires much practice.

Outline drawings made by means of the *camera lucida* should have their scale stated and this can be done quite simply by using the apparatus (with the mirror remaining at precisely the same angle at which it was set for the original drawing) to trace on the drawing paper a section of the stage-micrometer scale.

The use of a separate reading lamp to illuminate the drawing paper greatly simplifies the balancing of the illumination of the microscope image and that of the pencil point and drawing paper.

## 2.7 USE OF THE MICROSCOPE AS A MICROPROJECTOR

There may be times when it is desired to demonstrate a microscopic preparation to a small group of people but there is no microprojector available. As, in essence, a microprojector is an ordinary microscope fitted with a mirror inclined at 45° over the eye-piece and supplied with additional illumination, a little ingenuity in fitting these extras will enable an ordinary microscope to be used as a microprojector with some degree of success and as a temporary expedient.

If the preparation is 'dry' the microscope is simply laid in a horizontal position, the rays emerging from the eye-piece being directed on to a suitable vertical screen *placed not more than, and preferably less than, 3 metres away.* It will almost certainly be necessary to make a slight adjustment to the position of the objective in order to focus the image on the screen.

If the preparation is 'wet' and likely to 'run' the microscope stage must, of course, be kept horizontal. In these circumstances the rays emerging from the eye-piece can be directed either on to a white ceiling — which makes observation just that much more difficult — or, alternatively, a front-silvered mirror fixed at an angle of 45° to the emergent rays can be used to direct the image on to a vertical screen.

There are, however, a number of drawbacks to the use of an unmodified microscope. The illumination may be insufficient and uneven. This can be partly overcome by the use of an almost point-source of illumination of sufficient intensity, such as that provided by a 'quartz-halogen' electric bulb. The objective will work less efficiently, because of optical errors introduced when the objective is adjusted (and hence the tube-length altered) to focus the image on the screen. The image on the screen may be distorted, because the ordinary ocular is designed to produce an image which the eye sees at the optimum visual distance, whereas the screen is much farther away from the ocular. The last two errors can be overcome by the use of a modified low-power ocular in which only the eye-lens is adjustable. When this is used the rays emerging from the eye-piece take a more nearly parallel path, rather than a divergent path, towards the screen.

For really successful results, however, and particularly when working with larger groups for whom a greater screen-distance is essential, it is preferable to purchase a good proprietary microprojector designed for the work it is required to do. Such instruments are fitted with voltage-regulating devices for the control of illumination; heat-resistant glass; water-cooled troughs for demonstrating living specimens, pond life, etc.; they are reasonably trouble-free and they can be professionally serviced.

A simple test for the efficiency of a microprojector for class demonstration work is that it should give a clearly defined image of cell division in *Rhabditis*, provided the microscope preparation has been well made.

Where it is not possible to darken a room really efficiently and the microprojector is not fitted with a special 'projection head', reasonably good images may be obtained by using a 'rear-projection' screen. A sheet of suitable translucent material, such as 'Bexoid' (clear matt/matt), 'Celastoid', or 'Vulite' is stretched over a wooden frame of suitable size and placed between the microprojector and the viewers, whose number must necessarily be limited.

## 2.8 OTHER TYPES OF OPTICAL MICROSCOPE

Although the form of microscope previously described is the one most likely to constitute part of the equipment of the elementary laboratory, it is possible that the junior student may, at some time, be given an opportunity to examine objects through one or other of the more sophisticated types of optical microscope. They include the following.

## The Binocular Microscope

The binocular microscope (Fig. 2.10), as its name implies, is an optical microscope with two eye-pieces, a feature tending to reduce eye strain. A series of prisms below each eye-piece is so arranged as to direct light from the objective through each of them. The eye-pieces, which are usually parallel with each other, may be set vertical or inclined at an angle of 45° to the draw-tube. The type chosen is largely a matter of personal preference, based on comfort and convenience in use.

Although some binocular microscopes are made to be used permanently as such, there are occasions when it is convenient to be able to change from a binocular to a monocular arrangement. Instruments have therefore been designed with detachable binocular additions which slide into the body-tube in place of the monocular, thus permitting easy interchange.

The binocular arrangement results in an increase of as much as $1\frac{1}{2}$ times in the effective tube-length. This increase is allowed for in manufacture by the introduction of suitable correction lenses into the optical system. In such instances the correct working tube-length for the objective may be assumed.

### *The low-power, stereoscopic, dissecting binocular ('Greenhough Binocular')*

Binocular microscopes for high-power work are designed to be used with a single objective. It is useful, however, when dissecting or when doing other manipulations under the microscope, to work under low-power but with a *stereoscopic effect.* This is achieved in the *'Greenhough Binocular'* (Fig. 2.11) by the use of two objectives of equal power and two eye-pieces. A further refinement, by the use of additional prisms, results in images that are both erect and correctly orientated.

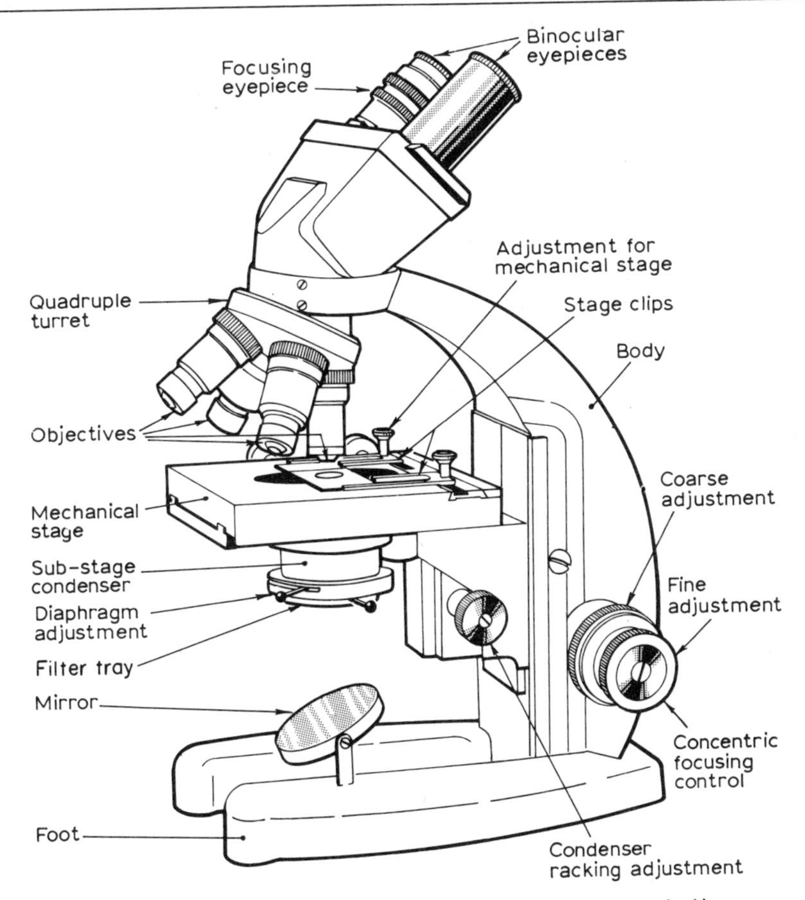


Fig. 2.10 A typical binocular microscope (*Vickers Instruments Ltd.*).

The source of illumination may be built into the foot of the instrument and worked direct from the mains electricity supply or through a transformer, or it may be separate from the instrument, when the microscope will be fitted with a mirror.

The magnification given by the dissecting binocular is quite low, up to about x75.

## The Phase-contrast Microscope

In an earlier part of this book (p. 6) the reader was reminded that in an unstained or living tissue we can distinguish different parts only when the light we receive has undergone changes of phase by the different parts. This is shortly expressed by saying that the parts visible to us have different refractive indices. If, however, the object under examination is either very thin, or very transparent, or both, an ordinary microscope will not provide sufficient contrast to enable the observer to distinguish different parts. It is, therefore, in the high-power examination of very thin or very transparent living cells, such as those of the smallest protozoa, or in the examination of the inclusions in the cytoplasm of living cells that the *phase-contrast microscope* is of the greatest use.

### *Principle of the phase-contrast microscope*

The principle underlying the construction of the phase-contrast microscope is precisely the same as that used in the ordinary microscope, namely, the use of interference effects to enable the observer to see the object.

In the phase-contrast microscope, however, these interference effects are deliberately increased

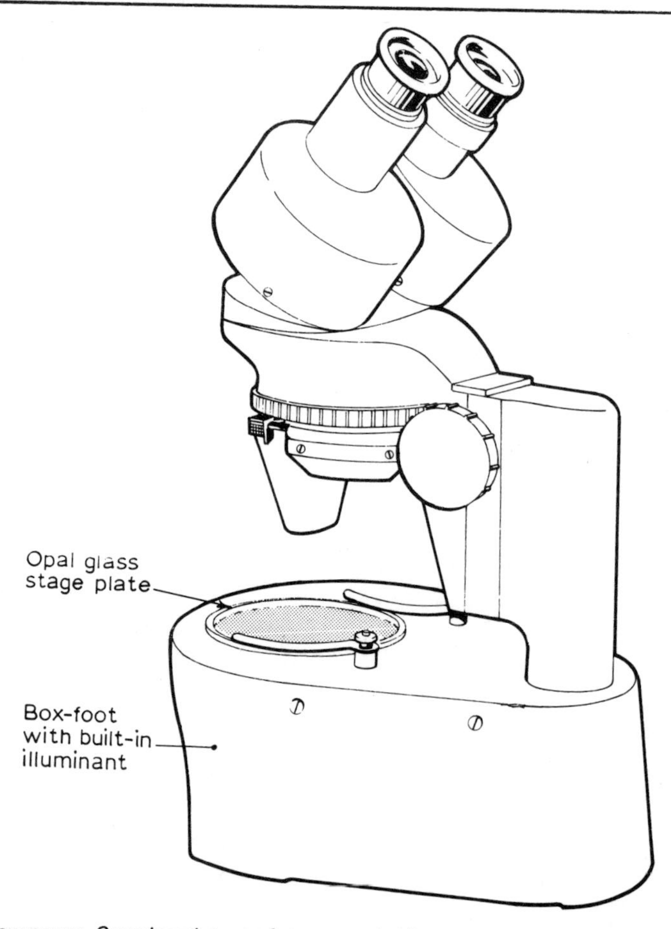


Fig. 2.11 A low power, Greenhough type of stereoscopic binocular microscope. (*W. Watson & Sons Ltd.*)

by causing different rays of light to pass through two different thicknesses of glass, a process which retards the rays which pass through the thicker glass. The interference between the emergent rays, on combination, is thus increased. This makes the change in phase between the direct and diffracted light apparent as a change in *amplitude* of the wave i.e. a change in intensity.

A diaphragm having a circular slit in it and sometimes referred to as an annular diaphragm, is placed below the condenser. This results in the focusing of a hollow cone of light on the object. Above the back-lens of the objective there is placed a glass plate – the *phase-plate* – on which is etched an annulus corresponding in size exactly with the image of the annular slit in the sub-stage diaphragm. Where the phase-plate is etched the glass is fractionally thinner (Fig. 2.12 ii). Rays passing through this area will emerge out of phase with those passing through the thicker, unetched, area.

Direct light passes through the sub-stage annular diaphragm, through the condenser and the objective and is imaged onto the etched annulus in the phase-plate. Rays diffracted from the object which have been retarded in phase by about $\frac{1}{4}$ of a wavelength, however, do not pass through the etched annulus but through the thicker portion of the phase-plate. Hence they are further retarded and emerge $\frac{1}{2}$ a wavelength out of phase with those rays that have passed through the etched annulus. Interference, and hence amplitude differences, result – provided that steps have been taken to arrange that the (direct) rays of light passing through the etched annulus of the phase-plate are of intensity similar to that of the diffracted rays not passing through the etched annulus.

In the majority of instruments light from a source (S) (Fig. 2.12 i) is directed into the microscope by the mirror (M). An annular diaphragm (D) is located in the back focal plane of the condenser, close to the position normally occupied by the iris-diaphragm.

The phase-plate (P) is located in or near the back focal plane of the objective (O). An image of the diaphragm is thus formed on the groove in the phase plate and hence all the direct light passes through this area.

As the light diffracted from the specimen arises from a different conjugate plane, it will pass equally through the whole area of the phase-plate. This light, already retarded $\frac{1}{4}\lambda$ in phase or thereabouts by the specimen, will then be further retarded by the extra thickness of glass which it has to traverse in the phase-plate.

Reference should be made to the Bibliography for further information about the theory and technique of the phase-contrast microscope.

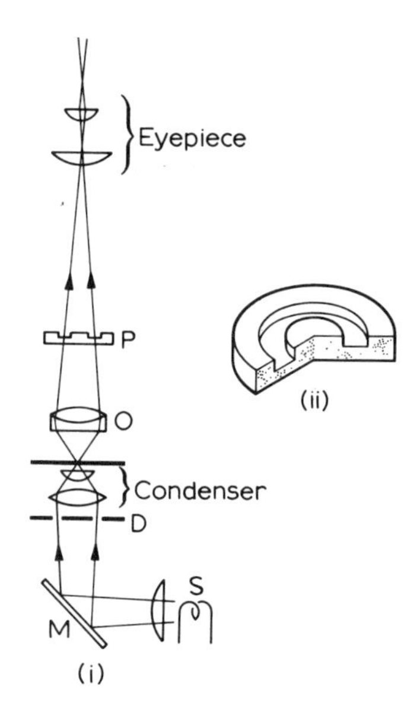


Fig. 2.12 (i) A diagram of the optical system of a phase-contrast microscope.
(ii) Phase plate in section.

**The Interference Microscope**

The interference microscope is a development of the phase-contrast microscope and works on similar principles to those described in the previous paragraph. By means of this microscope it is possible to produce effects resembling those produced by differential staining of the object and to measure accurately the phase changes introduced by different regions of the object. The interfering light waves, which, depending on the construction of the instrument, may be in a double beam or in a multiple beam, are produced by a device known as an interferometer built in to the microscope. The use of the interference microscope is outside the scope of this elementary work.

## 2.9 THE ELECTRON MICROSCOPE

As its name implies, the electron microscope is *not* an optical microscope. Instead of using light it makes use of a beam of electrons to give even greater resolving power. As a result, it is possible to make direct observations of viruses, cellular components, and even of the largest molecules, for the electron microscope has a resolving power of about 0.3 nm. It is a highly expensive piece of apparatus and is used only in advanced work.

# 3

# Protoplasm and the cell

## 3.1 PROTOPLASM AND THE CELL

It is not the purpose of this book to make a study of cells (cytology), or of tissues (histology), but before trying to understand the processes involved in microtechnical work it will be well to have some knowledge of the material, protoplasm, and of the units of that material, cells, which will be subjected to the various processes. It is necessary, however, to remember that, in the biological field, what is thought to be true to-day may be found to be incorrect to-morrow. Only by constant, wide reading will the student keep himself up to date.

Bearing in mind therefore that our present knowledge of the cell is not complete and that new discoveries are constantly being made, the following summary indicates, in general terms, something of the structure and functions of protoplasm and the cell, as revealed by dark-ground illumination, phase-contrast, interference, polarizing and fluorescence microscopes, the electron microscope, and by micro-dissection, i.e. the dissection of living cells. More detailed information will be found in some of the books mentioned in the Bibliography.

## 3.2 THE NATURE OF PROTOPLASM

All cells are composed, primarily, of protoplasm, with which may be associated by-products of protoplasm and substances helping to manufacture it.

There is no completely satisfactory answer to the question, 'What is protoplasm?' because protoplasm is *living* and in the process of chemical analysis it is killed. There is, therefore, no guarantee that what is found on chemical analysis is the same as that which was present in the living protoplasm.

### Living Protoplasm

Modern work points to the conclusion that living protoplasm is an emulsoid,* but in physical structure it is by no means homogeneous. Indeed, it would seem that living protoplasm is, in fact, a mixture of sol and gel in constantly changing proportions.

### Dead Protoplasm

On death, protoplasm becomes a gel, but, unless kept at a temperature of about 0° C, there is then a change to the sol state due to the action of intracellular enzymes in dissolving tissues. The process is called *autolysis*. This liquifaction is continued

* An emulsoid is a particular class of *colloidal solution*. It consists of two immiscible phases called, respectively, the *disperse phase*, and the *continuous phase* or *dispersion medium*. An emulsoid can exist in two states, namely, the *(hydro)sol* and the *(hydro)gel*. When an emulsoid is a sol the disperse phase is the less fluid of the two components and is suspended in the more fluid continuous phase (dispersion medium). Owing to molecular bombardment the particles of the two fluids are in a state of constant, dancing, movement known as *Brownian motion*. When an emulsoid is a gel it is believed that the disperse phase assumes a net-like structure and that the dispersion medium moves within the network. This may account for the combination of great viscosity with great elasticity which is a property of gels.

under aseptic conditions and is not to be confused with that caused by putrefying bacteria.

Dead protoplasm is a complex mixture of proteins, fats, carbohydrates, mineral salts and water, with no fixity of composition.

## 3.3 THE FUNCTIONS OF THE CELL

The cell is a living thing. Vital functions comprise respiration (anabolic and catabolic processes often, but not necessarily, involving the intake and circulation of oxygen, and always resulting in the production of energy); nutrition (including the securing of food materials, their conversion into substances suitable for anabolism and their circulation within the organism); excretion (the removal of unwanted products of metabolism); reproduction; differentiation; development; irritability (sensitivity); (loco) motion; selectivity; and rhythm.

The individual, living, cell, whether it exists alone or forms part of a community of cells that form part of a specialized tissue, performs all the functions of a living thing in greater or smaller degree. Indeed, one of the most remarkable features of individual cells is the high degree to which *intra-cellular differentiation and organization* are developed, a capability stemming from the very nature of the living protoplasm from which they are made. Furthermore, it is the fact of intra-cellular differentiation that results in the phenomenon of *homeostasis*, the maintenance of a stable state of internal economy, not only within the individual cell but also as between the different cells of a multi-cellular organism.

## 3.4 THE STRUCTURE OF THE CELL

Stated in the simplest terms the major features of almost any and every cell are: an outer boundary wall, the *plasma-membrane* or *cell-membrane* that encloses a cavity containing *cytoplasm*. In the cytoplasm there occur numerous living, protoplasmic, inclusions called *organelles*, of which the biggest is the *nucleus.* The nucleus is enclosed within a *nuclear-membrane* and may contain a *nucleolus.* The cytoplasm also contains *metaplasmic inclusions* which are the *non-living* products of cell metabolism. Some cells contain spaces called *vacuoles.*

### The Plasma-Membrane or Cell-Membrane

Limiting the cell is the *plasma-membrane* or *cell-membrane*, between 7 and 10 nm thick (see p. 10). As visualized with the electron microscope it appears as a double entity, the so-called *'unit membrane'*. The cell-membrane contains a high proportion of phospholipids* combined with proteins to form lipoprotein membranes. Such membranes have certain characteristics that help in the regulation of the cells' internal economy and in the maintenance of homeostasis.

Were it not for the spatial limits imposed by the plasma-membrane the cell would tend simply to assume a spherical shape. As it is, variations in the form of the plasma-membrane result in different cells assuming different shapes. This variety is, however, limited for physical reasons directly connected with the chemical metabolic processes going on in the cell. Many of these processes involve the movement of substances in and out of the cell, through the plasma-membrane. In the absence of any form of true circulatory system the distances travelled by the various substances in the cell must, somehow, be minimized and the distribution surfaces maximized.

Now, as the volume of a sphere varies as the cube of the radius but the surface area varies only as the square of the radius, it is clear that the bigger the volume of the cell, the greater the problem of providing sufficient surface area of plasma-membrane to allow of the maintenance of homeostasis. The tendency is, therefore, for cells to assume flattened and elongated rather than spherical shapes. Furthermore, the total surface area may be much increased by convolutions of the plasma-membrane.

### The Pellicle or Cuticle

The requirements of individual cells, or of the organism as a whole, may necessitate the cells having a tougher limiting layer than that provided

* Regrettably, there is much confusion of nomenclature where fats and their relations are concerned. In these pages a *fat* (true fat or neutral fat) is regarded as a combination of glycerol and one or other of the fatty acids; a *lipid* (lipide, lipin, lipine) is regarded as a substance soluble in a fat solvent (such as benzene, chloroform, ether, or hot alcohol) and which may either contain a fatty acid combined with a nitrogenous base, sometimes together with phosphorus (phospholipids) or sulphur, or not, (e.g. carotene, terpene, steroids, and sterols, although these may, sometimes be combined with fatty acids).

by the plasma-membrane alone. In such instances, due sometimes to the size of the cell or to its position within the organism, the plasma-membrane is able to secrete a layer outside itself. This may take the form, for example, of a very thin, non-cellular, *pellicle* (*cuticle*), which may itself be thickened in exposed places by the deposition of the substance *keratin* (as on the cells of the stratum corneum of mammalian skin), of the fibrous protein *collagen* (as in the epidermis of *Lumbricus terrestris*), or even of a cellulose-like material (as in the Ascidians).

### The Cell-Wall

Most plant cells (*protoplasts*) have their plasma-membranes strengthened by the external deposition of a dead cell-wall of *cellulose*, a fibrous, polysaccharide carbohydrate. This provides the plant body with a skeleton. Again, the cell-wall may be modified by the deposition, for example, of gum-like polysaccharides called *pectins*; or of *suberin*, a corky material; or of *lignin*, a woody material. In the fungi the cell-wall is composed of *chitin-cellulose*, a horn-like substance resembling *chitin.*

### Inter-Cellular Adhesion

While it can readily be understood that the presence of a skeletal-like system of cellulose deposited between adjacent plant cells gives the collection of cells some form, it may equally readily be asked, what prevents a number of adjacent animal cells from falling into an amorphous mass? Is there some adhesive substance between the cells? The electron microscope reveals that there is. Adjacent plasma-membranes lie about 15 to 20 nm apart and in the intervening space there is a mucin-like substance that causes *inter-cellular adhesion.*

#### *Desmosomes*

In animal tissues likely to suffer strain, inter-cellular adhesion seems to be improved by the presence of small patches or discs called *desmosomes.* These are very small, between 1.0 $\mu$m and 2.0 $\mu$m in diameter, and their nature is not fully understood. Just as the plasma-membrane may sometimes be thickened and strengthened by a deposit of keratin, so apparently may the desmosomes be strengthened by fibrils of keratin protruding from them.

#### *Plasmodesmata*

Reference has already been made to the fact that in plant tissues the living plasma-membrane may be toughened externally by the deposition of a cellulose cell-wall. This wall, however, is dead and were it not for some connective material between the cells, each would be leading a solitary life. The connective material exists in the form of *plasmodesmata*, fine threads of cytoplasm which run through, between, and in and out of adjacent cells, thus forming a continuous living structure.

### The Cytoplasm

A large portion of the contents of the cell consists of *cytoplasm* and it is believed that the major quantity of proteins is synthesized in it (see 'Protein Synthesis', p. 31). Cytoplasm is living protoplasm in the form of a (usually) clear, heterogeneous liquid, or sap, of fairly constant chemical composition. It is composed of aqueous solutions of sugar and inorganic salts, certain sorts of proteins (as colloids in the emulsoid condition, with a continuous aqueous phase), a most important substance called *ribonucleic acid* (RNA), and about 80% water. The protein portion sometimes forms a clear network called the *hyaloplasm*. The cytoplasm also contains phospholipid membranes that help to form some of the living *intracellular organelles* (see below) which are closely connected with the maintenance of homeostasis. These are of various shapes, all are very small and some are visible only with the electron microscope. Finally, there are numerous non-living inclusions (see p. 29).

The various metabolic processes enumerated above would appear to necessitate some system of circulation within the cell. It may be that this is provided either by a general flowing movement of the cell contents as required or by a *contractile vacuole* (see 'Vacuoles', p. 30) which may act as a sort of pump. See also under 'Mitochondria' (below).

The *cytoplasm* generally is *basic*, will stain with *acid* dyes, and is therefore termed *acidophil.* Certain parts, however, contain RNA and, of course, are *acidic*, stain with *basic* dyes, and are, therefore, termed *basiphil.*

## INTRACELLULAR ORGANELLES

It will be observed that many of the organelles mentioned below include particle-covered membranes as part of their structure. Such membranes are frequently concerned with the production of proteins. As protein synthesis is not an outstanding feature of most plant cells it will be appreciated that the membranes concerned are not usually so noticeable a feature of plant cells as they are of animal cells.

### *The Golgi body*

Apart from the nucleus the Golgi body is the largest of the organelles and is present in all cells except those of bacteria and some plants.

Seen with the electron microscope it appears as a group of smooth membranes flattened into cisternae and associated at their periphery with small vacuoles. There are grounds for believing that it may be the focal point for the formation of various organelles (e.g. lysosomes) in the cell. It is well developed in cells differentiated especially for secreting.

Recent research has associated the Golgi body with the synthesis of carbohydrate materials, e.g. mucus, in animal cells and in the formation of cell wall and extracellular materials in plant cells.

### *The mitochondria*

In order of size, next below the Golgi body are the *mitochondria* which vary in diameter between 1.0 μm and 2.0 μm. They are found in quantity in all cells (except those of the blue-green algae and very small bacteria) and are particularly numerous in cells where great activity goes on. They are either sausage-shaped or rod-shaped, may have a granular appearance, and consist of a double membrane, the inner membrane being much convoluted to form plates known as *cristae* and enclosing a fluid matrix.

Mitochondria contain numerous enzymes, some dissolved in the matrix, some lying on, or adsorbed on, the cristae. The function of the enzymes is to govern the citric acid cycle which is the complex series of processes of oxidation leading to the release of the energy required for *phosphorylation*. This is the synthesis of high-energy substances, such as adenosine triphosphate (ATP) which is stored in the mitochondria and which can supply energy for endothermic reactions in the cytoplasm. The mitochondria are thus the chief places in the cell where combustion takes place and where energy is produced.

Reference was made earlier to the possibility that the contractile vacuole acted in some way as a pump. It is interesting to note, therefore, that in Protozoa the vacuole is seen to be surrounded by mitochondria which may, in some way, supply energy for the operation of the vacuole.

It is not yet known how mitochondria originate, but they have been observed to fragment transversely.

### *The Endoplasmic reticulum*

This has been recognized by electron microscopy as a system of tubules or flattened membranous sacs or cisternae extending throughout the cytoplasm and connecting with the nuclear envelope. The form of the system may vary considerably but two major divisions are recognized, one in which the cisternae are studded on their cytoplasmic surfaces with the dense particles called ribosomes, and one in which the ribosomes are absent from the membranes or cisternae. The *granular* or *rough-surfaced endoplasmic reticulum* is associated with extensive cellular protein synthesis whilst the *agranular* or *smooth-surfaced endoplasmic reticulum* has been associated with such cellular activities as glyconeogenesis and glycogenolysis and steroid synthesis.

### *The ribosomes*

The *ribosomes* are the smallest of the organelles within the cytoplasm and are about 0.01 μm in diameter. As indicated in the previous paragraph, they occur as dense particles on the membranes of the granular endoplasmic reticulum. They also occur free in the cytoplasm and are also found in the nucleolus (see p. 31).

The ribosomes consist of about two thirds RNA and one third protein and are the site of protein synthesis (see p. 31).

Cells producing great quantities of protein, e.g. gland cells, embryonic cells and rapidly growing bacteria are particularly rich in RNA, but it is noteworthy that in cells where the ribosomes are free of the endoplasmic reticular membranes the cell products are retained rather than secreted.

*The centrosome*

The *centrosome* lies near the nuclear membrane together with the Golgi body (p. 28). It is an area of differentiated protoplasm free of particles, but with fine filaments or microtubules radiating from it.

*The centriole*

The optical microscope reveals the *centriole* as a tiny particle, about 0.2 μm in diameter, frequently, but not universally, present. It stains deeply and is seen in cells (except those of the higher plants) in the centrosome area during interphase.*

Just before prophase it splits into two halves which travel to opposite ends of the cell to form the centre of the aster (if present) and the poles of the radiating spindle filaments.

When seen with the electron microscope it is interesting to note that the centriole bears a resemblance to the basal granule at the base of a cilium. Indeed, the centriole appears to be connected to the axial filament of cilia and flagella.

*Lysosomes*

These are particles of varying morphology which have been shown to contain acid hydrolases, especially nucleases and acid phosphatase. They involved in the digestive activities of the cells and may be released outside the cell to destroy extra cellular material. Lysosomes are vital for the processes of phagocytosis, the lysosome fusing with the ingested material in the pinocytotic vacuole to give a so-called *digestive vacuole*, and of cell remodelling.

*Plastids*

The *plastids* are units of self-propagating protoplasmic material found in the cytoplasm of plant cells. They are of various shapes and sizes and may be coloured or colourless.

CHLOROPLASTS One of the most characteristic features of the cells of mature green plants are the *chloroplasts*. A chloroplast is rather larger than a mitochondrion and consists of a single-walled, membranous sac enclosing groups of parallel membranes, the *grana*, lying in a diffuse supporting material, the *stroma*. Also present are enzymes, believed to lie on the grana, and the green pigment *chlorophyll* whose function is to absorb radiant energy from the sun.

The function of the chloroplasts is the production of sugars from atmospheric carbon dioxide and water. On leaving the chloroplasts the sugars are burnt in the mitochondria to provide energy for the production of adenosine triphosphate (ATP). ATP may also be produced in the chloroplasts themselves.

CHROMOPLASTS Chromoplasts are plastids which contain the pigments *carotin* and *xanthophyll* as minute droplets. (Chromoplasts are sometimes referred to as chromatophores, but it is suggested that this term is best reserved for the pigment-containing *cells* of such animals as the Crustacea, *Rana* and *Chamaeleo*.) See also 'Inclusions ii' below.

LEUCOPLASTS Leucoplasts are minute, colourless bodies of irregular shape and are concerned with the conversion of sugar to starch which appears as granules of characteristic shape. The leucoplasts may also contain crystals of protein substances.

PYRENOIDS Pyrenoids are somewhat spherical protoplasmic bodies sometimes associated with chloroplasts and found in some unicellular green plants. They contain protein in crystalloid form and small starch granules.

*Spherosomes*

These are small spherical organelles, between 0.5 and 1.0 μm in diameter, which occur in nearly all plant cells. They are rich in protein and in oil and some authors believe they also contain hydrolytic enzymes. This latter fact would seem to relate them to the lysosomes.

NON-LIVING INCLUSIONS IN THE CYTOPLASM

These inclusions are products of cell metabolism.

(i) *In animal cells*

*Fats* and *oils* in the form of globules, usually compounds of oleic, palmitic and stearic acids;

* Interphase is the resting stage of the nucleus. Prophase, metaphase, anaphase and telophase are successive stages of nuclear division.

*glycogen*, as granules or in solution in the cytoplasm; *mucinogen*; *yolk*, in granular or disc-like form, a mixture of protein, fats, lecithin and cholesterol.

(ii) *In plant cells*

SOLIDS *Protein substances*, mainly globulins, as *aleurone grains* of round or irregular shape, sometimes containing several crystals; *calcium carbonate*, as *cystoliths*; *calcium oxalate*, as single crystals, or as bundles of needle-shaped crystals (*raphides*), or as collections of crystals radiating from a centre (*sphaeraphides*); *inulin*, as *sphaerites* (sphere crystals). Included in chromoplasts are *pigments, protein crystals,* and *starch granules*, either flat, roundish oval or spherical.

LIQUIDS *Cell sap*, which occurs in the vacuoles; it may contain *acids* (citric, malic, tartaric), *protein substances, alkaloids, amides, glucosides, glycogen, inulin, mucilage, pigments* (e.g. *anthocyanins, anthoxanthins*), *sugars, tannin. Ethereal oils, fats* and *resins*, if present, occur in vacuoles.

**Vacuoles**

Vacuoles are cavities within the cytoplasm.

*Vacuoles in plant cells*

Many plant cells are noteworthy because of the large size of the vacuole which may occupy the major part of the cell. In such instances the cytoplasm, with the nucleus embedded in it, may be pushed against the plasma membrane. Sometimes the nucleus is placed more centrally, especially in younger cells, and then the vacuole becomes subdivided into smaller vacuoles by sheets of cytoplasm extending from the nucleus to the plasma-membrane.

The vacuole acts as a store for sugar and other substances in solution. The liquid, or cell sap, is isotonic with the cytoplasm, but the osmotic pressure maintained above that of the extra-cellular liquids helps to maintain the turgidity of the cell and prevent its collapse. The fact that the cytoplasm is pressed against the plasma-membrane results in a shortening of the distances involved in molecular diffusion.

*Food vacuoles*

These are cavities formed temporarily in Protozoa, and in the monocytes, macrophages and polymorphonuclear leucocytes of vertebrates for the purpose of ingesting food. The process is called *phagocytosis*. The cell moves membrane-like pseudopodia around the food particle and engulfs it, the enclosing cavity thus formed being the *food vacuole*. Once the food particle has been ingested, it is digested by the lysosomes.

*Pinocytosis vacuoles*

When cells are examined under the electron microscope it is possible to see minute sacs invaginating from the plasma-membrane. It may be that these are vacuoles used for taking liquids into the cell. The process is called *pinocytosis.*

*Contractile vacuoles*

Contractile vacuoles are found in some Protista, especially the fresh-water species, and in fresh-water Porifera. They periodically and rhythmically expand, fill with water (which may contain excretory products in solution), contract and discharge their contents to the outside. As mentioned under 'Mitochondria' (p. 28), in Protozoa the contractile vacuole is surrounded by mitochondria which may be concerned with the provision of energy for the operation of the vacuole.

**The Nucleus**

The nucleus is usually ovoid or spherical and about 10 μm in diameter. It is thus the largest of the intracellular organelles. It consists of a *nuclear envelope* which encloses the *nucleoplasm.*

*The nuclear envelope*

The nuclear membrane is composed of phospholipid and is pierced by many exceedingly small holes or *nuclear pores*. It is visible during interphase but when the cell is actively dividing it disappears at the beginning of metaphase and reappears during late telophase. It is now known that the nuclear envelope is continuous with the endoplasmic reticulum.

*The nucleoplasm*

The nucleoplasm contains both basiphil and non-basiphil material, the latter being referred to as *nuclear sap.*

The basiphil material consists partly of *deoxyribonucleic acid* (DNA) and partly of *ribonucleic acid* (RNA). The DNA forms a complex with proteins and becomes aggregated to form the *chromosomes* which, although not always seen as such (unless mitosis has followed very quickly upon mitosis), are nevertheless present during interphase and form part of the permanent structure of the nucleus.

Within the chromosomes lie the *genes*, the units of inheritance. Each gene is believed to be a fractional part of a DNA molecule and contains, as it were, instructions for making one particular protein (see 'Protein synthesis').

The *nuclear sap* (non-basiphil material) contains proteins and is the site of certain nuclear enzymes.

*The chromatids*

Towards the end of interphase or, in some organisms, during very early prophase, the chromosomes split longitudinally into two halves, the *chromatids*, which at first remained joined at their centres.

*The centromere*

The *centromere* is a small, non-staining constriction which appears just before or during metaphase on the paired, but as yet unseparated, chromatids. The centromere is, in fact, an integral part of the structure of each chromosome. For any given pair of chromatids it always appears at the same point, but it may appear at different points on different pairs. It becomes the point of attachment of the chromatids to the spindle fibres. At the end of mitosis the centromere, with the rest of the chromosome, becomes invisible.

*The nucleolus*

That part of the basiphil material which consists of RNA is combined with proteins to form one or two small, dense bodies within the nucleus, called *nucleoli*. These are produced by certain regions of the chromosomes but disappear at the end of prophase and reappear during late telophase.

The nucleolus also contains particles resembling ribosomes and it is believed that they consist of 'Messenger RNA' (see 'Protein synthesis', below).

*Function of the nucleus*

The nucleus may be said to be the *raison d'être* of the cell. Without their nucleus all cells die.* The nucleus, then, is responsible for the continued life of the cell for, not only does it contain the genetic apparatus necessary for self-replication of the cell, it also controls its whole structure, functions and way of life.

## 3.5 PROTEIN SYNTHESIS

The structure of the DNA molecules formed in the nucleus is such that it is believed that each acts as a particular sort of 'template' for the formation of molecules of the nearly-related RNA. The 'templates' vary according to their base sequences of adenine, thymine, guanine or cytosine. These particular molecules of RNA, formed from the DNA molecules in the chromosomes, are known as '*Messenger* RNA'. They leave the nucleus by way of the pores in the nuclear-membrane, pass out into the cytoplasm, and there link with the ribosomes and supply them with the necessary 'code' for synthesizing a particular type of protein. Meanwhile, in the cytoplasm, different amino-acids have, with the aid of selective enzyme action, become attached to molecules of another sort of RNA known as '*Transfer* RNA'. These combinations of particular amino-acids with molecules of transfer RNA also enter the ribosomes. Here they meet with the appropriate molecules of 'Messenger RNA' and the amino-acids of the transfer RNA's are linked together to form protein chains. The molecules of protein then pass out of the ribosomes into the cytoplasm. For the details of this process, one of the text books listed in the Bibliography must be consulted.

* Mammalian erythrocytes, which have no nucleus, are *not* an exception to this statement. When in the myeloid tissue of bone marrow they *are* nucleated but, on passing into the blood stream, lose their nuclei and henceforth have a life limited to about one hundred days.

### 3.6 CONCLUSION

This chapter must be concluded with a reiteration of the reminder and the warning given at its commencement: We do not yet know everything there is to be known about protoplasm and the cell. Some of the facts we now believe to be true may be found, at best, to be half-truths and, at worst, to be untruths. For the student there are two things to do, namely, *to read as widely as possible* in order to try to keep up to date, and to keep an open mind.

# 4

# Microtechnical processes– principles and techniques

It is only in exceptional circumstances not likely to be experienced by the beginner that cells and tissues retain anything approaching their living state when under microscopical examination. For this reason it is necessary to subject material to a series of microtechnical processes designed to enable it to be examined under the microscope and yet to retain it in as lifelike a condition as possible.

The name given to the art of conducting these processes is *microtechnique*. This is not an end in itself, but merely one method used to assist in the interpretation of structure. Thus when an examiner asks a candidate to 'investigate the stem of . . . ' he means the candidate to do much more than simply cut and mount a transverse section – which is the point at which a good many candidates stop.

As far as microtechnique is concerned the investigation should ideally include the production of *serial* sections, and not only serial *transverse*, but also serial *radial longitudinal* sections and *tangential longitudinal* sections in order to build up a picture of the organ and the organism as a solid object. Further reference is made to this most important feature of microtechnical work on page 18.

## Microscopical Preparations

*Microscopical preparations* may be either *temporary* (i.e. they will only remain suitable for microscopical examination for a comparatively short time, perhaps even an hour or less) or *permanent* (i.e. they can be stored and should remain suitable for microscopical examination for many years, although even some permanent preparations are liable to deteriorate with age).

Unfortunately, microtechnical processes are almost bound, indeed some are specifically designed, to have some effect on the protoplasm and other cell contents. The result is the production of *artifacts* which may be only distorted images of the real object. Error and confusion in interpretation may thus arise through lack of consideration of the possible effects of microtechnical processes and this fact must *always* be borne in mind when examining cells and tissues microscopically. 'Even the best preparation has undergone a series of manipulations – killing, drying and sectioning, for example. It is in this sense an 'artifact' . . . it must always be borne in mind that the best of 'good' preparations is still an artifact. The task of the biologist is not to avoid artifacts, but to interpret them and never to accept them for more than they are.'*

While it is true that the precise sequence and the manner in which the various microtechnical processes are used will vary with the particular method chosen for making a microscopical preparation, the fact remains that there is a logical sequence appertaining to the whole. Thus, fundamentally, the production of a microscopical preparation may be said to involve the use of the following microtechnical processes in the sequence indicated, viz:

* Picken, Dr. L. E. R. (1955). *School Science Review*, **XXXVI**, No. 129, 263.

SUMMARY AND SEQUENCE
OF THE CHIEF
MICRO-TECHNICAL PROCESSES

*Note: Processes shown within parentheses are not necessarily obligatory and their use will depend on the particular technique chosen*

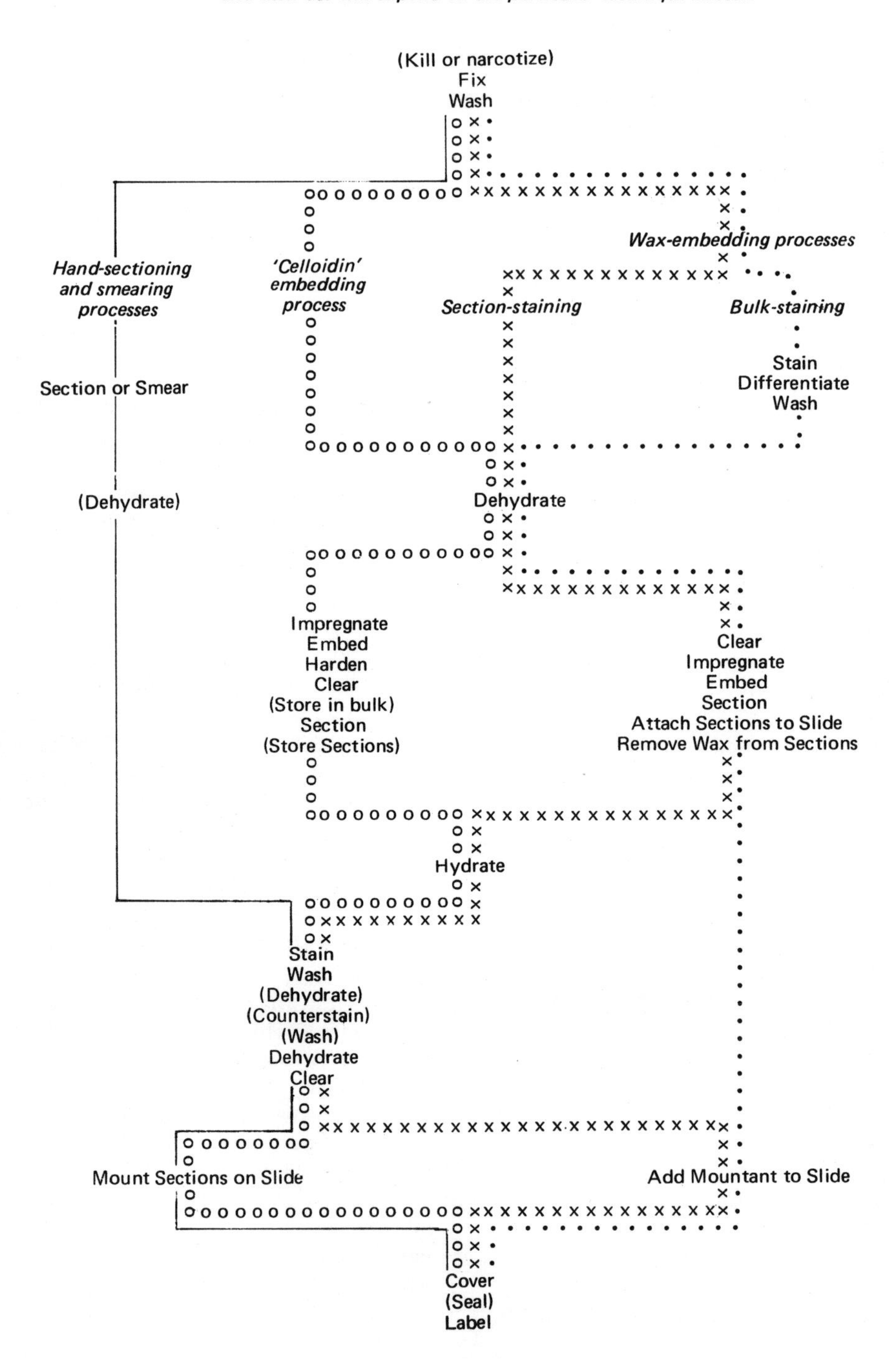

In the following pages descriptions of these fundamental processes are arranged in the above order because it is the actual sequence of one of the standard processes which the student will learn. There are, however, certain other processes which may be used from time to time. They are:



These processes are not fundamental to microtechnique (though their use is essential in certain instances) and therefore explanation is generally deferred until the later pages of this chapter.

To enable the reader more easily to follow the course of the different techniques while he learns about the processes, their purposes and underlying principles, a summary table is given on the page opposite.

## PRINCIPLES, PURPOSES AND TECHNIQUES OF THE VARIOUS MICROTECHNICAL PROCESSES

Under each numbered heading there is given, where appropriate, first a statement of the *principle(s)* underlying, and the *purpose(s)* of carrying out, the process. This is followed by a statement of the *technique* involved. It is suggested, therefore, that the beginner with a background knowledge of protoplasm and the cell, and alert to the possibility of the formation of artifacts, should first study the principles and purposes as a whole. With these in mind he will then be better equipped to study and to master the techniques when working systematically through the standard methods for making preparations given in Chapter 5.

### 4.1 FIXING AND HARDENING

Fixing is a mode of preservation intended to prevent shrinkage, swelling, distortion of parts, evaporation, and decay – whether by bacteria or by moulds or by enzymes (autolysis). Fixation may be by heat or by chemical action. In the fixed condition the cell and its components should be insoluble in the succeeding reagents.

#### Principles and Purposes

1 *To stabilize or fix the cell contents and the tissue in as unchanged a condition as possible so that they may be subjected to further treatment (e.g. to the processes of impregnation, embedding, sectioning, and mounting) which would otherwise damage them.*

2 *To modify the refractive index of some of the components of the cell or tissue, so that they may be the better distinguished from other components not affected to the same degree.*

We can see, and distinguish between, objects around us because they reflect light of varying intensity and colour. If a piece of glass is immersed in a mixture of chloral hydrate and glycerol the glass is indistinguishable from the liquid. This is because the glass and the liquid have the *same* refractive index and hence we receive light of the *same* intensity and colour from both. Thus, in an unstained or uncoloured tissue we can distinguish different parts only if they have *different* refractive indices resulting in our receiving light of *different* intensity from the different parts.

3 *To make the cells and tissue resistant to distortion by dehydration and solutions of varying osmotic pressures.*

Here it may be said that some authorities consider that as soon as the fixative begins to operate the cell no longer reacts to different osmotic pressures* whether hypertonic (i.e. of osmotic

* Tellyesniczky, quoted by J. R. Baker, *Cytological Technique*, Methuen.

pressure greater than that of the cell contents) or hypotonic (i.e. of osmotic pressure less than that of the cell contents).

4 *To harden the tissue and so enable it to withstand after-treatment – especially by the cutting blade – without distortion.*

The ordinary fixation processes render most plant and some animal tissues hard enough to be cut into thin sections, but certain tissues must be submitted to further treatment to make them sufficiently rigid.

5 *To make the cells and the tissue resistant to high temperatures such as may be necessary in the processes of impregnation and embedding.*

6 *To improve the effects of certain stains that may be used later to make the cell structure and tissue structure more visible.*

The worker must familiarize himself with the after-effects of fixatives from the point of view of staining and, of course, be careful to use only those stains which give good results after the particular fixative in use or, conversely, to use only those fixatives which best precede the desired stain(s).

7 *To prevent the loss of tissue constituents and changes in the spatial relationships of organelles and macromolecules.*

These requirements of a fixative are assuming more importance as the use of histochemical techniques and of electron microscopy become more widespread.

In addition to the foregoing desired effects, there are other undesired effects on the tissue, namely, its shrinkage or swelling to a varying degree according to the fixative used.

It is now a common practice to prepare sections of material which has not been fixed by heat or chemical action but which has been frozen very rapidly. Such material is cut on a cryostat, which is a microtome mounted in a refrigerated cabinet. Cryostat sections are used for histochemical work because the proteins and enzymes are not denatured and because there is no loss of freely soluble components (e.g. some carbohydrates).

While the main object of fixation is to retain the tissue structure unchanged, one may say that, with certain exceptions, its general and immediate cytological effects are:

(*a*) to kill the protoplasm (opaqueness of the cell or tissue may result);
(*b*) to raise its refractive index from about 1.35 to 1.54;
(*c*) to make protein sols more viscous, or to convert them into aqueous gels.

The number and quality of chemical fixatives is many and varied, and the beginner will do well to confine himself to one or two, making sure that he is well acquainted with their use and effects.

Some chemical fixatives penetrate tissues slowly, some quickly; some toughen tissues, others soften them; some are oxidizing substances, others reducing; some are acidic, some basic; some are single substances, some mixtures. When a mixture is used, the object is that certain components shall make up for what one may term the 'fixation deficiencies' of the others, but care must be taken lest the substances mixed are incompatible with each other. For example, chromium trioxide is an oxidizing agent; formaldehyde acts as a reducing agent; they must not be mixed until immediately before use. The single substance that

| **Proteins coagulated** | | **Proteins not coagulated** | |
|---|---|---|---|
| Protoplasm usually transformed into a network | | Protoplasm not transformed into a network. Protein sols are made more viscous or converted into transparent aqueous gels. Protein gels are stiffened. | |
| *Chemical* | *Standard concn.* | *Chemical* | *Standard concn.* |
| Acetone | 100% | ACETIC ACID | 5% w/v aq. |
| CHROMIUM TRIOXIDE | 0.5% w/v aq. | FORMALDEHYDE | 4% w/v aq. |
| ETHYL ALCOHOL | 100% | OSMIUM TETROXIDE | 1% w/v aq. |
| Hydrochloric acid | 0.5 N | POTASSIUM DICHROMATE | 1.5% w/v aq. |
| MERCURIC CHLORIDE | Satd. aq. | | |
| Methyl alcohol | 100% | | |
| Nitric acid | 0.5 N | | |
| PICRIC ACID | Satd. aq. | | |

Names in capital letters indicate substances most commonly used

will, with perfect satisfaction, fix all the cell or tissue components is unknown. Again, some fixatives are better for histological work, some for cytological, and some are equally good for both.

Summarizing, it may be said that:

*Fixation by heat* results in the coagulation of the proteins. It tends to distort tissues but is useful for blood smears (heat to about 110°C for ½–1 *min*).

*Fixation by chemicals* may or may not result in coagulation of the proteins. Hence chemical fixatives may be classified according to their residual effects (see table opposite).

*Freezing or Cryostat techniques* do not denature proteins or enzymes or allow loss of soluble compounds and are thus now much used for advanced histochemical studies.

**Chemical Fixatives**

The more common chemical fixatives and fixative mixtures are arranged in alphabetical order in the following table (pp. 38–41), which contains a summary of their main characteristics and mode of use. Where the fixative is a mixture of two or more substances, and no information has been given in certain columns, it may be assumed that their characteristics are by way of being a balance between those of their components. If, otherwise, no information is given, none sufficiently accurate for inclusion is available.

Chemical fixatives suggested for general use in more elementary work are indicated by a thick vertical line to the left of the Table.

**Technique of Fixation**

1 Fixation should be carried out as soon as possible after the animal has been killed, or the plant tissue gathered, in order that the tissue shall not shrink by drying, or decompose by putrefaction or autolysis. Methods for killing are, if necessary, given in Chapter 6.
2 Before deciding on the fixative, refer to the summary in the following pages. Some simple, type-methods are given below. It will be found that they are quite effective for ordinary purposes and the beginner should try them first.
Certain tissues are best fixed by special methods. Information for these will be found in Chapter 6, 'Methods for Specific Material'.
3 For histological work cut the tissue into pieces no bigger than 1 cm x 1 cm x 0.5 cm and treat it for about 18 h. If the tissue can, without distortion, be cut thinner, fixation will be more rapid. Use the fixative and tissue in the proportion, by volume, of 100 to 1 respectively and carry out the process in flat-bottomed specimen tubes (approximate internal measurements: length, 9 cm; diameter, 3 cm) fitted with corks. Smaller pieces may be treated in watch-glasses.
4 For cytological work the tissue must be cut into very small pieces no thicker than about 1.0 mm. The time taken for fixation is, of course, proportionately reduced.
5 For really successful work, air should be removed from the tissue by carrying out the fixation in a vacuum which may be obtained by means of a filter pump.
6 After fixation, *thorough washing in the liquid most appropriate for use after the particular fixative is absolutely essential if subsequent processes are not to be ruined.* This is especially true when mercuric chloride and acid fixatives have been used. Even after apparent thorough washing, acid has been known to come out of the tissue when in storage, and, as a result, successful staining has been impossible. Suitable liquids and times for washing after fixation are given in the table of fixatives (pp. 38–41). *As a precaution, always re-wash stored material prior to working with it.*

**Simple Methods of Fixation**

*A. Animal Tissue*

(*a*) *For very rapid fixation of small pieces of fresh tissue.*
  **1** Drop into hot water at 90°C. (1 min)
  **2** Transfer to alcohol (70%). (1 min)

(*b*) *For general use.*
  **1** Cut the tissue into pieces not larger than 1 cm x 1 cm x 0.5 cm.
  **2** Transfer to formol-saline (strong) (p. 215). (24 h)
  **3** Transfer to alcohol (50%), or (70%), or (90%). Avoid water. (1 hour in each)

**Summary of characteristics and mode of use of fixatives**

| Fixative and Main Uses | General Notes | Penetration and Time required for Fixation of Small Pieces | Mode of Washing Fixed Tissue | Shrinkage or Swelling Effect | Hardening Effect | Effect on subsequent Staining | Action |
|---|---|---|---|---|---|---|---|
| ACETIC ACID. (Animal nuclear cytology.) | Best fixative for nuclei and chromosomes. Cytoplasm and fats not fixed. Action on Golgi bodies uncertain. Mitochondria are not seen. | Very rapid About 1 h. Must not be allowed to act for long. | Alcohol (50% or 70%). | Swells tissues very much, especially white connective tissue fibres. | None, Leaves tissues soft and incapable of being hardened by alcohol. | Neither helps nor hinders. | Precipitates (in an unlifelike way) nucleoproteins and mucin. Does not coagulate albumen. |
| 'ACETIC-ALCOHOL.' | See Clarke's Fluid. | – | – | – | – | – | – |
| ALCOHOL. (ETHYL.) (Animal and plant histology.) | Ethanol tends to become oxidized, therefore do not use with chromium trioxide, osmium tetroxide, or potassium dichromate. Dissolves some fats and phospholipids, hence attacks mitochondria and Golgi bodies. Does not fix chromosomes. Do not use at very low temperatures. Concentration of alcohol used during and subsequent to the precipitation of glycogen must be at least 50%. | Very great and Very rapid 1–3 h. | In alcohol of the same strength as the fixative. | Shrinks tissues very much. Cytoplasm may retreat to centre of cell. | Very great. | Tissue difficult to stain, but haematoxylin and, for small specimens, alum-carmine, effective. Albumen and globulin tend to stain more easily. | Precipitates both albumen and globulin in an insoluble and denatured form. Precipitates nucleic acid and glycogen in a water-soluble form, the latter as a cloud of fine granules, or in amorphous masses. |
| BOUIN'S FLUID. (Mammalian histology and delicate plant and animal material.) | Good fixative for chromosomes. Bad fixative for mammalian kidney. Does not fix mitochondria. For work on embryos dilute with 25% or 50% of its volume of distilled water. A good example of the combination of properties in a fixing mixture. See column 8. | Considerable and rapid. 12–18 h (not more). | Do not use water. Wash in alcohol (50%) and (70%), or in lithium carbonate [satd. soln. in alcohol (70%)]. | Hardly shrinks cytoplasm. Cf. *Acetic Acid, Formaldehyde, and Picric Acid.* | Not great. | Tissue easily stainable, especially with Heidenhain's iron haematoxylin. If using basic aniline dyes, especially safranin o, see that all picric acid is out before staining. Do this by placing sections in lithium carbonate [satd. soln. in alcohol (70%)] (2 min.) | Probably the picric acid checks the action of the formaldehyde and keeps the tissue fairly soft; the formaldehyde checks the action of the picric acid on the cytoplasm, and of the acetic acid on the nucleoproteins; the acetic acid checks the later shrinking effect of the formaldehyde, and fixes the chromosomes. |
| CARNOY'S FLUID. (Cytology, especially chromosomes.) | As Clarke's Fluid (see below) but with chloroform added to hasten its action. | – | – | – | – | – | – |
| CHROM-ACETIC. (Plant histology.) | Does not precipitate some cytoplasmic elements. Useful for annelids. | Slow but good. 24 h, but longer time has no ill effects. Pieces of tissue must be *very* small, if possible not thicker than 1.5 mm. | Running water 24 h, then distilled water 12 h, then transfer to alcohol (50%, or 70%, or 90%). | Little change. Swelling by acetic acid counteracted by shrinkage due to chromium trioxide. | Cf. *Acetic Acid and Chromium Trioxide.* | No deleterious effects. | |

| Fixative and Main Uses | General Notes | Penetration and Time required for Fixation of Small Pieces | Mode of Washing Fixed Tissue | Shrinkage or Swelling Effect | Hardening Effect | Effect on subsequent Staining | Action |
|---|---|---|---|---|---|---|---|
| CHROMIUM TRIOXIDE ('Chromic acid')<br>(Animal cytology, and plant histology, especially algae.) | Weakly acid. An oxidizer, therefore do not use with alcohol or formaldehyde.<br>Does not fix fats, but causes globules to coalesce.<br>Does not fix lipids. Destroys mitochondria.<br>Light may cause outer pieces of fixed tissue to dissolve. Fixes outward form and internal structure.<br>Preservation with chromium trioxide improved if 0.75% NaCl is added to fixative. | Fairly slow, and not very penetrative. 12–24 h.<br>Pieces of tissue must be *very* small, if possible not thicker than 1.5 mm. | Wash thoroughly for 12 h in running water. Transfer plant material to alcohol (50%, or 70%, or 90%) and keep in the dark. | Shrinkage of nucleus medium, but of cytoplasm considerable. | Powerful and rapid. | Cytoplasm rendered acidophil; chromatin more basiphil. Aqueous stains may be used. | Precipitates all proteins as insoluble compounds, and chromatin as a reticulum. |
| CLARKE'S FLUID. ('Acetic-alcohol')<br>(Cytology, especially chromosomes.) | Fixes cytoplasm and nuclei.<br>Dissolves lipids, Golgi bodies, and sometimes mitochondria. Is not a good fixative for use prior to embedding because the acetic acid has a softening effect. Conversely, it is useful for squashes and hence for cytological work. | Rapid; $\frac{1}{2}$ h. Must not be allowed to act for long. | Alcohol (100%), several changes. Washing in alcohol (100%) is unnecessary if aceto-carmine or aceto-orcein stains are used subsequently. | Shrinkage less than by alcohol, owing to effect of acetic acid. | None. | No deleterious effect on any staining method. | Cytoplasm fixed and glycogen precipitated by alcohol. Nucleoprotein fixed by acetic acid. |
| 'Corrosive-Acetic.' | See 'Mercuric-Acetic'. | – | – | – | – | – | – |
| 'Corrosive-Formaldehyde.' | See 'Mercuric-Formaldehyde'. | – | – | – | – | – | – |
| 'Corrosive Sublimate.' | See 'Mercuric Chloride'. | – | – | – | – | – | – |
| FLEMMING'S SOLUTION.<br>(Animal and plant cytology. The standard fixative for chromosomes.) | The oxidizing substances ('osmic' and 'chromic' acids) must not be mixed with the organic acid (acetic) until immediately before use. | Poor. 1 h for chromosomes. Use weak soln. for very small objects. | As for chromium trioxide | Moderate shrinkage. | Slight. | | |
| | | ← Cf. *Acetic acid, Chromium trioxide and Osmium tetroxide.* → | | | | | |
| FORMALDEHYDE.<br>(Animal histology.)* | A reducer, therefore do not use with chromium triooxide or osmium tetroxide, or potassium dichromate.<br>Does not make albumen insoluble. No effect on fats. Makes outline of nucleus less clear. Mitochondria appear as rows of spheres.<br>Do *not* use for mammalian testis. (Great shrinkage – reason unknown.) | Very considerable but slow. 1–2 d. | Do not use water. Wash in alcohol (70%, or 90%). | Little shrinkage at the time, but great shrinkage afterwards in alcohol (90%, or 100%).<br>Much shrinkage with mammalian testis. | Very great (probably by acting on lipids of cell membrane). Does not harden albumen but prevents its subsequent hardening by alcohol. (Baker, *Cytological Technique*.) | Helps staining by haematoxylin. Makes staining by acid dyes (e.g. eosin Y) difficult. | Does not coagulate albumen or nucleoproteins. |
| FORMALIN-ALCOHOL.<br>(Plant histology.) | A good general fixative. For rapid fixation of *small* pieces, or sections, of fresh tissue, algae. Material may be left in fixative till required for use. | Rapid. 15 min. for small pieces. Longer for larger pieces. | Alcohol (70%). Small pieces, 2 min. | ← Cf. *Alcohol and Formaldehyde.* → | | | |

* The commercial product is available as a solution in water at a concentration of approximately 40% w/v. This is often known under the trade name of 'Formalin'. It is best to express the concentration of fluids containing formaldehyde in terms of their *formaldehyde* content e.g. Formalin diluted with 9 times its volume of water or saline is best called 4% formaldehyde, rather than 10% Formalin.

| Fixative and Main Uses | General Notes | Penetration and Time required for Fixation of Small Pieces | Mode of Washing Fixed Tissue | Shrinkage or Swelling Effect | Hardening Effect | Effect on subsequent Staining | Action |
|---|---|---|---|---|---|---|---|
| FORMOL-ACETIC-ALCOHOL. (Plant histology; algae.) | ← Cf. *Formaldehyde, Acetic acid and Alcohol.* → | | | | | | |
| FORMOL-PROPIONIC ALCOHOL.† (Plant histology.) | ← Cf. *Formaldehyde, Propionic acid, and Alcohol.* → | | | | | | |
| FORMOL-SALINE. See Formaldehyde. | Opinions differ as to the advisability of diluting the formaldehyde with saline instead of water, but Carleton (*Histological Technique*) considers it gives better results.‡ | Slow. 24 h. | ← Cf. *Formaldehyde.* → | | | | |
| HELLY'S FLUID. | See Zenker-Formol. | – | – | – | – | – | – |
| MERCURIC-ACETIC (Histology of very small animals; whole mounts; micro-anatomy.)* | A very useful fixative. Differentiation helped. | Very rapid. About 1 h. | As for mercuric chloride. | Shrinkage by mercuric chloride is counter-balanced by the swelling due to acetic acid. ← Cf. *Acetic Acid and Mercuric Chloride.* → | | No deleterious effect. Carmine stains are especially good. | |
| MERCURIC CHLORIDE. (Animal histology and plant cytology.)* | May be mixed with the other fixatives. No effect on lipids and mitochondria. Fat globules coalesce. Nucleus fixed in an unlifelike manner. | Rapid. 1–2 h. Material should be removed from fixative as soon as opaque. | Wash in alcohol (70%) made the colour of dark sherry by the addition of a saturated solution of iodine in alcohol (70%). As colour disappears replace by fresh iodine solution. Remove iodine colour with 'hypo.' (p. 249). | Shrinkage of tissues fairly considerable and that of cytoplasm great. | Moderate. | Staining, especially with carmine, easy, and with safranin o and haematoxylin quite good. | Precipitates proteins. Precipitates are soluble in saturated sodium chloride and potassium iodide. Fixes by denaturing (see mode of action of alcohol) the proteins. Fixes nucleus in an unlifelike manner. |
| MERCURIC-FORMALDEHYDE. (Animal histology, and some cytology.)* | Preserves with minimum distortion. Useful for red and white blood corpuscles. | Fairly rapid. 12 h. | As for mercuric chloride. | ← Cf. *Formaldehyde and Mercuric Chloride.* → | | | |
| 'OSMIC ACID.' ⁂ | See Osmium Tetroxide. As used in this book the name 'osmic acid' refers to perosmic acid, $H_2OsO_5$, which is the aqueous solution of osmium tetroxide (perosmic anhydride) $OsO_4$. Strictly speaking, osmic acid, $H_2OsO_4$, is the aqueous solution of osmium trioxide, $OsO_3$. | | | | | | |

† Suggested by C. A. Willoughby, B.Sc., University of Bradford.
‡ Carleton's work has since been confirmed by Young (*Nature*, **135**, 824; May 18, 1935), who recommends that *all* fixatives for *marine* animals should be made up in isotonic saline.
* Mercuric chloride is very poisonous.
⁂ The vapour of osmium tetroxide may damage the cornea of the eye.

| Fixative and Main Uses | General Notes | Penetration and Time required for Fixation of Small Pieces | Mode of Washing Fixed Tissue | Shrinkage or Swelling Effect | Hardening Effect | Effect on subsequent Staining | Action |
|---|---|---|---|---|---|---|---|
| OSMIUM TETROXIDE. ('Osmic acid'). (Animal cytology, especially microscopic animals; plant histology.) *‡ | An oxidizer. Do not mix with alcohol or formaldehyde. Fixes cytoplasm in a lifelike way, but nuclei badly. Does not precipitate proteins. Fixes fats, lipids, and mitochondria. If acidified with 15% of glacial acetic acid it fixes cytoplasm well but nucleoproteins in an unlifelike way. One of the standard fixatives used for electron microscopy. | Poor. Action on proteins slow. 1–2 d. If vapour is used for small animals, 30 sec. | Running water, 12 h. After use of vapour wash in chromic acid (1% aq.) (1 h), then water (10 min), then bleach with hydrogen peroxide (p. 228). | Swelling slight, but may shrink after subsequent treatment. | Slight | Hinders staining, but methyl green or haematoxylin useful. | The unsaturated fatty bodies are oxidized, reducing the peroxide to oxide which forms black compounds with the fatty substances. |
| PICRIC ACID.* (Animal cytology; plant histology, especially algae.) | Fairly strong acid. May be mixed with any other fixatives mentioned. No effect on lipids. Fat globules coalesce. Mitochondria appear as rows of spheres. | Fairly rapid. Very small objects 2 min; large pieces 24 h. | Wash with alcohol (50%, or 70%, or 90%). See 'Bouin's Fluid' for treatment of picric acid-fixed tissue. | Great shrinkage. | Very little. | Staining easy, especially with picro-carmine. Tissues have little affinity for basic dyes. | Precipitates all proteins by formation of protein picrates, all insoluble in water. |
| 'PICRIC-ALCOHOL.' (Plant histology, especially algae.) | | Fairly rapid. 3–4 h. | As picric acid. | | | No deleterious effect. Borax carmine especially good. | |
| | | | ← Cf. *Alcohol and Picric Acid.* → | | | | |
| POTASSIUM DICHROMATE. (Animal cytology.)* | Best not used by itself because nuclei are not properly fixed. Cytoplasm fixed in a lifelike fashion. An oxidizer, therefore do not use with alcohol or formaldehyde. If acidified it fixes like chromium trioxide. Fats not affected. Mitochondria fixed but tend to thicken. | Fairly slow especially action on proteins. Therefore fix for several days. | Running water, 12 h. Avoid alcohol till after staining, especially with carmine. | Shrinkage little but may increase during subsequent operations. | Slow, but good effect. | Helps staining of mitochondria. Hence useful to use another suitable fixative and then place tissue in potassium dichromate (3%) for 3 d. (Post-chromatization.) Stains well with carmine and haematoxylin. | Probably fixes by combination. Does not precipitate proteins when used by itself but renders them insoluble. |
| PROPIONIC ACID. [*Used in conjunction with alcohol and formaldehyde* (*q.v.*) for plant anatomy, e.g. growing points, and esp. for immediate fixation in the field.] | Modifies hardening and shrinkage effects of alcohol and formaldehyde; chromosome fixation reasonable; preserves nuclear detail; very useful for study of cell walls. | Good | Alcohol (70%), until smell of propionic acid disappears. | Tends to swell tissue. | Tends to soften tissue. | Reduces staining of cytoplasm. May be followed by Heidenhain's haematoxylin and orange G. | Fixes nucleoprotein. |
| | | ← Cf. *Alcohol and Formaldehyde.* → | | | | | |
| WATER (HOT). (Animal histology.) | A rapid method for *very small* pieces of tissue when the work is urgent and especially good results are *not* required. Temperature should be about 90°C. | 1 min. | Transfer to alcohol (70%). | | | | Albumen coagulated. |
| ZENKER-FORMOL. (Vertebrate histology; cytoplasmic inclusions; histology.) | Although this fluid contains a mixture of an oxidizing agent (potassium dichromate) and a reducing agent (formaldehyde), it is a good fixative for the porposes indicated. Make up fresh before use. Not good for plant tissues. | Moderately slow. 12–24 h. | Running water 16 h, then as for mercuric chloride (q.v.). | Rather liable to distort certain tissues. | | | |
| | | | | ← Cf. *Formaldehyde, Mercuric Chloride, and Potassium Dichromate.* → | | | |

* Young (*Nature* 135, 824; May 18, 1935) recommends that *all* fixatives for *marine* animals should be made up in isotonic saline.

‡ The vapour of osmium tetroxide may damage the cornea of the eye.

(*c*) *For protozoa, Paramecium, Vorticella, spermatozoa, coelenterata, Hydra, polyzoa, and aquatic organisms,* see Chapter 6.
(*d*) *See also 'Animal Tissue'*, Chapter 6 (p. 98).

*B. Plant Tissue*

(*a*) *For rapid fixation of small pieces or sections of fresh tissue; algae.*
1 Foraline alcohol (pp. 39, 187). (15 min)
2 Wash in alcohol (70%). (2 min)

(*b*) *For general use.*
1 Cut the tissue into pieces not larger than 1 cm x 1 cm x 0.5 cm.
2 Chrom-acetic (pp. 38, 199). (24 h)
3 Wash in running water. (12 h)

(*c*) *See also 'Plant Tissue'*, Chapter 6 (p. 158).

## 4.2 SECTIONING

### Principles and Purpose

Most pieces of tissue are too thick to allow sufficient light to pass through them for microscopic examination and study of intercellular and intracellular relationships. Exceptions are very thin, small, whole objects; pieces of very thin tissue; and liquid or semi-liquid tissues which may be thinly smeared or squashed on a glass slide or cover-slip. Generally it is found necessary to cut thin sections of the tissue. *Living* tissues are not easily sectioned sufficiently thinly and uniformly and, in any case, the cells may be damaged. Sections of *dead* tissue can usually be stained better than living tissues.

If the tissue is fairly hard and stiff as, for example, plant tissue which has been fixed and hardened beforehand, *free-hand sectioning* is reasonably satisfactory. With practice, and provided the tissue is somehow held firmly, it is possible to obtain sections as thin as 8 µm and the aim should be to get them not thicker than 12 µm as a maximum.

Hand-sectioning is rarely completely satisfactory for animal tissues, owing to their general lack of rigidity. If, however, the tissue has been well hardened during fixation it is possible to make very moderately satisfactory hand-sections of animal tissue.

Sections of more constant thickness, particularly of plant material, can be made if the tissue is supported by being surrounded by paraffin wax or pith or expanded polystyrene and cut in a *hand microtome.* This is an instrument (of moderate price) by means of which a measured quantity of the tissue is delivered and the section cut off by means of a hand-operated knife. The mechanism is then turned to deliver a further section-thickness of material and can be adjusted to give sections of 30 µm, 20 µm, and part-sections of 10 µm thickness. The hand microtome is particularly useful for cutting sections of 'Celloidin'-embedded material (p. 66) because this particular technique does not lend itself to the production of sections thinner than 20 µm.

More accurate work and thinner sections are obtained by first impregnating the tissue and then embedding it in some suitable material, such as paraffin wax (p. 62), in order to produce a block of stiff material. The block is then placed in a *mechanical microtome.* This is a much more expensive instrument which not only incorporates the cutting blade but automatically delivers, continuously, sections of pre-determined thickness. Using this it is therefore possible to obtain a ribbon of serial sections. A study of serial sections is a great aid to the formation of a mental picture of the three-dimensional nature of organisms.

### Technique of Free-Hand Sectioning

*The razor* must be of shaving sharpness.* To strop a razor see 'Razor, to sharpen' (p. 242).

For ordinary work, sections should be from 8 µm to 12 µm thick (µm = $\frac{1}{1000}$ mm).

1 Hold the tissue firmly between two pieces of carrot or elder pith (Fig. 4.1) which has been stored in alcohol (70%).
2 Place on the razor some of the liquid in which the tissue has been standing and cut through supporting medium and tissue, keeping the razor horizontal and drawing it towards the body with a long, oblique, sliding movement (see Fig. 4.1). Do not stop at one section; cut

* Not everyone seems able to acquire the art of sharpening the 'cut throat' type of razor. A suitable alternative is a 'safety razor' blade mounted in a suitable holder. When the blade becomes too blunt for the successful production of thin sections it can be thrown away and a new blade brought into use. *Great care must be used in pushing the blade into the holder* and the blade is best held *in a pair of pliers, care being taken not to damage the edge of the blade.* Suitable holders are obtainable from suppliers of biological apparatus.

several before proceeding to step **3**.
When cutting transverse sections of plant stems and roots do not, at first, attempt to cut complete sections. Be content with the thinnest representative sectors you can cut at right-angles to the main axis of the tissue.

**3** By means of a camel-hair brush quickly transfer sections to more of the liquid in which the tissue has been stored.

**4** Select sufficient of the thinnest sections and transfer them
(*a*) for an unstained preparation either to clearing agent (p. 53) or to mountant (p. 55);
(*b*) for a stained preparation to the desired stain (p. 47).

### Technique of Sectioning with the Hand-Microtome

1 Material must either be hardened before sectioning or embedded in 'Celloidin' (see p. 66 *et seq.*) or supported by means of expanded polystyrene (see note (d), on p. 44).
2 Plant material may be hardened by either,
(i) soaking in alcohol (90%) (24 h) or,
(ii) bringing material, previously fixed, up to alcohol (70%) or,
(iii) using an alcoholic fixative.

**1** Cut the material (whether embedded in 'Celloidin' or not) into lengths of approximately 1.25 cm.
**2** Trim the ends so that the cut end is at right-angles to the long axis of the material.
**3** Stand the material in the microtome-well so that it is near the front edge of the microtome-platform, i.e. away from the operator.
**4** By means of the microtome mechanism lower the material until its exposed end is below the level of the microtome-top-plate.
**5** Pour molten paraffin wax (m.p. approx. 45°C–50°C) into the microtome-well until the material is completely covered. Add more molten wax as the wax in the well cools and contracts.
**6** Allow the paraffin wax to set completely.
**7** Adjust the mechanism so that the wax (with the contained material) is pushed up the well.
**8** With an old scalpel pare away the surface wax until the material is exposed.
**9** Cut away a portion of wax on the side of the material *facing* the operator so that the section-cutting blade will first cut the tissue and not wax.
**10** Flood the cutting knife and the block of wax and material with alcohol (70%).
**11** Place the special cutting-knife between the

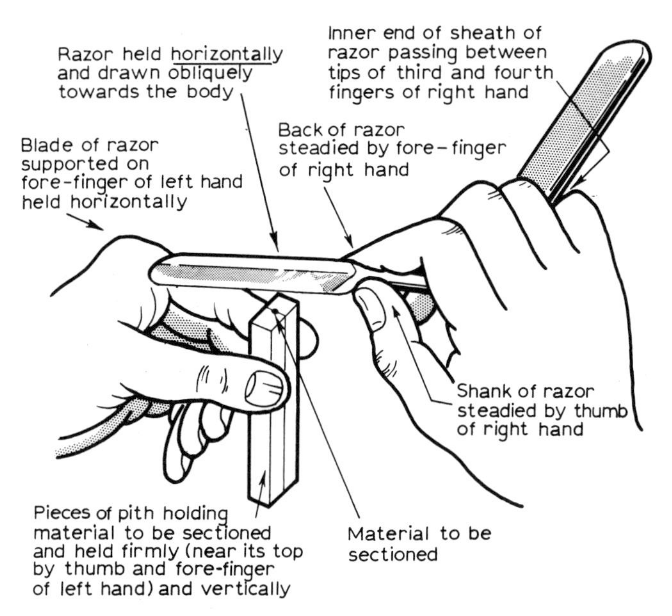


Fig. 4.1 Hand cutting sections with a razor.

operator and the material with the cutting edge facing forwards, i.e. away from the operator.

**12** With an oblique, sliding motion push the cutting edge forwards and sideways through the material.

**13** Transfer the section to alcohol (70%).

**14** Remove any loose wax from the microtome-plate by means of a brush or soft cloth.

**15** Adjust the mechanism to bring a further thickness of material up the microtome-well for sectioning.

**16** Re-flood both knife and material with alcohol (70%).

**17** Repeat processes from **12** onwards until enough sections have been cut.

*Note:* (*a*) Until some experience has been gained it is best not to attempt to cut sections thinner than 30 μm. With practice, sections of 20 μm can be cut, and part-sections of 10 μm.

(*b*) 'Celloidin' sections must not be cut thinner than 20 μm.

(*c*) The further treatment of 'Celloidin'-embedded sections is described on page 67.

(*d*) Fresh or fixed plant material (and some animal tissues) are most easily cut in the hand microtome if they are not embedded in paraffin wax but placed between two pieces of expanded polystyrene which are trimmed to fit into the microtome well. Elder pith was formerly used for this purpose, but polystyrene provides a much firmer support.

### Technique of Sectioning Wax-Embedded Tissue with the Mechanical Microtome

*Note:* (i) This follows the embedding process described on p. 63.
(ii) In using the mechanical microtome the sections should come off in a ribbon.

**1** Remove the wax block from its mould and pare away the wax so that none is left at the sides of the tissue, very little at the top and bottom, and *so that the upper and lower surfaces of the block are parallel.* Remove the corners of the block on its front face. This enables the wax ribbon to be divided easily when required (Fig. 4.2).

**2** Melt the wax on the chuck of the microtome with the heated blade of an old scalpel.

**3** Press the block firmly on to the warmed chuck, arranging the long side of the block so that it will be parallel with the edge of the razor (Fig. 4.2).

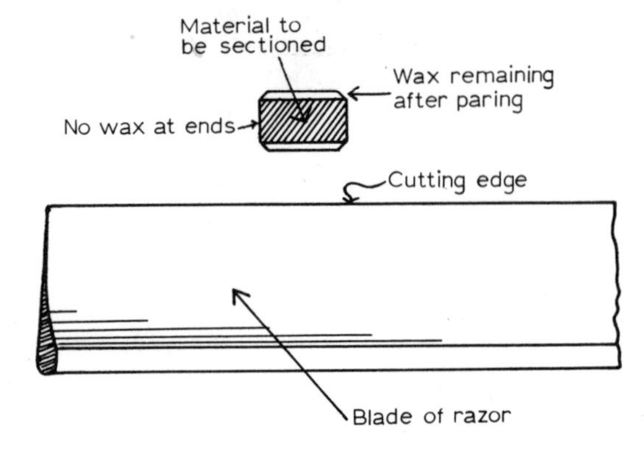


Fig. 4.2 Relation of microtome knife and trimmed wax block.

**4** Allow to cool.

**5** Fix chuck on microtome and cut sections of desired thickness, usually 8 μm–12 μm. Support the ribbon of sections on a finger of the free hand.

**6** Place the ribbons of sections onto a sheet of black paper. Avoid draughts.

**7** If desired, divide the ribbon into portions by cutting with a scalpel blade (Swann-Morton no. 22), using a gentle rolling motion.

**8** Mount the sections onto glass slides, as outlined in the paragraph 'Technique of attaching wax-impregnated sections to the slide' (p. 64).

*Note:* If the sections do not come off in a ribbon:

(i) The wax is probably too hard; warm it gently or coat the block with wax of m.p. 40°C;
(ii) The knife may be too cold; warm it gently. If the atmosphere is cold place an electric bulb about 5 cm away from the knife;
(iii) The knife may be greasy; wipe it with a cloth soaked in xylene;
(iv) The upper and lower surfaces of the block may not have been pared parallel; remedy obvious;
(v) The xylene used before the final impregnation may have been imperfectly removed; return

the block for further impregnation in pure wax.

If the wax tears from round the sections the relative hardness of wax and tissue must be adjusted suitably.

If crumbling occurs the wax is too soft. The best remedy is to re-embed the tissue.

If the sections and tissue tear:

(i) The razor may be blunt;
(ii) The razor may be set at the incorrect angle;
(iii) The tissue may not have been fixed properly;
(iv) The fixative may not have been washed out;
(v) Subsequent treatment, especially dehydration and impregnation, may have been imperfectly carried out.

Remedies for the above are obvious.

## 4.3 SMEARING

### Principles and Purpose

Some tissues, e.g. blood, do not lend themselves to sectioning. Again, it may be desirable to make a preparation of fresh unhardened tissue, e.g. fresh spinal cord or contents of seminal vesicles of earthworm. In these instances the tissue, if of a sticky consistency, is smeared very thinly on glass.

### Technique of Smearing

Depending on the technique to be used later, the tissue may be smeared either on the centre of a slide or on a cover-slip. The aim is to obtain a smear of approximately the same area as that of the cover-slip. The amount of material required to give the correct area of smear is determined by trial and error but, whatever the area, *the smear must be very thin.*

Depending on the type of tissue, it may be convenient to obtain the smear by pressing the slide, or the cover-slip, on the tissue or, alternatively, by transferring a sufficient quantity of tissue to the slide, or cover-slip, by means of a needle, preferably glass rather than steel (unless otherwise stated) lest there be interference by the iron with subsequent staining methods.

If the tissue has some rigidity, it may be convenient to mount it in a drop of suitable medium (p. 55) and then, if necessary, dissociate it into smaller pieces by teasing it apart with two needles, again bearing in mind the proviso in the previous paragraph.

Methods for the preparation of certain smears, e.g. bacteria, blood, *Monocystis*, spinal cord, etc., are given under the appropriate headings in Chapter 6, 'Methods for Specific Material' (p. 93). Otherwise, the tissue may be treated as for material in very thin sections.

*Note:* The process of smearing is sometimes regarded as synonymous with squashing, but the two processes are not precisely the same by any means, because material for the production of squashes strictly requires certain pretreatment which is not necessary for the production of smears.

## 4.4 SQUASHING

### Principles and Purpose

Certain plant materials, notably, rapidly growing parts such as anthers, leaf tips, ovaries, petals, root tips and tendrils are neither sufficiently soft to make a smear nor sufficiently rigid to be sectioned without being previously embedded in some supporting material. Preparations of such material can, however, be made quite rapidly without previous embedding by means of *squashes.*

The method is not quite so straightforward as might be imagined from its name for, before squashing, the constituent cells of the material must first be separated. To do this it is necessary to remove the pectic cementing materials which help to form the middle lamella and bind adjacent cells together. This is done in the process of maceration (below). The separated cells are then squashed on to a slide by pressure on the cover-slip.

### Technique of Squashing

A typical technique for making squashes is given in Chapter 6 under the heading 'Chromosomes, Mitosis, Squash Techniques', to which reference should be made.

## 4.5 MACERATING* (Plant Material)

### Principles and Purpose

It is sometimes desirable, and more particularly

* In part, after Lorna I. Scott, University of Leeds.

so when attempting to visualize the three-dimensional nature of plant structures, to make a study of individual cells or of groups of cells.

Between adjacent cellulose cell walls there is a cementing and stiffening layer known as the *middle lamella* and before individual cells can be examined this layer must be broken down. This is achieved by the process of *maceration* which is also an essential preliminary to the production of squashes of plant material.

In herbaceous (soft) tissues the middle lamella consists largely of pectic substances. In woody tissue it becomes more ligneous. Hence the particular technique of maceration adopted will depend on the botanical nature of the material under examination. For example, in very soft material it may be sufficient simply to use boiling water. Rather harder material may require treatment with dilute alkalis. Still harder material may require treatment with acidified alcohol (to convert the pectins to insoluble pectic acid) with subsequent treatment with ammonium oxalate (to convert pectic acid to soluble pectic oxalate; and calcium compounds to calcium oxalate). More ligneous material may require treatment with chromic acid (to dissolve calcium pectate etc.), while really woody material must be treated much more drastically, as for example, with a mixture of nitric acid and potassium chlorate.

**Techniques of Maceration of Plant Material***

(i) LEAVES

1 Soak leaves in alcohol (95%) to remove chlorophyll.
2 Transfer to potassium or sodium hydroxide (5–8% aq.) and warm, preferably on a water-bath. Do *not* boil. (45 min or until the tissue swells and the epidermis separates from the mesophyll)
3 Wash gently in running water. (2 h)
4 Transfer to hydrochloric acid (10% aq.) (6 h)
5 Wash gently in running water. (2 h)
6 If desired, store in formaldehyde (5%). (For further treatment see 'Leaf' (p. 142).

* See also, 'Bundle Ends' (p. 112); 'Chromosomes' (p. 114); 'Leaf' (p. 142); 'Phloem' (p. 157); 'Xylem' (p. 180).

(ii) HERBACEOUS TISSUE

(*a*) *Delicate material* (*Fresh*, sectioned)

1 Soak in chromic acid (5% aq.). (24 h)
2 Wash thoroughly in running water. (2 h)
3 Wash in distilled water.

(*b*) *Tough material*

1 Boil in potassium hydroxide (10% aq.).
2 Wash thoroughly in water.
3 Soak in chromic acid (5% aq.). (Thick sections 24 h or longer if necessary)
4 Wash thoroughly in water.

(iii) ROOTS

(*a*) *Root tips* (For mitosis)

1 Soak in hydrochloric acid (N/1) at 60°C on a water-bath. (6–10 min)

*Note:* The hydrochloric acid (i) by hydrolysis, frees the aldehyde groups from the nucleic acid in the chromosomes. The aldehyde groups subsequently combine with the Schiff's reagent used in the Feulgen technique to stain the chromosomes violet; (ii) dissolves the middle lamella of the plant tissue, thus allowing the preparation of squashes for the study of mitosis.

(*b*) *Fleshy roots*

1 Soak the material in acidified alcohol (see 'Macerating Fluids', p. 232, for special formula). (24 h)
This process may be hastened by warming the fluid gently.
2 Wash in running water. (1 h)
3 Transfer to ammonium oxalate (0.5% aq.). (1 h)
4 Mount in ammonium oxalate (0.5%) on slide.
5 Tap the cover-slip gently. The cells will fall apart.

(iv) WOODY MATERIAL

*Note:* Thin sections of timber or other woody stems and roots may be obtained in the form of shavings cut with a very sharp smoothing plane. The shavings will tend to curl but each shaving will include an area sufficiently large and flat for further treatment.

(*a*) *Modified Franklin's Method* *

1 Place the woody material in a flask fitted with a reflux condenser.
2 Half fill the flask with a mixture of equal volumes of glacial acetic acid and hydrogen peroxide (20 vol).
3 Reflux gently. (1–8 h)
4 Allow the flask and contents to cool.
5 Neutralize the contents with sodium carbonate.
6 Decant the liquid.
7 Wash the woody material with several changes of water.

*Note:* The period required for maceration must be determined by trial and error, as it varies with the size and thickness of the block or shaving, with the nature of the wood and the degree of softening required. As a rough guide soft woods may require 1 h, hard woods 1½ h or longer; up to 8 h in the hot liquid followed by 12 h in the cold may be needed for complete disintegration. If desired the softened wood may be stored after washing in a mixture of alcohol/formaldehyde/acetic acid (see p. 215).

For a temporary preparation the woody shaving may be stained in acid phloroglucinol (p. 239) which colours lignin red.

For a permanent mount proceed by one of the following methods:

1 Wash in alcohol (30%).
2 Stain in light green SF yellowish in clove oil (Fast green FCF in clove oil is a suitable alternative).
3 Rinse off excess stain in clove oil.
4 Clear in cedar wood oil.
5 Mount in 'Euparal'.

(*b*)

1 Boil woody shaving in potassium hydroxide (10%).
2 Wash thoroughly in water.
3 Place in chromic acid (20–30% aq.). (Few min or until soft)
4 Wash thoroughly in water.
5 Stain and mount as required.

* After Franklin, G. L. (1945). Preparation of Thin Sections of Synthetic Resins and Wood-resin Composites, and a New Macerating Method for Wood. *Nature*, **155**, 51, modified by Crowther, R. F. and Fontana, J. W., The Grammar School, Burton-on-Trent.

(*c*)

1 Place very thin shaving in a mixture of chromic and nitric acids made according to the formula on p. 232. (24 h or until the ends of the piece begin to fray)
2 Wash thoroughly in water.
3 Tease if necessary.
4 Mount in glycerol (10%) to which a drop of methylene blue has been added.
5 Cover; gentle tapping or pressure on the cover-slip should cause the cells to fall apart.

(*d*)

*Note:* This method is very drastic and should be used with the greatest care. It is best carried out in a fume cupboard.

1 Bring about 50 ml Schulze's macerating fluid (p. 246) to the boil. (Great care)
2 Place the tissue in the hot macerating fluid.
3 When the tissue can be teased apart easily, pour the tissue and fluid into a large excess of water.
4 Wash tissue thoroughly in running water. (Several h)
5 Stain and mount as required.

## 4.6 STAINING

### Principles and Purpose

In dealing with the object of fixation it was remarked that in an unstained tissue the only parts distinguishable from one another were those having different refractive indices. By staining, i.e. dyeing the tissue, the phenomenon of colour can be introduced. Those parts of the cell or tissue which stain differently because of chemical and/or physical differences can thus be more easily distinguished. This is particularly helpful when different components which, because of their like refractive indices, would remain indistinguishable, stain with different dyes or with different intensities of the same dye, and hence become well defined.

Summarized then, one may say that the object of staining is to render parts of the tissue more obvious.

**Theories of Staining***

In the past there has been much discussion between those who held that staining was a purely physical phenomenon and those who regarded it as a process of chemical combination. While there are arguments for and against both views the border-line between certain aspects of physics and of chemistry is so tenuous that neither a purely physical nor a purely chemical explanation is necessarily correct in every instance. Sometimes the explanation may lie in the realm of physical chemistry. It is known, however, that the physical processes of absorption, adsorption, capillary action, diffusion, osmosis and solution can, in their turn, play their part while, on the chemical side, it is clear that chemical reactions sometimes take place even if the result is not always an entirely different substance with entirely different properties. Histo-chemical techniques are, indeed, based upon chemical reactions forming a coloured end-product.

**Classification of Stains**

Stains, i.e. dyes, are coloured organic substances (often salts) capable, by their inherent properties, of being held by tissues even though treated later by a solvent in which they were themselves dissolved.

Dyes must contain both *chromophores* (atomic groupings which are associated with colour) and *auxochromes* (other groups which impart to the whole compound the ability to form a union with the tissue end-group).

The classification of dyes is arbitrary and to some extent depends on the point of view of the user. In general terms they may be classified as:

(i) *Basic*, when they consist of a coloured organic base combined with an uncoloured acetate, chloride, or sulphate radicle. They may dissolve in water and/or alcohol. Examples are safranin O, and haematoxylin.

(ii) *Acid*, when they consist of a metallic base, usually sodium or potassium, combined with a coloured organic acid radicle. They, also, may dissolve in water and/or alcohol. Examples are light green S.F. yellowish, and eosin Y.

(iii) *Neutral*, when they are compounds 'of an acid dye and a basic dye in which both anions and cations contain chromophore groups'.* Neutral dyes may dissolve in water, more usually in alcohol, and often give colloidal solutions. One example is neutral red.

A more precise classification is based upon the nature of the chromophore. Although this may not classify them in relation to their *colour*, nevertheless it is useful because it groups together those with a similar chemical structure. Among some of the more important groups are

(i) Nitroso dyes, such as napthol green B.
(ii) Nitro dyes, such as napthol yellow S.
(iii) Azo dyes, such as orange G, Bismarck brown and chlorazol black E.
(iv) Aryl methane dyes, such as Fast green FCF, acid fuchsin, Victoria blue.
(v) Xanthene dyes, such as pyronin Y and rhodamine B and the eosins.
(vi) Acridine dyes, such as acridine orange.
(vii) Quinone-imine dyes, including the azocarmines, safranin O, thionin and the azures.
(viii) Natural dyes such as carmine and haematoxylin.

Many of the above groups have several subgroups; for a full list see the work by H. J. Conn cited above.

Another classification of stains is based on the affinities of different parts of the protoplasm for different dyes. Thus, stains may be classified as:

(*a*) *Nuclear*, when they tend to stain the nucleus. The nucleus is rich in nucleic acid and *has an affinity for basic stains*. The nucleus, and other parts of the cell which are of an acid nature, are therefore described as *basiphil*. When treated with a basic stain the acid is believed to combine with the coloured, basic part of the dye to form a coloured, insoluble salt. Hence, *nuclear* stains are *basic* stains.

(*b*) *Cytoplasmic*, when they tend to stain the cytoplasm. The cytoplasm is usually regarded as more basic and *has an affinity for acid stains*. It is therefore described as *acidophil*. When treated with an acid stain the basic portion of the cell component is believed to combine with the coloured, acid radicle of the dye to form a coloured, insoluble salt. Hence, *cytoplasmic* stains are *acid* stains.

* For a full discussion of the various theories of staining the reader is referred to Conn, H. J. (1969). *Biological Stains*, ed. R. D. Lillie, 8th edn. Baltimore, Williams and Wilkins.

* Defined thus by the American Commission on Biological Stains; quoted from H. J. Conn, *ibid.*

It should be noted that the terms 'nuclear' and 'cytoplasmic' must not be used in too restricted a sense, because basic stains, i.e. so-called 'nuclear stains', always stain the cytoplasm to some degree. Again, some acid stains, in addition to staining the cytoplasm, are also selective for certain nuclear elements.

This particular basis of classification which, as indicated, results in a distinction between those parts of the cell which are basiphil and those which are acidophil, also serves to distinguish those parts which are *eosinophil*, a term applied to acidophil granules having a particular affinity for the acid dyes eosin Y, and orange G; and *neutrophil*, a term applied to certain cells (e.g. certain white blood corpuscles) which have an affinity for neutral dyes and which dye strongly and impartially with eosin Y (an acid dye), and methylene blue (a basic dye).

**Mordants**

From what has gone before it may have been assumed that in the staining process the dye, in some way or other – physical, chemical or physico-chemical – attaches itself directly to the tissue, i.e. that the staining process is *direct*. While this is true in some instances it is not true in others. Some dyes will *not* attach themselves directly to the tissue and so the *indirect* process must be used. This involves the use of a substance (usually a metallic ion such as Al, Cr or Fe) acting as a sort of intermediary between the tissue and the dye. This substance is called a *mordant* and the process is known as *mordanting.*

The tissue is first mordanted, i.e. treated with the mordant, which incorporates itself (? combines) with some part or parts of the tissue. On the addition of the dye it is believed that the colouring matter forms a stable 'lake' probably by surface adsorption on the mordant. In some processes the tissue is first mordanted and then stained, while in others the mordant is mixed with the staining solution. An example is the use of iron alum as a mordant for Heidenhain's haematoxylin.

**Metachromasy**

Some of the basic anilin dyes do not stain all the cell and tissue components the same colour as they themselves possess. For example, safranin O stains cytoplasm in varying shades of red and cartilage matrix yellow. This phenomenon is known as *metachromasy*, and is of value in histochemical technique.

**Specificity**

Certain dyes, given specific conditions, stain only certain tissues or components. This phenomenon is called *specificity* and the stains concerned are said to be *specific* for the tissue concerned. Examples of specificity are the blue-to-black colour given to yellow elastic fibres by Weigert's elastin stain; the bright red colour given to lignin by phloroglucinol; the bright yellow given to the same tissue by anilin chloride; and the blue colour given to cellulose by Schulze's solution.

**Methods of Staining**

Apart from specific staining techniques for particular purposes, there are certain general methods which may form part of a specific technique. They are:

1. *Progressive staining*

This depends on the fact that certain dyes, e.g. carmine and haematoxylin, stain first the nucleus and then the cytoplasm. The tissue is placed in diluted stain until the desired intensity of colour in nucleus or, later, in nucleus and cytoplasm is obtained. If sectioned tissue is being stained, the degree of progress may be watched by placing the staining vessel on the microscope stage and examining under low power. Cytoplasmic stains and counterstains are frequently used progressively, and, although opinions differ and the progressive method is slower, the beginner is advised to use it.

2. *Regressive* (*retrogressive*) *staining*

The tissue is placed in a stock solution of stain, deliberately overstained and then *differentiated* or *destained*, i.e. excess stain removed by a suitable agent. The beginner will find some difficulty in judging the correct degree of differentiation and the tissue must be examined frequently under the microscope as in the progressive method. Further information will be found under 'Differentiating' (p. 50). Nuclear stains are frequently used regressively.

3. *Counterstaining* (*differential staining*)

The phenomenon of *selectivity* is frequently used in the processes of counterstaining, when first one part of the cell or tissue is stained with a suitable dye and the other parts are afterwards treated with a stain of contrasting colour. It should be understood that in many instances the process of counterstaining really involves the displacement of one dye by another. The dye first used (e.g. safranin O) stains all the tissues. The dye next used (e.g. Delafield's haematoxylin) will also stain all the tissues, but the two dyes operate together by differential displacement till, finally, for example, the lignin is stained red and the cellulose blue.

4. *Double staining; triple staining; quadruple staining*

These terms are, to a degree, synonymous with counterstaining but should, strictly, be applied only to the use of a mixture containing two (or, respectively three or four) stains of contrasting colours; they are sometimes also applied to two or more stains used in a particular sequence.

### Technique of Staining

Tissues may be stained as sections, or as smears or squashes, or in bulk.

SECTION STAINING. This is the most satisfactory method and should always be used for large pieces of tissue and for botanical work unless otherwise specified.

SMEAR AND SQUASH STAINING. This is quite satisfactory if the smear or the 'squash' is very thin.

BULK STAINING. This is quite satisfactory for small whole animals, e.g. protozoa, small crustacea, chick embryo, but should be avoided for large pieces of tissue and for botanical work unless otherwise specified. It is difficult to judge when the tissue is sufficiently stained and it will be found that the stain is rarely evenly distributed.

Staining, differentiation, counterstaining, dehydration, and clearing of loose sections, and of smears on cover-slips, are best done in very small watch-glasses kept covered to exclude dust. In this way several sections or smears may be dealt with at once, and they are under better control than if the operations are carried out on a slide and the appropriate reagents added drop by drop.

In certain instances (e.g. smears of blood, etc.) it may be necessary to stain the material on the slide.

Before commencing to stain, consult Chapters 6 (p. 93) and 7 (p. 183) to find the best stain to use for the given tissue, the specific action of the stain chosen, and the composition of the stain. If there is still doubt about the best stain to use, *the beginner should confine himself to the methods given under 'Animal Tissue — general histology'* (p. 99) *and 'Plant Tissue — general histology'* (p. 159). *These methods are all perfectly satisfactory for most histological work.*

Remember that *if an alcoholic stain is used, the tissue must first be dehydrated up to the strength of alcohol used as a solvent* (usually 50% or 70%).

If a diluted stain is recommended, care must be taken that the stain is diluted with the solvent in which it is made up. See Chapter 7 (p. 183).

The time occupied in staining, counterstaining, differentiating and washing varies with the type of tissue and its size, the type of stain, and its strength and condition.

The following may be taken as a *very rough guide:*

| | (Sections) | (Bulk) |
|---|---|---|
| Staining and counterstaining | (2 min) | (1 week) |
| Differentiating | (*For as long as the tissue was in the stain*) | |
| Washing | (2 min) | (12 h) |

Where this guide, *which is admittedly very general*, is not sufficient, explicit directions are given. Nevertheless, it must always be remembered that circumstances alter cases and, very often, the best results will be obtained only after careful and patient trial and possible error.

It is useful to keep a written record of the results of the various methods.

## 4.7 DIFFERENTIATING

### Principles and Purpose

Differentiation, or destaining, is carried out during the process of retrogressive staining. The purpose is, as its name implies, to differentiate the degree of staining of various parts of the cell or tissue and to remove excess stain.

The most usual differentiating agent is acid alcohol, i.e. alcohol (70%) to which 1% of acetic acid or 0.5% of concentrated nitric or hydrochloric acid has been added, but it is rather drastic and apt to diffuse the stain, and for these reasons retrogressive staining is not always to be recommended for the beginner.

Acid alcohol is not of universal use as a differentiating agent and in some instances the agent varies with the stain, e.g. clove oil is used to differentiate crystal violet; iron-alum solution (p. 187) is used to differentiate iron-haematoxylin.

### Technique of Differentiating

1 Place the tissue in a watch-glass in acid alcohol (p. 186) (unless some other differentiating agent is advised for the stain in use), *until the required density of colour is obtained.* If sections attached to slides are being differentiated, carry out the process in flat-bottomed corked specimens tubes – internal measurements approximately 9 cm x 3 cm or in Coplin jars. From time to time place the watch-glass or slide under the low power of the microscope and observe the progress of differentiation.
2 Wash in alcohol (70%).
3 Counterstain, if required.
4 Dehydrate in 96% and absolute alcohol.
5 Clear in xylene and mount in synthetic resin such as D.P.X.

## 4.8 DEHYDRATING

### Principles and Purpose

Water will not mix with the resinous media in which stained and sectioned material may finally be mounted, nor with the paraffin wax with which it may be necessary to impregnate material before sectioning. The purpose of dehydration is to remove *all* traces of water from the tissue before either impregnating or finally mounting.

A dehydrating agent in common use is *ethyl alcohol*, for it is miscible not only with water but also with the *solvents* used for the resinous mounting media and for paraffin wax. Unfortunately, as indicated below, alcohol is liable to distort tissues unless it is used in graded strengths, and therefore the process of dehydration is slower when alcohol is used. Furthermore, absolute (100%) alcohol is expensive. To reduce the expense, *industrial methylated spirit** (99.24% . 74° O.P.) may be used for most microtechnical purposes instead of alcohol (100%), especially if it is dried out by standing on anhydrous copper sulphate. It may be received only under licence issued by the Customs and Excise Department to whom application can be made on the appropriate form.

Although ethyl alcohol occupies a time-honoured place in the process of dehydration it will be found that *isopropyl alcohol*, which is much cheaper, will successfully perform all the functions required of its more expensive relation.

Another alcohol is available for dehydrating before impregnating with wax, namely, *n-butyl alcohol* which is considerably cheaper than ethyl alcohol and which has the added advantage that it is miscible with paraffin wax, thus rendering clearing before wax-impregnation unnecessary.

Dehydrating agents are not limited to alcohols. *Acetone*, for example, may be used in the later stages of dehydration. One of the most useful substances, however, is 2 ethoxy ethanol† which is miscible with water, with xylene, and is also a solvent for certain stains. The use of 2 ethoxy ethanol shortens the dehydration process very considerably.

*Note:* The use of dioxan (diethylene dioxide) is NOT now recommended for purposes of dehydration. It is known to give off a poisonous vapour which may have long-term effects not yet known.

* The nomenclature of the different grades of alcohol seems to be used somewhat loosely. The following is an attempt to clarify the terminology and reduce the confusion.

*Absolute alcohol* is ethyl alcohol (100%).

*Ethanol* is ethyl alcohol produced by synthesis (as opposed to its production by distillation from, for example, molasses or potatoes).

*Industrial spirit* is a term loosely applied to industrial ethyl alcohol or ethanol. Its content of ethyl alcohol varies from (96%) to (98%).

*Industrial methylated spirit* consists of approx. 95% ethyl alcohol and approx. 5% wood naphtha (crude methyl alcohol). It is sold in two grades, namely, 60° O.P. and 74° O.P., the latter containing (99.4%) alcohol. It is colourless.

*Purple methylated spirit* consists of approx. 95% ethyl alcohol and approx. 5% wood naphtha (crude methyl alcohol) but it also contains mineral naphtha (paraffin), pyridine and methyl violet.

*Proof spirit* contains 49.28% ethyl alcohol by weight (57.10% by volume) and has a sp. gr. of 0.91976 at 15.55°C.

*'Degrees over proof'* (°O.P.) signifies the increase in volume obtained when 100 volumes of spirit are diluted with water sufficient to obtain proof spirit.

*Rectified spirit* is a term loosely applied to ethyl alcohol distilled or re-distilled from the crude spirit. The percentage of alcohol varies with the number of times it has been re-distilled and may range from (90%) (the B.P. figure) to (96%), or (98%), or even higher.

*Methanol* is methyl alcohol produced by synthesis (as opposed to its production by distillation from wood).

†See *Watson's Microscope Record*, H. F. Frost, No. 34, 19; Jan. 1935; and R. H. Thorp, No. 38, 22; May 1936.

**Technique of Dehydrating**

Sections may be dehydrated in watch-glasses. (When absolute alcohol is in use the watch-glass must be kept covered.) Bulk tissue and slides with sections attached (p. 65) should be placed in flat-bottomed corked capsules — internal measurements approximately 9 cm x 3 cm.

METHOD A. USING ETHYL ALCOHOL OR INDUSTRIAL METHYLATED SPIRIT

It is a saving of time to have a portable wooden rack made to carry a series of small bottles containing the following alcohols: 30% (in a larger wash-bottle); 50%; 70%; 90%; 100%.

While certain tissues may be transferred direct from (say) water to absolute alcohol without damage to their structure, this is by no means usual. Most tissues when transferred direct from water to alcohol (100%) are rapidly plasmolysed, i.e. the water is removed from them too rapidly, and as a result they shrink and may be distorted. Shrinkage and distortion are avoided by gradual dehydration with strengths of alcohol gradually increased, and this should be accepted as a standard method whatever the tissue, unless an exception is specifically recommended.

Start the dehydration with the strength of alcohol immediately above that in which the tissue was last placed; e.g. if the tissue has been in an alcoholic stain, first consult Chapter 7 to find the strength of alcohol in which the stain was dissolved.

| | | | (Bulk Tissue) | (Sections) |
|---|---|---|---|---|
| 1 | Transfer to alcohol | (30%) | (30 min) | (1 min) |
| 2 | " " " | (50%) | (30 " ) | (1 " ) |
| *3 | " " " | (70%) | (30 " ) | (1 " ) |
| 4 | " " " | (90%) | (6 h) | (2 " ) |
| 5 | " to fresh " | (90%) | (6 ") | (2 " ) |
| †6 | " to " | (100%) | (6 ") | (2 " ) |
| †7 | " to fresh " | (100%) | (6 ") | (2 " ) |

*Notes:*

* Tissues already fixed and washed may be brought to this stage of dehydration and preserved in alcohol (70%).

† When using cedar-wood oil as the clearing agent the final dehydration should be in alcohol (97%), and when using benzene-phenol or clove oil the final dehydration may be in alcohol (96%) containing 5% phenol.

Absolute alcohol is very expensive and it is more economical and quicker to do the final dehydration in two successive changes of small volumes of alcohol rather than in one large volume. For the first of these changes the alcohol from the *last* change of a *recent final* dehydration may be used.

**The bottle of absolute alcohol will not remain absolute if you leave it unstoppered. The dehydration with alcohol (100%) must be done in a small closed vessel. When transferring sections to alcohol (100%) make sure that the camel-hair brush is not impregnated with alcohol weaker than 100%.**

Remember that the dehydration — as well as the final alcohol — must be absolute! Slackness here — as shown by a whitish film when the tissue is subsequently immersed in benzene or xylene (if either of these be used) — spells complete disappointment later.

METHOD B. USING RECTIFIED SPIRIT* AND ISO-PROPYL ALCOHOL OR ACETONE

Processes **1** to **3** as METHOD A.

| | (Bulk Tissue) | (Sections) |
|---|---|---|
| **4** Transfer to rectified spirit (90%) | (6 h) | (2 min) |
| **5** Transfer to fresh rectified spirit | (6 ") | (2 " ) |
| **6** Transfer to isopropyl alcohol or acetone | (6 ") | (2 " ) |
| **7** Transfer to fresh isopropyl alcohol or acetone | (6 ") | (2 " ) |

N.B. — Shake off excess isopropyl alcohol before clearing.

METHOD C. USING *n*-BUTYL ALCOHOL

Refer to Method (p. 87) and proceed from process **5** to process **9** (inclusive) thereunder.

METHOD D. USING 2 ETHOXY ETHANOL

2 ethoxy ethanol is miscible with water, with alcohol and with xylene. As it does not distort thin pieces of tissue there is no need to grade the dehydration, nor is there any necessity to clear the tissue. It should *not* be used for dehydration of material in bulk.

*** See footnote* on page 51.**

Material for dehydration is transferred direct from water or from any strength of alcohol (if, for example, it has been preserved in alcohol, or if it has been in an alcoholic stain) into 2 ethoxy ethanol. Dehydration of sections takes about one minute and they may then be mounted immediately in synthetic resin. 2 ethoxy ethanol is also miscible with clove oil so that material dehydrated in 2 ethoxy ethanol may be transferred direct to a clove oil solution of a stain such as would be used in the safranin O and light green S.F. yellowish method given on page 160.

The method of using 2 ethoxy ethanol when tissue is to be wax-impregnated will be found under method 20(D) (p. 88).

## 4.9 CLEARING AND DE-ALCOHOLIZATION

### Principles and Purpose

The low refractive indices of such dehydrating agents as ethyl alcohol and ethanol make the tissues penetrated by them less transparent than is desirable for critical optical examination. Furthermore, neither ethyl alcohol nor ethanol is miscible with the wax used for impregnation; and 2 ethoxy is not miscible with the resinous media, such as Canada balsam or synthetic resins, frequently used as permanent mountants. For these reasons ethyl alcohol and 2 ethoxy must be removed from tissues before wax-impregnation and prior to mounting tissues in Canada balsam. Before dehydrating agents other than ethyl alcohol were used, the somewhat clumsy name 'de-alcoholization' was given to this process.

It will obviously be advantageous if the substances used for 'de-alcoholization' are also miscible with the solvent used for the paraffin wax or with the solvent used for the resinous mounting media, or with both. Such substances are known. They include benzene, toluene, xylene, terpineol, cedarwood oil, clove oil, and others. It so happens that all these substances have refractive indices higher than those of ethyl alcohol and 2 ethoxy ethanol and hence tissues penetrated by them become more transparent, or clear. The process is, therefore, known as *clearing*, a term frequently used, rather loosely, to include 'de-alcoholization', although the two terms are not necessarily synonymous.

Apart from any biological, chemical, or other physical considerations, the art of clearing is that of striking a working balance between the high transparency of an unstained tissue impregnated with a clearing agent of high refractive index, and the greater visibility of the components of a similar tissue impregnated with a medium of low refractive index. While it will be borne in mind that some clearing agents are also solvents for mounting media, the aim should be to use media for 'de-alcoholization' and for clearing, and as mountant-solvents and as mountants, that have refractive indices approximating to, or slightly less than, that of fixed and cleared tissue; and approximating to, or slightly more than, that of crown glass. A table of refractive indices is given on pages 255–256.

The choice of clearing agent will, of course, also depend both on the object or tissue in course of preparation and on the general method of preparation; that is, whether the preparation be temporary or permanent and, if permanent, whether or not it is to be embedded.

### Clearing Agents

(*a*) *For temporary preparations*

(i) ANIMAL TISSUE: Isotonic saline.

(ii) PLANT TISSUE: Chloral hydrate, clove oil, eau de Javelle.

(*b*) *For permanent preparations.* (*Plant and animal tissue*).

As indicated above, for making permanent preparations the clearing agent must be capable not only of de-alcoholizing the tissue but also of mixing with paraffin wax and with the resinous media used for mounting. A number of liquids satisfy these requirements but none is without some disadvantage, such as a tendency to make tissue brittle or to cause some shrinkage or to have some solvent action in certain stains. The following clearing agents are among those commonly used and their number is more than sufficient for the elementary student.

(i) XYLENE

This is one of the most commonly used substances but it has two characteristics. One is the disadvantage that it tends to cause shrinking and hardening of the tissues. The other is that it forms a whitish temporary emulsion with any residual water in an incompletely dehydrated specimen. This is a warning sign that dehydration must be continued. If no other clearing agent is available, and xylene must be used, then, in every 100 ml xylene dissolve 5 g of phenol crystals.

### (ii) BENZENE

This is strongly recommended by Baker.* It does not shrink nor harden the tissue to the same extent as xylene but, unfortunately, it also emulsifies with water. Baker avoids this, and the high cost of absolute alcohol, by doing the last dehydration in alcohol (96%) containing 5% phenol and adding 5% phenol to the benzene.

### (iii) TERPINEOL

Terpineol† may be used as a substitute for the much more expensive cedar-wood oil and has the advantage that tissues may be transferred to it from alcohol (80%). Although the clearing process is rather slow, terpineol does not make tissues brittle. It has been recommended‡ for small whole mounts of fresh-water microfauna. For paraffin wax embedding, tissues should first be dehydrated up to alcohol (95%) and then transferred to terpineol.

### (iv) AMANN'S MEDIUM (LACTO-PHENOL)

This substance is particularly useful for clearing delicate algae and fungi and for such organisms as small nematodes. It can be used when the nature of the tissue is such that sections must be thick, and it has the added advantage that material can be transferred to it from concentrations of alcohol as low as (90%).

### (v) BERLESE'S FLUID

This may be used for clearing small whole insects (p. 190).

### (vi) BEECHWOOD CREOSOTE

This is useful for clearing whole mounts of such organisms as *Taenia solium, Distomum hepaticum*, and small fresh-water fauna. Beechwood creosote (B.P.) should be specified, i.e. the substance listed in the British Pharmacopeia.

* *Cytological Technique* (1960). London, Methuen.
† Terpineol is sometimes sold as artificial oil of lilac or lilacene and should be distinguished from terpinol.
‡ Gray, P. (1936). *Watson's Microscope Record*, 37.

### (vii) CLOVE OIL

This is one of the most time-honoured substances for clearing plant tissue and, indeed, it was at one time thought that its use was essential for making the best preparations of plant tissue. It has certain advantages, namely, that it can be used to clear thick sections and that it appears to have a slight dehydrating action. Indeed, sections can be transferred to it from alcohol (95%) or even (90%).

On the other hand, it has certain distinct disadvantages. It is liable to make objects brittle. It removes many stains, e.g. haematoxylin, crystal violet, orange G, and safranin O; when used for clearing sections stained with those dyes it should be followed quickly by cedar-wood oil unless the solvent action of the clove oil is used deliberately to afford some degree of differentiation in staining. However, probably its greatest disadvantage is the fact that before the preparation is mounted in Canada balsam or synthetic resin it is *vital* to remove all traces of oil by passing the tissue through xylene.

### (viii) CEDAR-WOOD OIL

For work on animal tissue cedar-wood oil has held the same time-honoured position as has clove oil for plant tissue. It has certain advantages. Though clearing more slowly than xylene or benzene, it is the least likely to shrink or harden the tissue. It mixes only in certain proportions and with certain strengths of alcohol. Baker recommends final dehydration in alcohol (97%) and transference of the tissue to a 50/50 mixture of cedar-wood oil/absolute alcohol and then to pure cedar-wood oil for equal periods. There is no limit to the time during which tissues may be left in cedar-wood oil.

As with clove oil, however, so with cedar-wood oil. All traces of it must be removed by passing the tissue through xylene before mounting it in Canada balsam. Possibly the greatest disadvantage in the use of cedar-wood oil is its price, even if the cheaper sort used for clearing is specified instead of the more expensive sort formerly used for oil-immersion lenses. Indeed, there seems to be nothing that cedar-wood oil can do that terpineol cannot do at least as well and probably better.

(ix) METHYL BENZOATE

This will clear from alcohol (95%) and hence is useful for yolky material that would be hardened by alcohol (100%); material so cleared and intended for wax embedding must be transferred to benzene or cedar-wood oil because methyl benzoate is not completely miscible with paraffin wax.

(x) CHLOROFORM

Chloroform is a useful de-alcoholization agent, especially for small pieces of tissue before embedding in wax. It will also remove water from tissues.

**Technique of Clearing**

Clearing of sections, smears on cover-slips, and small pieces of tissue can be done in a watch-glass. Bulk tissue and sections attached to slides should be treated in flat-bottomed corked capsules – internal measurements, 9 cm x 3 cm approx.

Before using any clearing agent, see notes on Refractive Indices (p. 255).

*A. Temporary preparations of animal tissues.*
Saline (isotonic salt) solution (p. 244).

*B. Temporary preparations of plant tissues.*
(*a*) **1** Eau de Javelle (p. 211). (2–3 min)
**2** Wash with distilled water.
**3** Wash with dilute acetic acid.

or (*b*) Chloral hydrate (p. 198). (overnight)
or (*c*) Clove oil after dehydration as far as alcohol (95%).

*C. Permanent preparations of animal and plant tissues. (Small whole objects, bulk tissue, and sectioned tissue.)*

Place the clearing agent of choice in a small specimen tube and add the tissue, transferring by means of a brush or pipette from the final dehydration medium. If sections are to be cleared, dip the whole slide bearing the section in the clearing agent.

The time for clearing bulk tissues varies with the clearing agent and the tissue and its size. Twenty-four hours may be considered a maximum. Half an hour may be sufficient. If xylene is used, make the time as short as is consistent with complete clearing. Two minutes in xylene suffices for clearing stained sections prior to mounting in resin.

See Chapter 6 (p. 93) for special methods for clearing algae, fungi, insects, crustacea.

## 4.10 MOUNTING AND COVERING

**Principle and Purpose**

The principle and purpose of mounting the tissue is to preserve it for as long as desired and to enable it to be examined under the microscope. These ends are achieved by placing the tissue on a *slide* (a piece of thin, plane glass of suitable dimensions), surrounding the tissue with a *mountant* (a liquid or semi-liquid medium appropriate for the particular preparation), and covering both tissue and mountant with a *cover-slip* (a *very* thin piece of plane glass) to exclude air and dust and provide the requisite optical conditions for microscopy.

**Mountants**

The medium in which any particular tissue is mounted will vary with the type of preparation but, as the refractive index of the contents of a cell after fixation and clearing is about 1.54 the mountant should, if possible, have a refractive index approximating to this figure. A list of refractive indices is given on pages 255–256.

If the preparation is required only temporarily then the mountant is liquid to prevent the tissue drying.

If the preparation is to be of a permanent nature then the medium is usually gelatinous or resinous for the sake of preservation.

TEMPORARY MOUNTANTS FOR ANIMAL TISSUE

(i) *Saline (isotonic sodium chloride) solution.*
(ii) *Glycerol* (p. 219).

This is useful for small or delicate objects that might be damaged by too much manipulation. *The tissue should be rinsed in distilled water before being mounted*, but there is no need to dehydrate or clear.

TEMPORARY MOUNTANTS FOR PLANT TISSUE

(i) *Alcohol* (30%).
(ii) *Glycerol* (p. 219).

See remarks above.

PERMANENT MOUNTANTS FOR ANIMAL AND FOR PLANT TISSUE

(i) *Glycerol.*

See remarks above. The preparation must be sealed (p. 59). Follow the special technique given on page 58.

(ii) *Glycerol-jelly.*

Uses as for glycerol (above) but it is rather easier to use. The preparation must be sealed. Follow the special technique given on page 59.

(iii) *Farrants' medium.*

Uses as indicated for glycerol-jelly. The preparation must be sealed. Follow the special technique given on page 59.

(iv) *Amann's medium.* (*Lacto-phenol*).

This is a convenient mountant both for temporary and permanent preparations because it can be used as a base for various stains. It is, however, rather fluid, and *permanent preparations must be sealed.* Its refractive index is rather low, viz. 1.440.

(v) *Polyvinyl alcohol – Lacto-phenol.*

The addition of polyvinyl alcohol to lacto-phenol has the effect of producing a mountant less fluid than lacto-phenol. Polyvinyl alcohol—lacto-phenol is especially useful as a mountant for insect larvae, small whole insects and their various parts, and other small arthropods. Its refractive index varies between 1.447 and 1.469 according to the precise composition of the mixture. A mixture of suitable viscosity and which will dry in about six weeks at temperatures around 15°C to 18°C will have a refractive index of 1.458.

(vi) *Canada balsam in xylene* (p. 193).

Canada balsam is best kept in wide-mouthed bottles (painted black outside to prevent ingress of light and consequent acidification of the balsam) containing a small glass rod and supplied with a domed glass stopper which fits outside the neck of the bottle. Avoid cork stoppers; the cork disintegrates and fouls the balsam. If the balsam thickens, dilute it slightly with the appropriate solvent (either xylene or benzene). On pouring out fresh Canada balsam always wipe the inside of the neck and the stopper of the stock bottle with a lint-free cloth soaked in xylene. This prevents the stopper sticking and obviates much annoyance later. When removing the rod bearing the drop of balsam for mounting, be careful to lift it clear of the neck of the bottle to prevent fouling.

Permanent preparations mounted in Canada balsam cannot be handled safely until the balsam has at least partly hardened, and they cannot be examined to the best advantage until the balsam has had full time (at least a week) to penetrate uniformly.

In the course of time Canada balsam tends to become acidic and turns a darker yellow.

(vii) *'Euparal'*

This is used in the same way as Canada balsam but it has the advantage that it also acts in some measure as a clearing agent. This means therefore that *slight* amounts of water remaining in the preparation are tolerated and this mountant should be used if the dehydration is suspected of being incomplete.

(viii) *Synthetic mounting resins*

Various proprietary resins (e.g. D.P.X., 'Micrex', Xam, etc.) are now available. These are neutral and remain completely colourless even after the preparation is several years old. They are used in exactly the same way as Canada balsam in xylene.

(ix) *Polyester resin*

A recent paper by Senior* recommends the use of polyester resin for both thick whole mounts and for stained sections mounted on slides. The specimens are stained (Carmalum and Fast green FCF are good) dehydrated and cleared in xylene. They are then soaked in the uncatalysed resin for a period which varies from 15 minutes for sections to 48 hours for large mounts of embryos before mounting under a no. 1 cover-slip in fresh resin containing 0.25% of catalyst.

After curing overnight at room temperature and for 2 hours at 60°C, the preparations are ready for examination. Such preparations it is claimed are much less liable to shrinkage of the mountant than those mounted in balsam in the usual way and the cover-slip does not need supporting. A further advantage is that the mount is completely hard within a week and the specimen

* Senior, W. J. (1970). *Microscopy,* **91**, 207–210.

movement which is often so troublesome with thick whole mounts in balsam is prevented. The original paper should be consulted for full details of the technique and for sources of supply of resin etc.

**Technique of Mounting and Covering**

The plane glass slides in general use measure approximately 7.5 x 2.5 cm. At first the beginner should use circular cover-slips (19 mm diameter) and then try 2 cm square slips. For long specimens use rectangular slips 6.4 cm x 2.50 cm. Until really proficient, use slips No. 2 thickness, to avoid excess breakages. Afterwards use slips No. 1 0.13 mm in thickness, although $1\frac{1}{2}$ slips (0.17 mm thick) are more suited to critical microscopy if they can be obtained.

It is well to give the slide and cover-slip a final polish with a piece of clean linen kept for the purpose. To clean the cover-slip, hold opposite edges between the finger and thumb of one hand and polish it very gently with the linen held between finger and thumb of the free hand.

The object should be mounted in the middle of the slide. When the cover-slip has settled on the mountant, the latter should spread just to the edges of the slip — no less — no more. There may be a little difficulty in judging the correct quantity of mountant to ensure this. Perfection will come with practice.

MOUNTING — GENERAL TECHNIQUE

1 Place a drop of mountant (see above) on the centre of a *clean* slide.
2 By means of a small camel-hair brush place the object in the mountant.
3 Place one edge of a *clean* cover-slip on the slide to one side of the mountant, gently lower it by means of a mounted needle, and *allow it to settle itself* (Fig. 4.3).

   Alternatively, if stained sections which have been stuck onto slides are to be mounted, the correct quantity of mountant can be more easily estimated if it is placed on the cover-slip, the slide with its section is then inverted and lowered on to the drop of mountant.

If, by bad manipulation, air bubbles are included, warm the slide *very* gently over a small, non-luminous, gas flame.

The position of minute objects on the slide may be indicated by applying to the cover-slip a ring of Indian ink surrounding the position. The ink is best applied with the thinnest sable brush obtainable, or else by a fine mapping pen, while the slide is revolved on a turntable (see 'Sealing', p. 59).

If the object is thick and in danger of being crushed use one or other of the following devices to raise the cover-slip off the slide, thus:

(i) For a quick, temporary mount support the cover-slip on a thin ring of 'Plasticine' of diameter equivalent to that of the cover-slip.

(ii) When examining live animals: Make four balls of 'Plasticine' each about the size of a large pin's head and place them at the four corners of a dry, square cover-slip. Place the animal in a drop of water on a clean, dry slide. Invert and lower the cover-slip gently on to the slide over the drop of mountant. Gently, but firmly, press the cover-slip down, corner by corner. Keep the animal under observation meanwhile.

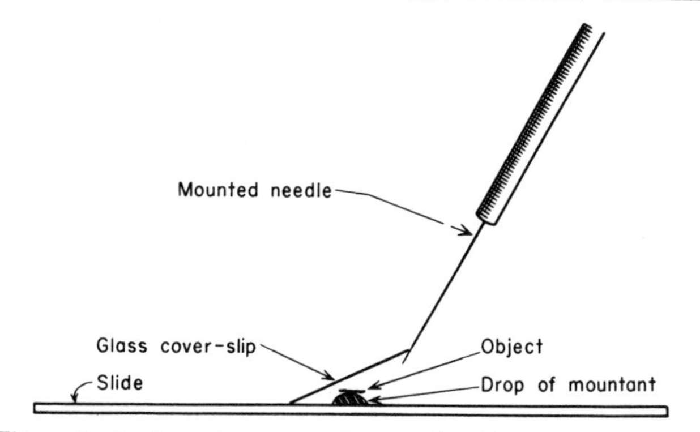


Fig. 4.3 The method of lowering a cover-slip onto the object and mountant medium.

(iii) Cut a square or circular frame of mill-board or very thick paper of the same shape and area as the cover-slip and mount the object in the space thus enclosed (Fig. 4.5a).

(iv) Cut strips of glass from a slide or a cover-slip the same length as the width of slip to be used. Place two strips in position corresponding with the ends of the cover-slip. Mount the object between them (Fig. 4.5b).

(v) With the aid of a turntable (p. 60) build up a series of superimposed rings of shellac or varnish (p. 246) by successive applications and dryings on the slide. Mount the object inside the ring (Fig. 4.4a and b).

(vi) Build up four raised spots of shellac or varnish to fit just inside the four corners of a cover-slip placed over them (Fig. 4.4c). Mount the object between the four spots.

(vii) Use a ring of tin-foil, lead-foil, or very thin sheet aluminium. Before use, flatten by pressing between two slides.

MOUNTING – SOME SPECIAL TECHNIQUES

(i) *Glycerol.*

(*a*) For delicate objects.

**1** Wash object in distilled water.
**2** Drain.
**3** Transfer either (i) to glycerol (10%) or, (ii) to a solution of

| | |
|---|---|
| Distilled water . . . . . | 5 g |
| Industrial spirits . . . . | 4 g |
| Glycerol . . . . . . . . | 1 g |

**4** Allow the glycerol or the solution to concentrate by evaporation at room temperature. (*Several d*)
**5** Transfer the object to a drop of pure glycerol on a cover-slip.
**6** Invert the cover-slip on to a slide provided with four legs of varnish, or cement, or tea-chest foil punched into discs 1–2 mm in diameter.
**7** Coat the margin of the cover-slip (which will not be touched by the glycerol) with paraffin wax.
**8** By means of a hot wire, melt the wax and run it under the slip to fill the space between the mountant and the margin of the slip.
**9** When the wax has set, remove the excess with a warmed scalpel.
**10** Seal with shellac varnish (p. 247).

(*b*) For large objects.

**1** Wash object in distilled water.

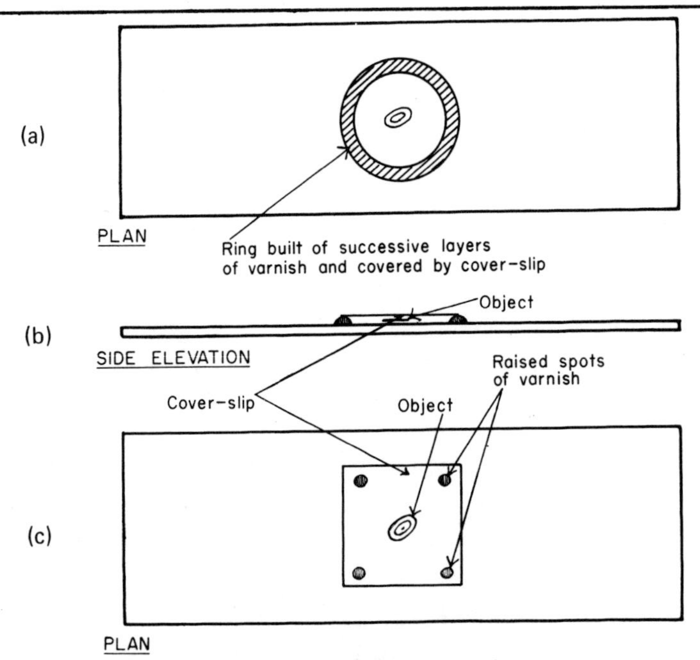


Fig. 4.4 Devices for raising the cover-slip above a thick preparation. (For temporary preparations use 'Plasticine' instead of varnish.)

2 Drain.
3 Mount glycerol (p. 219).
4 Cover.
5 Seal cover-slip with gold size (p. 247).

(ii) *Glycerol jelly.*
1 Wash object in distilled water.
2 Drain, and soak object in glycerol (40%). (3 min)
3 Melt the glycerol jelly (p. 220) on a water-bath.
4 Place object on cover-slip.
5 Feed the fluid jelly on to the object with a warm pipette.
6 Invert cover-slip on to a warmed slide.
7 Seal cover-slip with gold size (p. 247) when preparation is cool.

This method obviates the use of small cubes of jelly which may easily overheat and entrap air bubbles.

(iii) *Farrant's medium.*
1 Wash object in distilled water.
2 Drain thoroughly.
3 Soak object in Farrant's medium (p. 213).
4 Breathe on a slide and add the specimen.
5 Add a drop of Farrant's medium to the specimen.
6 Breathe on a cover-slip and lower it, damp side downwards, on to the specimen. (The dampness prevents bubbles forming in the medium.)

*Note:* Special methods for mounting protozoa, coelenterates, platyhelminthes, crustacea, insects, small algae, fungi, etc., are given in Chapter 6 (p. 93).

## 4.11 SEALING (RINGING)

### Principles and Purpose

In course of time the liquid mountants and the solvents of the resinous mountants evaporate, and it sometimes happens that a tissue cannot well be preserved permanently in a resinous medium. In such instances it is necessary to mount in a more liquid medium and to run a ring of sealing medium round the edge of the cover-slip to exclude air and prevent evaporation of the mountant. This process is known as *sealing* or *ringing* and is sometimes used even for synthetic resin mounts when it is desired to give a particularly fine finish to a slide. Preparations mounted in fluids should first

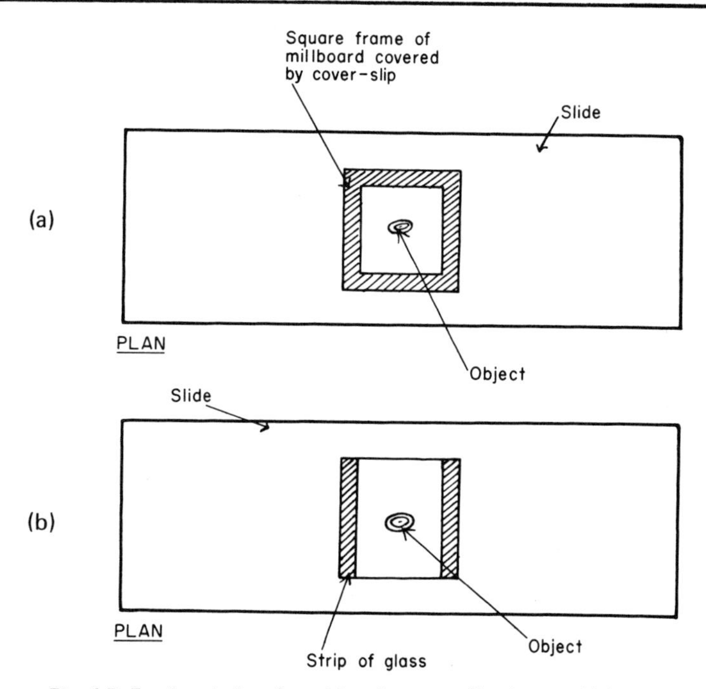


Fig. 4.5 Further devices for raising the cover-slip above a thick preparation.

be ringed with glycerol jelly before the final seal is applied.

### Sealing Media

A comprehensive list of sealing media with, in many instances, instructions for their preparation and use, is given under the heading 'Sealing Media' (p. 246 *et seq.*).

### Technique of Sealing (Ringing)

The sealing medium, which should be fairly stiff and approximately of the consistency of the gum commonly sold by stationers, should be carried on a finely-pointed No. 1 or No. 2 best-quality sable brush. The medium is applied in a narrow band to the edges of the cover-slip and to the adjacent part of the slide.

The medium must be applied in successive layers, each very thin, with sufficient time for thorough drying between each application, until a thick layer has been built up. It will be found that one very small drop of sealing medium on the end of the brush is sufficient for one application.

If a circular cover-slip is to be sealed, the process is more easily done by holding the slide under clips on a simple rotating turntable as shown in Fig. 4.6a and b. If the rings become uneven or too wide, the turntable should be revolved at a fairly fast speed and the point of the blade of a penknife used to push the sealing medium to the required position.

If it is desired to build up a ring to raise a cover-slip off a specimen, or to make a cavity for purposes of irrigation, the turntable should be used. A piece of white card, the same size as the turntable, should be cut ready to fit upon it. By means of a finely-pointed pen two concentric circles are drawn with their centres corresponding with the centre of the card. One circle should be of diameter very slightly larger than that of the cover-slip to be used; the other very slightly smaller. The card is now fixed to the turntable and the slide clipped upon it so that the circles appear in the centre of the slide. A ring of sealing medium is now applied to the slide within the area delineated between the circumferences of the concentric circles on the card beneath. A thick ring is gradually built up as described above.

If the cavity formed by the ring is to be used for holding an irrigated specimen, about one-eighth of the ring should be cut away with a razor-blade to allow the introduction of the irrigating fluid (para. 4.13).

## 4.12 LABELLING

### Principles and Purpose

These would appear to be so obvious as to need no mention. Yet it is surprising to find how many students are content to make a reasonably

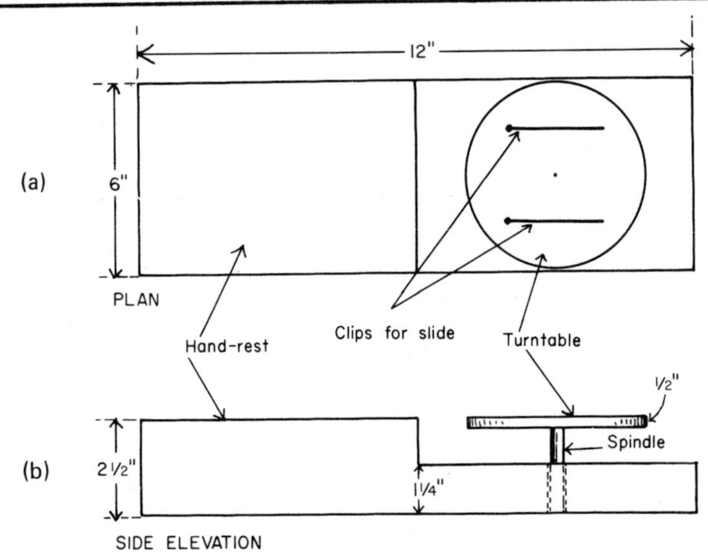


Fig. 4.6 A turntable for ringing slides.

good preparation and then leave it unlabelled, with no indication of the nature of the tissue or of the method of staining (on which future identification and interpretation may well depend), let alone the date on which it was made or even the maker's name. If the preparation is bad there may be an element of shame attached to the omission but, after all, failure can well be a spur to future success. The only advantage possessed by an unlabelled slide appears to be that, provided the preparation is of reasonably good quality, it can be used later for 'spot testing' during the course of the revision of work. On the whole, however, failure to label is *not* something to be recommended.

### Technique of Labelling

*(a) Capsules*

Capsules – flat-bottomed specimen tubes used for carrying tissue in bulk and sections attached to slides – should be labelled:

(i) outside, to indicate the liquid they contain.
(ii) inside, to indicate the tissues under treatment. This is best done in pencil, writing on a piece of plain white paper slipped inside the capsule.

*(b) Slides*

After mounting and covering the tissue, the slide should be labelled and endorsed, preferably in Indian ink, with:

(i) the name of the tissue and location of the section;
(ii) the methods of fixation and staining (this is important for purposes of interpretation);
(iii) the date of preparation;
(iv) the maker's name.

Use labels with a good adhesive – bad stickers are a source of annoyance in a dry atmosphere. Labels should be about 2.5 cm x 1.75 cm and placed at one end of the slide. If the slide is to be stored on its long edge, the writing on the label should be parallel with the long side of the slide. If it is to be stored flat, the writing on the label should be at right-angles to the long side.

In damp atmospheres it is wise to protect written labels by brushing them over with a very thin coating of molten paraffin wax. Alternatively, the label may be protected by covering it with a strip of self-adhesive tape (such as 'Sellotape') of suitable width.

## 4.13 IRRIGATING

### Principles and Purpose

It is sometimes necessary, especially when dealing with isolated cells, small animals and plants, whether live or dead, to treat them with fluids while on a slide under the cover-slip. This is accomplished by *irrigation.*

### Technique of Irrigation

It is assumed that the object is already immersed in some fluid, and this must reach at least to two opposite sides of the cover-slip. The fluid to be introduced is placed in a drop at one edge of the cover-slip. A piece of filter paper (a useful size, cut ready for convenient handling, is 5 cm x 7.5 cm) is placed with one edge against the opposite side of the cover-slip. The filter

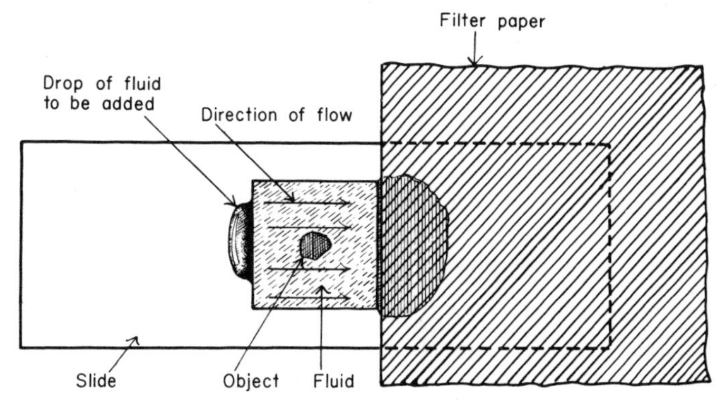


Fig. 4.7 Irrigation of a preparation with fluid.

paper draws out the liquid already under the slip, and the fluid to be added flows in to take its place (Fig. 4.7).

Irrigation should always be done gently to avoid washing the specimen out.

To enable an irrigated specimen to be examined with the microscope stage inclined to the horizontal, the specimen may be enclosed in a ring of shellac, of diameter very slightly larger than that of the cover-slip to be used, and built up gradually as explained under 'Technique of Sealing' (p. 60).

To enable the specimen to be irrigated from time to time, a sector of the ring approximating to one-eight of its circumference should be carefully cut out with a safety razor-blade. The irrigant may then be introduced by means of a Pasteur pipette, i.e. a finely-pointed glass tube fitted with a rubber bulb (or so-called 'teat') at the opposite end.

Alternatively, a 'stage plate' consisting of a glass slide 7.5 cm x 2.5 cm with a glass strip 0.25 mm wide cemented with D.P.X. on the lower edge of its upper surface may be used to mount the specimen (Fig. 4.8). The cover-slip rests against the glass strip and the irrigating liquid does not contaminate the microscope stage.

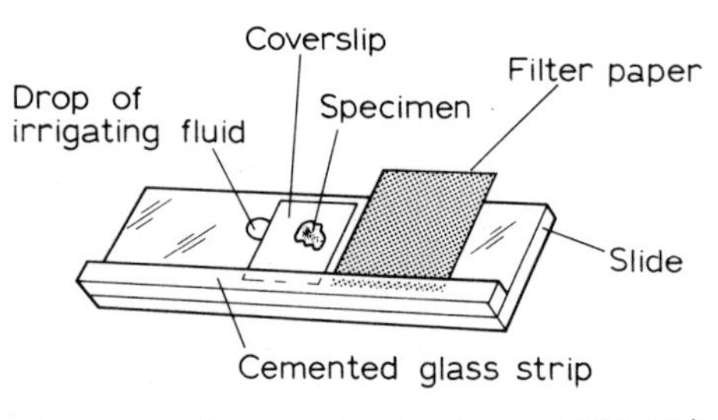


Fig. 4.8 A stage plate for irrigation of preparations when the microscope stage is in an inclined position.

## 4.14 WAX-EMBEDDING*

### Principles and Purpose

As indicated previously, reasonably thin sections of plant tissue may often be cut with a razor, free-hand. Animal tissues, being less rigid, rarely lend themselves to this method. For the finest work with both animal and plant tissue it is necessary to cut the thinnest of sections (not thicker than about 12 μm) with a mechanical microtome. For this purpose, and also when a hand microtome is in use, the tissue, after certain preliminary treatment, is either impregnated with and then embedded in a suitable stiffening material, or is frozen rigid.

### Impregnating Materials

The usual impregnating material is paraffin wax, but for certain tissues gelatine is a better material. 'Celloidin'* may be used to surround and support delicate tissues, but it does not impregnate them.

### Methods Employed for Wax-Embedding

In the preparation of wax-embedded sections two methods are employed. Either the material — after fixation, dehydration and clearing — is impregnated with and embedded in wax and then sections are cut and stained, or the material is first fixed, stained in bulk, dehydrated and cleared, and then impregnated, embedded and sectioned. Whichever method is employed, once the material is embedded in wax it may be stored for treatment later.

Suitable methods along both these lines are given in Chapter 5 under the heading 'Permanent Preparations from Wax-Embedded Tissues' (Methods 20–23; pp. 85–91). In carrying out these methods certain techniques, additional to those already described, must be used and these are explained below.

### Technique of Wax-Impregnation

The tissue is first fixed and washed according to the usual techniques. If paraffin wax is to be used for impregnating and embedding, the tissue must be dehydrated and cleared in the usual way. If, however, a water-soluble wax is to be used, the need for dehydration is eliminated.

The prepared tissue is gradually infiltrated and impregnated with molten paraffin wax. This is

* The reader may feel it a little illogical to have placed this section on wax-embedding so near the close of the chapter on techniques when it is basically concerned with the problem of tissue-sectioning. It will be appreciated, however, that as the processes of wax-impregnation and embedding involve many of the techniques already described the student without a knowledge of them would, as it were, be working blindfold.

* 'Celloidin' is a mixture of di-, tri-, and tetra-nitrates of cellulose (gun-cotton). It is soluble in acetone, ethyl alcohol (100%), clove oil, and ether. See para. 4.15, p. 66.

done by transferring pieces of tissue to small pannikins or wide and shallow specimen tubes (internal measurements: length, 9 cm; diameter, 3 cm), filled with wax to a depth sufficient to cover the tissue and kept in an oven at constant temperature not more than 5°C above the m.p. of the wax used. Unless very hard tissue has to be sectioned (when 'Ester wax' should be used), the paraffin wax should be of m.p. 56°C – *not higher*. If the wax used is of too high a melting point, the tissue may be cooked during the impregnation and difficulty may be found in getting a good ribbon of sections; over-hot paraffin causes shrinkage of the tissue and makes it very brittle.

Steedman ((1949). *Nature*, **164**, 1084) introduced a mixture which melts at 53°C but allows good sections to be cut even in rooms maintained at the temperatures current with modern central-heating installations.

*Steedman's formula.*

| | |
|---|---|
| Diethylene glycol distearate | 80 g |
| Ethyl cellulose (low viscosity) | 4 g |
| Stearic acid | 5 g |
| Castor oil | 4 g |
| Diethylene glycol monostearate | 5 g |

Replacement of the clearing agent by the paraffin wax is easier if the cleared tissue is first transferred to a mixture of clearing agent and wax and then to pure molten wax. Care must be taken to avoid getting xylene or benzene in the wax in the final stage of impregnating.

If an oven is not available, the pure wax for the final impregnation may be kept molten to a depth of about 2.5 cm in a small beaker by placing a small electric bulb about 10 cm or 20 cm above the wax. These simple devices have one advantage in that objects on top of the semi-molten wax do not get over-heated. Further, several receptacles for wax can be used; and waxes of different melting points can be used by standing the receptacles on wooden blocks at different distances from the source of heat.

It is a matter of common sense to avoid using any naked light for heating vessels containing xylene, benzene, and other inflammable substances mixed with the wax. Instead, use either, a low-power electric hot-plate, or an electrically heated oven or a small container heated by a water-bath.

The wax used for the second and third impregnation baths may be used time after time. It improves by use and continued reheating.

Waddington and Kriebel* suggest adding 0.50% of petroleum ceresin to embedding wax to give a fine texture on cooling. Add the petroleum ceresin to a mixture of wax having a m.p. slightly lower than that normally used.

When impregnating very fresh tissue, an acetone-paraffin wax mixture may be used instead of the benzene-wax or xylene-wax mixture.

Further details of the mixtures and times involved in impregnating by different methods are given under Methods 20 (pp. 85–88), 21 (p. 89) and 22 (p. 90).

**Technique of Wax-Embedding**

The wax-impregnated tissue is next embedded in a block of paraffin wax of size suitable for placing in the microtome. The block is made by pouring molten wax into a mould and, at the same time, the tissue is so placed and orientated in the mould as to enable it to be cut in the required plane.

It is first necessary to have some form of mould in which the tissue may be set and orientated. Three methods are indicated below.

(*a*) *Brass mould*

Cut two pieces of brass 1.5 mm thick, and 1.25 cm x 4 cm. Bend each piece into the shape of an L with the long side 2.5 cm and the short side 1.5 cm long. Stand on edge in the form of a box on a small sheet of glass. Warm before use.

(*b*) *Paper mould*

Make a stiff paper box 2.5 cm x 1.5 cm x 1.25 cm deep according to directions† below (see Fig. 4.9).

1. Always fold the same way (letters inwards).
2. Fold *aa'* and *bb'*.
3. Fold *cc'* and *dd'*.
4. Fold *AA'* by applying *Ac* against *Aa* and pinching out *AA'*.

* (1935). *Nature*, **136**, 685.

† Reproduced, with modification, by permission of J. and A. Churchill Ltd., from Bolles Lee's *Microtomist's Vade-Mecum.*

5 Repeat for *BB'*, *CC'*, *DD'*.
6 Turn the 'dog's ears' round against the ends of the box.
7 Turn down, outside, the projecting flaps that remain.

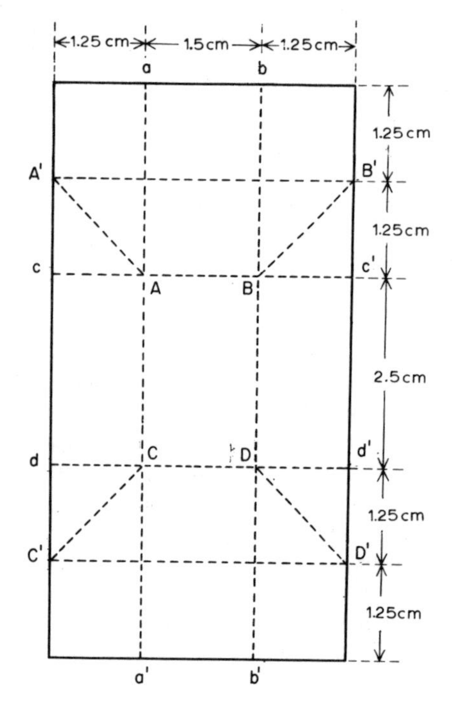


Fig. 4.9 The method of folding a sheet of paper to form a box for embedding tissues in wax. (After Lee, *Microtomists' Vade-Mecum*, Churchill, London.)

8 Smear the inside of the box with glycerol before use.

(*c*) *Watch-glass*

Useful for small objects. Lightly smear the concavity of the glass with glycerol before use.

## I. NORMAL METHOD OF WAX-EMBEDDING

1 Pour hot wax (m.p. 56°C) at not more than 58°C into a warmed mould.
2 Warm some forceps and quickly place the impregnated tissue into the molten wax.
3 Orientate the tissue as desired with a warm needle.
4 Quickly add more molten wax to fill the mould, if necessary still holding the tissue in the desired position.
5 While the wax is still molten it is well to insert a slip of paper bearing a description of the tissue, so that the paper protrudes at one corner of the mould between mould and wax. This paper will stick to the wax on cooling. Unlabelled wax blocks are a source of confusion.
6 Hold the mould on the surface of some cold water, blow gently on the surface of the wax and, as soon as a skin has been formed, immerse the mould in the water. In immersing the mould hold it at an angle to the surface of the water to prevent too sudden pressure of water on the half-solidified wax. Quick cooling of the wax helps to prevent crystallization and consequent difficulty in sectioning.
7 Remove the wax block from its mould. In this condition tissues may be preserved till they are required for sectioning.

## II. METHOD FOR WAX-EMBEDDING VERY SMALL OBJECTS

Place the object in a small piece of glass tubing. Tie a piece of silk over one end of the tube and invert the tube so that the object rests on the silk. Place the inverted tube in the wax to a suitable depth.

This method may be used for all processes from fixing to embedding.

### Technique of Sectioning Wax-Embedded Material

See pages 43–44.

### Technique of Attaching Wax-Impregnated Sections to the Slide

For ease of manipulation after sectioning, the wax-impregnated sections are best attached to a glass slide or, in some instances, to a glass cover-slip.

The adhesive used must be sufficiently strong to retain the section(s) attached to the slide, and must not dissolve off the slide during subsequent operations. On the other hand, it must in no way interfere with the final preparation. The substance in most common use is egg albumen, either alone or with glycerol.

After the sections have been attached to the slide, the wax with which they were impregnated must be removed. This is done by dissolving it in xylene.

A stock solution of egg albumen for use as a section adhesive may be made by separating the white from the yolk of an egg and diluting the egg white with an equal volume of 1% aq. sodium chloride solution. Any insoluble precipitate may be removed by centrifuging the mixture. Sodium *p* hydroxybenzoate may be added to a concentration of 0.2% w/v in order to preserve the solution against the growth of bacteria and moulds. (Baker & Jordan. (1953). *Quart. J. micr. Sci.* **94**, 237).

1 Dilute 1 volume of the stock solution of albumen with 50 volumes of distilled water.
2 Pipette about 2–3 ml diluted albumen onto a clean glass slide.
3 Place two or three paraffin sections from the ribbon onto the pool of albumen on the slide. The sections are best mounted with their shiny side towards the glass slide.
4 Warm the slide gently on a hot plate until the sections stretch and the folds in the section flatten out. Take care not to allow the wax in the sections to melt.
5 Drain off the surplus albumen by tilting the slide and then wiping carefully around the sections with a clean cloth.
6 Leave the slides in a 37°C incubator or oven to dry thoroughly.

An alternative procedure is to coat clean slides sparingly and evenly with undiluted albumen solution. (The ball of the thumb drawn from end to end of the slide produces an even smear.) Parts of the ribbon of sections are then flattened and stretched by floating them on the surface of water warmed to about 45°C in a thermostatically controlled tank. When stretched, a prepared slide is passed under the portion of ribbon which is then caught on the slide by lifting the latter obliquely out of the water. Draining and drying take place as outlined above.

*Note:* Slides with sections attached may be stored for future use. The prepared surface of the slide should be marked with a diamond pencil to avoid confusion.

**Technique of Subsequent Treatment of Wax-Impregnated Sections**

A. UNSTAINED SECTIONS

As stated under the paragraph on staining, it is usually preferable to stain tissue in sections rather than in bulk. Consequently the wax-impregnated sections are as yet unstained. Before they can be stained, the impregnating wax must be dissolved away with xylene and the xylene itself must then be removed by treating the sections with alcohol (100%).

Now the stain to be used may be dissolved in alcohol (usually 70% or 80%), or in water, so sections not attached to the slide must next be hydrated gradually by treatment with alcohol (90%), then with the strength of alcohol in which the stain is dissolved or, if an aqueous stain is to be used, with distilled water. The reasons for gradual hydration will be appreciated by a reference to those advanced for gradual dehydration.

Sections attached to slides are not harmed by passage from alcohol (90%) to water.

The technique of these operations is as follows:

*Note:* Processes **1–8**, inclusive, may be carried out (*a*) by pouring the reagents *gently* on the slide and allowing them to drain off after an appropriate lapse of time; or (*b*) by placing the slides in flat-bottomed specimen tubes (internal measurements: length, 9 cm; diameter, 3 cm) fitted with corks; or (*c*) in slide holders (p. 248) placed in vessels of suitable size; or (*d*) in more elaborate slotted jars known as Coplin jars.

1 Remove wax with xylene.* (2–3 min in jar)
2 Remove xylene with alcohol (100%). (1 min)
3 Transfer to alcohol (90%). (1 min)
4 Transfer to alcohol (70%). (1 min)

[If an aqueous stain is to be used, then **4a**. Transfer to distilled water (1 min).]

Treatment after hydration will involve staining, differentiating, dehydrating, clearing, mounting, covering, sealing and labelling.

5 Stain.
6 Differentiate.
7 Dehydrate.
8 Clear.
9 Mount.
Place synthetic resin on section(s) on slide; then cover.
10 Seal, if necessary.
11 Label.

* If a jar is used, it and the xylene it contains should be reserved for this particular purpose and no other, and labelled suitably.

Details of the processes **5** to **8**, inclusive, will vary according to the staining and dehydrating methods used.

It is advisable if slides are processed in tubes or jars to agitate them in the solutions with forceps during stages **1–8** above.

B. STAINED SECTIONS

All that remains to be done with sections from bulk-stained material, attached to slides as above, is to remove the wax from them, mount and cover.

**1** Remove wax from sections by *gently* pouring xylene on to the slide and allowing the solution to drain off.
**2** Wash gently with fresh xylene.
**3** Mount in synthetic resin by placing sufficient resin on the slide to cover the section(s).
**4** Cover.
**5** Seal, if necessary.
**6** Label.

## 4.15 'CELLOIDIN'-EMBEDDING

### Principles and Purpose

'Celloidin'-embedding serves the same purpose as wax-embedding, namely, to hold tissues rigid for sectioning. 'Celloidin', which is the trade name given to one type of low viscosity nitro-cellulose, does *not* impregnate the tissue but *surrounds* all loose structures. The method can therefore be used for soft tissues of animals and plants generally, but particularly where it is desired to reveal organs *in situ*, to preserve spatial relationships, and to avoid distortion of the tissue.

'Celloidin'-embedding is *not* satisfactory if sections thinner than 20 μm are required. It should therefore not be used for fine histological detail.

The process is considerably slower than wax-embedding.

### Technique of 'Celloidin'-Embedding

*Note:*

(i) The solvent used for 'Celloidin' in the following method is a 50/50 alcohol (100%)/ether mixture. *There must, therefore, be no naked lights in the laboratory when the method is being used.*

(ii) As the 'Celloidin' is required to *surround* the various tissues, closed structures (e.g. flower buds, ovaries, anthers, earth-worms, very small frogs, etc.) must have one end cut off to allow ingress of the 'Celloidin' solution.

(iii) Tissues should be fixed beforehand in an appropriate fixative, but fixatives containing picric acid should, preferably, be avoided as the picric acid tends to spread later into the 'Celloidin' and has a softening effect.

**1** Dehydrate the fixed tissue in the usual way, as far as alcohol (100%).

**2** Transfer the tissue to 'Celloidin' solution (4%) (see p. 200) in a firmly stoppered bottle or corked tube. Be sure that the tube is NOT left in a sunny place. (48 h – 1 week, depending on the nature of the tissue)

**3** Transfer the tissue to 'Celloidin' solution (8%, see p. 200). When it is judged that penetration is complete (48 h – 1 week) place the tissue in 8% 'Celloidin' solution in a suitable paper mould or embedding dish. It is often a help to orientate the tissue on a small 'brick' of junket. This is recommended by Baker (*Cytological Technique,* 3rd edn. 1950), who gives full details of the preparation of the junket.

**4** Cover the 'Celloidin'-containing mould with a bell jar and leave for 24 h in order to allow the bubbles of trapped air to rise to the surface.

**5** Harden the 'Celloidin' by allowing the solvent to evaporate very slowly. This is best done by removing the bell jar and covering the mould with a sheet of perforated zinc. The period of evaporation should be repeated for 2 h daily until the 'Celloidin' is a soft gel. If it shows signs of sinking in the middle of the block, run a sharp razor blade around the sides of the capsule; this will enable the gel to contract uniformly. When the upper surface of the 'Celloidin' block is of the consistency of soft india rubber it helps to remove the block from the mould and turn it upside down and replace it in the mould. Continue the daily hardening process until the whole block is of a hard rubbery consistency. This may take from 8–14 days or more.

6 Place the block in 70% alcohol to complete the hardening. Tissues must be stored in this until ready for sectioning. (24 h)

### Technique of Sectioning 'Celloidin'-Embedded Material

'Celloidin'-embedded material should be sectioned with a bench microtome in accordance with the technique described on page 43.

The block of 'Celloidin'-embedded material is supported on the microtome-chuck by means of Apáthy's adhesive (p. 185).

Sections should be cut at 20 µm with a plano-concave knife well flooded with 70% alcohol. They should be transferred to, and may be stored in, alcohol (70%).

### Techniques of Staining, Dehydrating, Clearing and Mounting 'Celloidin'-Embedded Sections

Apart from the particular advantages of the 'Celloidin'-embedding method already mentioned (p. 66), certain additional advantages become apparent towards the end of the process. Unlike the latter stages of the wax-embedding process, (when sections are attached to slides by a special method and when the removal of wax from the sections involves an additional operation), no special procedures are necessary preparatory to staining and mounting 'Celloidin'-embedded sections.

1 The sections have been placed, or stored, in alcohol (70%). Therefore, if it is decided to use an aqueous stain the sections must first be *hydrated* in alcohol (50%) (2 min), and alcohol (30%) (2 min).
If an alcoholic stain is to be used no action is necessary.
2 Stain in haematoxylin; or aniline blue W.S.; or brazilin; or chlorazol black. Other stains colour 'Celloidin' and must be avoided. The stain should be diluted with its solvent, otherwise there is a tendency to overstain and differentiation is difficult.
3 Dehydrate to alcohol (96%).
4 Clear in terpineol.
Do NOT attempt to clear in clove oil – it is a solvent for 'Celloidin'.
5 Mount in synthetic resin e.g. D.P.X.
6 Seal, if desired.
7 Label.

If it is desired to attach sections to slides before staining, a method will be found in Baker, *Cytological Technique,* 3rd edn. (1950), page 126.

## 4.16 'CELLOIDIN' – PARAFFIN WAX-EMBEDDING

### Peterfi's Method

This particular technique of embedding combines the respective advantages of 'Celloidin' and paraffin wax – the former helping to keep tissues in their correct positions relative to each other, the latter providing a firm basis for sectioning. It is particularly useful for such soft and complicated structures as the vertebrate eye, and for such small and delicate organisms as *Hydra.* Indeed, paraffin wax impregnation and embedding alone is not satisfactory for animals such as *Hydra*. The particular advantage of Peterfi's method is that it saves the necessity for following the whole sequence of both the 'Celloidin' and the paraffin-wax impregnation and embedding processes.

### Technique of Peterfi's Method

1 Usual processes of fixation and washing, according to the nature of the material.
2 Usual sequence of process of dehydration up to alcohol (95%).
3 Transfer to methyl benzoate. (Until the tissue is clear)
4 Transfer to:
'Celloidin' 1 g
Methyl benzoate 99 ml (3–12 h, according to size)
5 Transfer to fresh 'Celloidin' in methyl benzoate. (12–24 h according to size)
6 Again transfer to fresh 'Celloidin' in methyl benzoate. (12–24 h according to size)
(7 If desired, store in this solution)
8 Transfer to benzene. (15 min–12 h according to size)
9 Transfer to fresh benzene. (15 min–18 h according to size)
[10 Transfer large pieces to further fresh benzene. (24 h)]
11 Transfer to:
Benzene 100 ml
Paraffin wax Satis. (At 30°C for 15–30 min)
12 Transfer to pure paraffin wax.
13 Embed in paraffin wax.

## 4.17 FREEZING AND GELATINE-EMBEDDING

Although the best sections of animal tissue are likely to be cut if the material is held rigid, there are occasions when it is impossible to use either the paraffin-wax or the 'Celloidin'-embedding techniques for this purpose because either the alcohol used for dehydration or the xylene or chloroform used for clearing would affect the tissue. An obvious example is the investigation of a tissue for its fatty contents. Again, there may be special reasons for examining a tissue absolutely fresh, without prior contact with water or any other liquid. In such instances recourse may be had either to the *freezing technique* or to the *gelatine-embedding technique*, but neither of these should be attempted by the novice in microtechnique.

For both these techniques a *sliding microtome* is to be preferred, but it is possible to adapt some other types of microtome for the purpose. (A sliding microtome is one in which the tissue is held on a horizontal sliding bed and moves against the cutting blade which is also fixed horizontally and, preferably, fitted with a blade-freezing device.) A cylinder of liquid carbon dioxide is often required for both the freezing and the gelatine-embedding methods, although freezing can be achieved by means of ether* or by the use of Peltier-effect thermomodules.

A. THE FREEZING TECHNIQUE

### (i) Technique of Freezing and Sectioning

*Note:* Material may be sectioned without prior fixation or, provided fixation will not interfere with the investigation, after fixation in any of the usual fixatives for animal tissue.

1 Adjust the freezing microtome to cut sections at about 20 µm.
2 If possible, trim the piece of material so that it is approximately rectangular in shape.
3 Place a *small* quantity of water on the microtome chuck in order to freeze the tissue to it.
4 Place the tissue on the chuck and orientate it so that the blade will cut across it diagonally. This will give the blade a more gradual entry into the tissue.
5 Adjust the height of the bed so that blade and tissue are at the same height.
6 Apply carbon dioxide from the cylinder, *a little at a time in short bursts*, until the tissue is both frozen and frozen to the chuck.
*Note:* The amount of freezing necessary will depend on the tissue. Fat and connective tissue require less freezing than softer tissues such as spleen and liver. Over-frozen tissue will be brittle and show cracks; under-frozen tissue will tear when sectioned.
7 Cut sections as required.
8 *Either* (*a*) transfer sections by means of a dry sable brush to either distilled water or formol-saline (10%) and then proceed to (ii) below.
*or* (*b*) stain the sections before attaching to slides.

### (ii) Technique of Attaching Frozen Sections to Slide

1 Smear a slide, *very thinly*, with gelatine.
2 Leave the slide (partly inverted to protect the gelatine from falling dust) in a warm place for the gelatine to dry.
3 Make a section-lifter from a piece of glass rod drawn out to a point and bent at an oblique angle about 3 cm from the pointed end.
4 With one hand hold the slide, gelatined side uppermost, just below the surface of some distilled water in a Petri dish.
5 With the other hand use the section-lifter to lift a section from its dish of water (or formol-saline) and to lower it into the dish of water just over the centre of the gelatined slide.
6 Gently slide the section-lifter away from under the section and, almost simultaneously, gently raise the slide to catch the section on it.
7 Carefully drain off excess water from the slide.
8 Cover the section with a piece of very thin tissue paper (or cigarette paper) wetted on both surfaces.
9 Ensure attachment of section to slide and removal of excess moisture by very gentle vertical pressure with filter paper.
10 Carefully remove the filter paper and the tissue paper. If the tissue paper tends to

* Suggestions on the construction of a freezing microtome using ether will be found in an article by the Reverend M. T. Casey. (1947), *School Science Review*, **XXIX**, No. 107. 97.

stick to the section, apply a little alcohol (50%) containing 0.5% of pyridine.

[**11** Fix unfixed sections by exposing the slide to the vapour of warm formaldehyde (40%). (15 sec)]

**12** Transfer the slide to formol-saline (10%).

**13** Proceed to the desired staining method.
*Note:* Suitable methods for fat are given on p. 128.

### (iii) Handling of free-floating sections

Such sections may be transferred from solution to solution by means of the glass section-lifter described above or, alternatively, many sections may be handled together by placing them inside a small gravimetric crucible with a perforated bottom. This may then be passed from solution to solution carrying the sections with it. In this case the staining solutions are best contained in small pots – those in which certain fish and meat pastes are sold do very well for this purpose. Individual sections are best stained in small watch glasses containing the various solutions.

After the conclusion of staining the sections should be placed in a Petri dish of distilled water and mounted individually on clean slides (gelatined slides are not necessary) by the techniques outlined in stages **4–7** of A (ii) above. Frozen sections are best mounted in Farrants's medium (p. 213), or in glycerol jelly or Zwemer's medium (glychrogel, p. 253).

## B. THE TECHNIQUE OF GELATINE-EMBEDDING

### (i) Technique of Gelatine Impregnation, Embedding and Sectioning

**1** Fix and wash the tissue.

**2** Impregnate by placing it in gelatine (25%). (24 h at 37°C)

**3** Embed in gelatine (25%). (Till gelatine hardens. In a refrigerator. Several h)

**4** Trim the gelatine block to a convenient size for subsequent sectioning or storage.

**5** Place (and, if desired, store) the block in formaldehyde (10%) to render the gelatine insoluble in water. (A few h)

**6** Rinse in distilled water.

**7** Trim away the gelatine almost down to the tissue.

**8** Freeze the block onto the chuck of the freezing microtome by applying carbon dioxide from the cylinder.

**9** Allow the block to thaw until sectioning is just possible.

**10** Cut sections rapidly.

**11** Transfer sections *either* (*a*) to distilled water, *or* (*b*) to formaldehyde (10%) for storage.

*Notes:* The stock solution of gelatine should contain 0.2% sodium hydroxybenzoate to inhibit the growth of bacteria and moulds.

Do not maintain the stock solution of gelatine liquid for long periods as this tends to prevent the gelatine from forming a satisfactory gel on cooling.

Sections may be stained whilst they are 'free-floating' or after attachment to slides; the former method is quicker and usually more satisfactory.

### (ii) Technique of Attaching Gelatine-Embedded Sections to the Slide and their Subsequent Treatment

**1** Transfer a section from distilled water to a slide.

**2** Carefully drain off excess water.

**3** By means of a fine pipette place a *very small* quantity of previously warmed gelatine (1%) under the section.

**4** Dry the gelatine. (At 37°C for 5 min)

**5** Transfer the slide to formaldehyde (10%).

**6** Rinse in distilled water.

**7** Stain as desired.

**8** Mount in Zwemer's medium (p. 253).

**9** Cover and leave for a few h until the mountant sets.

## 4.18 RESIN EMBEDDING

This is a useful technique for the preservation and examination of whole mounts such as, for example, *Periplaneta* or small shells, or skulls etc.

**1** Measure very carefully into a clean container (glass, enamel, or porcelain):

Embedding resin* 100 g
Hardener 8 ml
As required (see **6** below) add
Accelerator 10 drops.

* A useful basic kit for this purpose, Mounting Kit Ceemar S51–100 (containing 'Ceemar' Embedding resin), is supplied by Messrs. Griffin and George.

2 Mix materials very thoroughly for at least 2 min.
3 Pour the mixed plastic into a polythene mould to a depth of approximately 3 mm.
4 Allow the plastic almost to set.
5 While the plastic is still tacky, position the specimen on the surface of this layer. If the specimen is large, pour a further 'holding' layer of plastic on top of the first layer.
6 While waiting for the first and successive layers of plastic to set it is best to keep the resin mix (preferably without the accelerator having been added) in a refrigerator.
7 When the first and 'holding' layers of plastic have set, add successive layers of plastic, *never more than* 4 mm *depth at a time*, until the specimen is covered, taking care to let each layer set before adding the next.
8 *Immediately* after use, and before any resin sets on them, clean all vessels and instruments in a strong solution of detergent in hot water.
9 Remove the cast block from the mould and cut to the required shape with a fine-toothed saw.
10 Polish with fine grades of emery cloth, finishing with metal polish on a soft rag.

# 5

# Standard methods for making microscopical preparations

In this Chapter there are outlined some common standard methods for making temporary and permanent microscopical preparations of animal and plant tissue. In order that confidence may be acquired in a small field the number of methods and of tissues suggested has been limited and the methods have been arranged in order of increasing difficulty.

The beginner is strongly recommended:

1 To read Chapter 2 (p. 3) so that he may learn something about the microscope and its care and use before he attempts to use it.

2 To collect beforehand all the apparatus and material likely to be needed and to arrange the various reagents near at hand and in some logical order of use. For this purpose it is useful to have at least three portable racks fitted with bottles, respectively, of

   (i) The most commonly used stains, e.g. Delafield's haematoxylin; eosin Y; fast green FCF; iodine; picro-aniline blue W.S.; safranin O.

   (ii) Distilled water (in a large wash-bottle); and alcohols for dehydrating, viz. (70%); (90%); and (100%); arranged in that order.

   (iii) Clearing agents and mountants, e.g. cedarwood oil; clove oil; xylene; glycerol; isotonic saline; D.P.X.

3 To cultivate the habit of putting bottles back in their proper places immediately after use. A bench littered with bottles of all sorts, here, there, and everywhere, leads only to confusion and mistakes. Some processes require only a few seconds for their completion and if the next bottle required is not immediately at hand in the right place, delay will occur and disappointment will ensue. In any case, unnecessary movement about a laboratory, especially if it is a crowded laboratory, suffices merely to raise dust, knock other people's elbows just when they are doing their best to hand-cut a thin section, shake other people's microscopes just when they have focused an object under high-power, and to create a disturbed atmosphere generally. It is far better to collect everything one is likely to need, beforehand, without, of course, hoarding to oneself the one and only bottle of some little-used reagent that someone else may require and that should be taken from and replaced promptly in its usual, and no doubt fairly central, position.

4 To make sure that his glass-ware is clean (p.218)

5 To make sure that his razor is sharp before attempting to cut sections (see p. 242).

6 To treat sections and small pieces of tissue in flat-bottomed watch-glasses of about 4.5 cm in diameter. Rather more costly, but less liable to be upset, are the so-called 'solid' watch-glasses. These are made of solid black or clear glass and have a watch-glass-like cavity. Whatever the type, watch-glasses should be kept covered, either by an inverted watch-glass or by a plane piece of glass of appropriate size, to prevent both the ingress of dust and, when

dehydrating in alcohol (100%), absorption of moisture from the air. Subsequent location of sections is facilitated if the watch-glasses are set out in a row on a piece of white paper. Mistakes are avoided if the name of the liquid in each vessel is written adjacent to it on the paper, and in the sequence in which each is to be used for the particular method being carried out.

7 To treat tissue in bulk (for fixation, washing, dehydration, clearing and impregnation) in flat-bottomed specimen tubes (approx. internal measurements: length, 9 cm; diameter, 3 cm) fitted with corks.

8 To treat sections attached to slides (for hydration, staining, washing, dehydration and clearing) in tubes as in 7, above. If the tubes are of the size indicated, they will carry two slides back to back – though the slides are rather liable to cling together. More elaborate apparatus made with slots to carry a great number of slides may be purchased from the usual dealers. A simple device is mentioned on page 248. Confusion is avoided if the surfaces of the slides bearing the preparations are first marked with a diamond pencil.

9 To label

(i) the tubes, to indicate the liquid they contain;

(ii) the inside of the tubes, to indicate the tissues under treatment. This is best done by pencil-writing on a piece of plain white paper slipped inside the tube.

10 To refrain from throwing away the various liquids after once using them. Provided there has been no deliberate or careless mixture of liquids they may mostly [perhaps with the exception of alcohol (100%)] be used over and over again, especially if the operations have been carried out in corked tubes. If the operations have been carried out in watch-glasses, the liquids should be returned to bottles appropriately labelled and kept specially for the purpose, i.e. they should *not* be returned to the stock bottles. The operator must use his judgment in deciding when the value of any particular liquid is exhausted.

11 To make a point of referring to the appropriate section of Chapter 4 (p. 33) to make sure he understands the underlying principles before he attempts to carry out any process. Without a knowledge of the underlying principles he is working in the dark and his work is bound to be slipshod and the final result poor.

12 To master the technique of each process and get really good results from each method before passing on to the next. In the pages that follow the techniques are merely outlined. They are explained in detail in Chapter 4.

13 To exercise care and patience in every process.

14 To work through the methods in this chapter in the order in which they are given.

15 *To try other interesting methods* [such as those given in Chapter 6, 'Methods for Specific Material', and in particular in the sections headed 'Animal Tissue' (p. 99 *et seq.*) and 'Plant Tissue' (p. 159 *et seq.*)] *but only after acquiring some facility with the standard methods here outlined.*

16 To bear in mind that "*the capacity for making full use of unstained sections and, in fact, the direct observation of living material are the foundation of biological training*".*

17 To recognize the microscopic appearance of 'foreign bodies' so that he may distinguish between them and the living material or the section he wishes to observe. To this end he should carry out the following preliminary exercises:–

**Recognition of Foreign Bodies**

Remember, dirty glass-ware and dirty lenses tend to give cloudy and 'fuzzy' images of low contrast.

(*a*) Place, in turn, some dust, a few sand grains, fibres of wool, cotton, linen, silk and a human hair on a clean slide. Examine and draw under a *low-power* objective. Do *not* examine under a high-power objective unless the objects are covered with a cover-slip.

(*b*) Note the microscopic appearance of air-bubbles. By means of a glass tube drawn out to a jet of suitable size (to be determined by trial and error), place a drop of water or glycerol in the middle of a clean slide. Mount

* Godwin, 1935. *New Phytologist*, **XXXIV**, No. 3.

a small quantity of any of the materials mentioned above at (*a*) in the mountant. Cover with a clean cover-slip according to the technique given on page 57. The mountant should spread to the edges of the cover-slip — no less and no more. At the first attempt air-bubbles will almost certainly be included, due either to bad judgment of the quantity of mountant required or to bad manipulation of the cover-slip, or both. Examine and draw the bubbles under low power and the objects under high power. Note the difference in appearance of the objects when mounted in a liquid to exclude air.

In future, regard the inclusion of any dirt, foreign bodies, or bubbles as a piece of bad workmanship.

### Temporary or Permanent?

The student may be confronted with a request 'to make a microscopic preparation of the tissue provided'. Does this mean a 'temporary preparation' or a 'permanent preparation'? Unless otherwise stated, it may be assumed that a temporary preparation is all that is required.

A 'temporary preparation' is one that will not remain fit for examination under the microscope for more than a limited time, perhaps for only a few minutes and certainly not for more than a few hours.

A 'permanent preparation,' on the other hand, should remain fit for examination for many years, although even the best microscopic preparations are liable to deteriorate and the stains perhaps to fade, after a very long period.

Even if a permanent preparation is required it is best always to make a temporary preparation before proceeding to one or other of the specialized techniques for permanent preparations. In this way it is possible to make a choice of the best piece of tissue or the best section for permanent preservation, and, in the long run, time will be saved.

## STANDARD METHODS

### A. Temporary Microscopical Preparations

### METHOD 1. UNSTAINED WHOLE MOUNT

*Material suggested:* Colonial algae; epidermis of onion leaf; hay infusion.

| *Process* | *Comment* |
|---|---|
| **1** Mount the material in water. | Place a drop of water in the middle of a glass slide. By means of a mounted needle or a pointed camel-hair brush transfer some of the material to the water. Purpose is to keep the material from drying during examination. |
| **2** Cover (p. 57). | Place a thin glass cover-slip over the object. Purpose is to prevent evaporation of the mountant, damage to the microscope objective and to provide the requisite optical conditions for viewing with the microscope. This process is normally assumed to be included in the mounting process. |

### METHOD 2. IRRIGATED WHOLE MOUNT

*Material suggested:* Colonial algae; epidermis of onion leaf; hay infusion.

| *Process* | *Comment* |
|---|---|
| **1** Mount in water. | |

| *Process* | *Comment* |
|---|---|
| **2** Cover (p. 57). | |
| **3** Irrigate with dilute iodine (p. 61). | Using the same piece of material as in Method **1**; the purpose is to observe changes wrought by the irrigant. With iodine, starch granules will be stained blue; protoplasm brown; protozoa will be killed; cilia will become more easily visible. |

### METHOD 3. UNSTAINED 'SQUASH'*

*Material suggested:* Pulp of fruit of tomato (*Lycopersicum esculentum*); pulp of snowberry (*Symphoricarpus racemosus*).

| *Process* | *Comment* |
|---|---|
| **1** Mount in water. | Cut the skin of the fruit and extract some of the fleshy material with the blade of a scalpel. Transfer a *small* quantity to a drop of water on a slide. Do *not* smear the material over the slide. (The aim is to have just sufficient material – no more, no less – to spread evenly beneath a coverslip after process **3**.) |
| **2** Cover with a cover-slip. | |
| **3** Squash. | Place a piece of filter paper over the slide and, using gentle, *vertical* pressure from one finger, squash the material so that it spreads evenly to the edges of the cover-slip. Pressure is *vertical*, without any sideways movement, to avoid lateral distortion of cells. The squash should be only a cell or two or three thick. The filter paper will blot up any excess mountant from the edges of the cover-slip. |

### METHOD 4. STAINED 'SQUASH'*

*Material suggested:* Pulp of snowberry (*Symphoricarpus racemosus*).

| *Process* | *Comment* |
|---|---|
| **1** Mount in iodine solution (p. 228). | Prepare the slide as in Method **3** but mount in iodine instead of in water. The iodine is the preliminary part of a method for staining the cellulose. |
| **2** Remove excess mountant. | Place the edge of a piece of filter paper at the outer limit of the drop of mountant. The filter paper will absorb any excess. |
| **3** Add sulphuric acid (70% aq.) or zinc chloride (conc. aq.) (p. 253). | By means of a fine pipette or glass rod add a *small* drop of the reagent to the material. Either reagent will cause the cellulose in the iodine-treated material to turn blue. |

* A true squash necessitates maceration of the tissue.

| Process | Comment |
|---|---|
| 4 Cover with a cover-slip. | |
| 5 Squash as in Method **3**, process **3**. | If some cells have absorbed too much acid they will first swell and then dissolve. Some cells may not have absorbed sufficient reagent and will remain yellowish owing to the iodine. |

## METHOD 5. UNSTAINED SMEAR

*Material suggested:* Squamous epithelium from cheek.

| Process | Comment |
|---|---|
| 1 Scrape some epithelial cells from the inside of the cheek. | Use the handle-end of a clean stainless steel scalpel or a clean wooden Tongue-depressor. |
| 2 Smear some of the cells on the middle of a slide.* | Smear should be thin (to show individual cells) and occupy about the same area as a cover-slip. |
| 3 Add a drop of isotonic (mammalian) saline solution (p. 244) to the smear. | This mountant prevents the cells from shrinking or swelling. |
| 4 Cover. | |

## METHOD 6. IRRIGATED SMEAR

*Material suggested:* Squamous epithelial cells from cheek.

| Process | Comment |
|---|---|
| 1 Smear the tissue on a slide.* | |
| 2 Add a drop of isotonic (mammalian) saline (p. 244). | |
| 3 Cover. | |
| 4 Irrigate with 1% acetic acid (p. 184). | This irrigant will render the nuclei more easily visible. |

## METHOD 7. UNSTAINED SECTIONS

*Material suggested:* Transverse sections of carrot.

| Process | Comment |
|---|---|
| 1 Section (p. 42). | Purpose is to have tissue so thin that light reflected from microscope mirror will pass through tissue and microscope lenses to observer's eye. Cut very thin transverse sections with a razor, freehand or with the aid of a hand microtome. Do not stop at one section; cut several at a time and do not reject small sectors of material. By means of a clean small camel-hair brush transfer the sections from the razor to a watch-glass of distilled water. |

* If preferred, the tissue may be smeared on a cover-slip, which would then be inverted in a drop of saline previously placed on the slide.

| Process | Comment |
|---|---|
| **2** Mount in glycerol (p. 219). | Place a drop of glycerol (50%) in the middle of a slide. With the camel-hair brush transfer the thinnest section to the drop of mountant. |
| **3** Cover. | |

## METHOD 8. IRRIGATED SECTIONS

*Material suggested:* Transverse sections of carrot.

| Process | Comment |
|---|---|
| **1** Section (p. 42). | |
| **2** Mount in water. | |
| **3** Cover. | |
| **4** Irrigate (p. 61) with anilin chloride solution (p. 189); or anilin sulphate solution (p. 189); or phloroglucinol (p. 239) followed by hydrochloric acid (conc.). | The purpose is to demonstrate lignified tissues (xylem). With anilin chloride or anilin sulphate lignified tissues stain yellow. With phloroglucinol followed by hydrochloric acid (conc.) they stain red. |

## METHOD 9. STAINED SECTIONS

*Material suggested:* Transverse sections of stem of white deadnettle (*Lamium album*); stem of sunflower (*Helianthus annuus*); root of buttercup (*Ranunculus repens*).

| Process | Comment |
|---|---|
| **1** Fix the tissue (p. 35). | Place the tissue in 'chrom-acetic' (p. 199) overnight. Purpose is to retain the tissue in as life-like a condition as possible and to harden it so that it may be sectioned more easily. (This may have been done for you beforehand but it is always well to know, or to ask, what fixative has been used, as this may affect subsequent staining processes.) |
| **2** Wash in distilled water | A very necessary process — to remove fixative which might otherwise interfere with the staining process. |
| [**3** Preserve in alcohol (70%). | This is not an essential process but will help to harden the tissue]. |
| [**4** Wash in distilled water. | To remove preservative which might otherwise interfere with staining by an aqueous stain]. |
| **5** Section. | |
| **6** Stain with Delafield's haematoxylin (p. 222). (3–10 min). (Although this is an alcoholic stain the concentration of alcohol is only about 20% and sections may safely be transferred from and to distilled water.) | Purpose is to render certain parts of the tissue more visible. Choose the thinnest sections, even though they may be only sectors of the stem, and transfer them to a watch-glass containing some stock solution of stain diluted about 1 in 3 v/v with distilled water. After 3 min place some of the sections on a slide and examine under the microscope to see if they are stained sufficiently. The |

| Process | Comment |
|---|---|
| | cell nuclei will be stained deeply; the cytoplasm less deeply. If not stained sufficiently, replace in stain and try again. |
| 7 Wash in distilled water. | To remove excess stain. |
| 8 Wash in tap-water. | To 'blue' the haematoxylin. If tap-water is very soft use dilute ammonia solution (p. 188). The nuclei will be stained blue. |
| 9 Mount in glycerol (p. 219). | |
| 10 Cover. | |

## METHOD 10. COUNTERSTAINED SECTIONS

*Material suggested:* Transverse sections of stem of white deadnettle (*Lamium album*); stem of sunflower (*Helianthus annus*); root of buttercup (*Ranunculus repens*).

| Process | Comment |
|---|---|
| 1 Fix the tissue. | As in Method **9** above. |
| 2 Wash in distilled water. | As in Method **9** above. |
| [3 If desired, preserve in alcohol (70%). | As in Method **9** above. |
| [4 Wash in distilled water. | As in Method **9** above. |
| 5 Section. | |
| 6 Stain with Delafield's haematoxylin (p. 222). (3–10 min). | Dilute the stain about 1 to 3 with distilled water. Check progress under microscope. |
| 7 Differentiate in acid alcohol (p. 186). (Momentarily) | Purpose is to remove the haematoxylin from the cytoplasm which, otherwise, would give a purplish-red colour when counterstained with eosin Y. |
| 8 Wash in tap-water or dilute ammonia. | To blue the haematoxylin. (See **8** above.) |
| 9 Counterstain with aqueous eosin Y (p. 211). (30–60 s). | Place the haematoxylin-stained sections in a watch-glass of aqueous eosin Y. Purpose is to stain cytoplasm pink. |
| 10 Rinse in tap-water quickly. | |
| 11 Mount in 50% glycerol. | |
| 12 Cover. | |

## METHOD 11. MACERATED UNSTAINED SECTIONS

*Material suggested:* Sections of any fleshy root, e.g. carrot.

| Process | Comment |
|---|---|
| 1 Section the material. | Prior to removing the pectin cement (middle lamella) between the cells. |
| 2 Place in hydrochloric acid (alcoholic) (p. 187). (24 h) | Purpose is to convert the pectins into pectic acid (insoluble in alcohol). |
| 3 Wash sections in water. | To remove acid. |
| 4 Place sections in ammonium oxalate (5% aq.). | Purpose is to convert pectic acid to ammonium pectate (soluble), and calcium to calcium oxalate which is precipitated. |

| Process | Comment |
|---|---|
| **5** Mount sections in ammonium oxalate on the slide. | |
| **6** Cover with a cover-slip. | |
| **7** Tap the slide gently. | Purpose is to cause the cells of the macerated sections to fall apart with their cellulose walls undamaged. |

**B. Permanent Microscopic Preparations**

## METHOD 12. STAINED WHOLE MOUNT

*Material suggested: Daphnia* or *Cyclops.*

For this method first make a container, suitable for holding a number of the animals, by tying a piece of muslin or silk over one end of a short piece of glass tubing having about 1 cm bore. Processes **1** to **9** inclusive are carried out by dipping the covered end of the tube in each liquid (placed, for convenience, in short wide specimen tubes) to a depth sufficient to cover the animals. When each process is complete, the tube is removed, allowed to drain for a moment or two, and then placed in the next liquid.

| Process | | Comment |
|---|---|---|
| **1** Kill and fix in Bouin's fluid (p. 191). | (10 min) | The picric acid in the fixative will also stain the chitin yellow. |
| **2** Wash in alcohol (30%). | (2 min) | |
| **3** Dehydrate in alcohol (50%). | (2 min) | It is proposed to use an alcoholic stain, i.e. a stain dissolved in (50%) alcohol. Therefore dehydrate to this stage before staining. |
| **4** Stain in borax carmine (p. 196). | (2 min) | |
| **5** Wash in alcohol (70%). | (2 min) | |
| **6** Dehydrate in alcohol (90%). | (2 min) | |
| **7** Dehydrate in alcohol (100%). | (2 min) | |
| **8** Clear in clove oil or cedar-wood oil. | (Till transparent) | Clove oil and cedar-wood oil can be used to de-alcoholize, even though a trace of water is present. Do not throw away the oil after use, it can be used again; transfer it to a special bottle. This stage may be omitted if dehydration is thorough and complete. |
| **9** Wash in xylene. | (1 min) | Purpose is to remove traces of oil which would show as globules under the microscope. |
| **10** Mount in D.P.X. (p. 209). | | Transfer contents of tube to a watch-glass and remove animals one by one to the mountant on the slide. This resinous medium seals the preparation and keeps it air-tight. |
| **11** Cover. | | |
| **12** Label. | | Stick a small white label at one end of the slide. On it write the name of the preparation; the method of staining; the date of preparation; and your initials. |
| **13** Seal (if desired). | | This involves running a ring of cementing material or varnish round the edge of the cover-slip. It is not essential but ensures the permanence of the preparation. |

## METHOD 13. STAINED SQUASH

*Material suggested:* Root-tips of broad-bean (*Faba vulgaris*) grown in culture soln. [equal vols. solns. (*r*) (i) and (ii), p. 206)].

| *Process* | *Comment* |
|---|---|
| **1** Cut off small pieces of root tips about 4 mm long. | If roots are grown in a culture solution they are less likely to be damaged. |
| **2** Transfer to a watch-glass containing a small quantity of a mixture of: lacmoid-acetic (p. 230) 10 ml hydrochloric acid (N/1) 1 ml. | Lacmoid-acetic is a combined fixative and stain. It will stain the chromosomes red. (If mounted in neutral balsam the colour will turn to blue.) |
| **3** Warm gently, until the liquid steams but does *not* boil. Repeat 2–3 times. | |
| **4** Allow to stand for 10 min. | |
| **5** Transfer a piece of material to a drop of lacmoid-acetic on a slide. | |
| **6** Gently tease out the material and remove any debris. | Use a glass needle for preference. |
| **7** Smear a cover-slip with egg albumen (p. 65). | The adhesive will ensure that the material is not lost from slide or cover-slip in processes that follow. |
| **8** Invert the smeared cover-slip over the material on the slide. | |
| **9** Cover the slide with a piece of filter-paper and, using the gentle, *vertical*, pressure of one finger, finger, squash the material under the cover-slip. | Pressure must be *vertical* and not lateral, otherwise the cells will be distorted. |
| **10** Invert the slide in a Petri dish of Clarke's fluid (p.199). (Until the cover-slip drops off). (5–10 min) | It is essential to note which are the prepared surfaces of slide and cover-slip. Clarke's fluid ('acetic alcohol') is a fixative. |
| **11** Transfer slide and cover-slip to alcohol (100%). (2 min) | To remove water. |
| **12** Transfer slide and cover-slip to fresh alcohol (100%). (2 min) | |
| **13** Drain off the alcohol and place a drop of (preferably old) 'Euparal' over the material on the slide. | This mountant has a low refractive index (1.483) and has the advantage that *traces* of water do not spoil the preparation. |
| **14** Gently lower the inverted cover-slip into position. | If too much mountant is used it will exude from the edge of the cover-slip. If too little is used it will not spread to the edge. |
| **15** Label. | |

## METHOD 14. STAINED SMEAR

*Material suggested:* Seminal vesicle of Earthworm (*Lumbricus terrestris*).

| *Process** | *Comment* |
|---|---|
| **1** Smear the cut surface of a seminal vesicle, very thinly, on a cover-slip. | Handle the cover-slip with forceps. |

* After Green, 1934 *School Science Review,* XV, 408.

| *Process* | *Comment* |
|---|---|
| **2** Allow to become almost dry in the air. | |
| **3** Fix in alcohol (70%–90%). (5 min) | This and succeeding processes should be carried out in covered watch-glasses. |
| **4** Stain in Ehrlich's haematoxylin (p. 222). (15 min) | |
| **5** Wash in alcohol (70%). | |
| **6** Differentiate in acid-alcohol (p. 186). (5–12 min – until pale reddish colour) | |
| **7** Wash in alcohol (70%). | |
| **8** Wash in alcohol (90%). | |
| **9** 'Blue' in alkaline-alcohol (p. 186) or in ammonia vapour. | The stain itself is a dark red. A blue colour develops in the presence of alkali. |
| **10** Dehydrate in alcohol (90%).<br>**11** Dehydrate in alcohol (100%).<br>**12** Dehydrate in fresh alcohol (100%). | Purpose is to remove all the water before mounting in a resinous medium, with which water will not mix. This is done gradually to prevent shrinkage of tissue. Continue each stage for 2 min. Cover the vessels of absolute (100%) alcohol with another watch-glass to keep out water-vapour. |
| **13** Clear in benzene-phenol (p. 190). (2 min or until transparent) | Purpose is to remove alcohol, which will not mix with the resinous mountant. |
| **14** Mount by inverting the cover-slip in a drop of D.P.X. on the slide. | |
| **15** Label. | |

## METHOD 15. COUNTERSTAINED SMEAR

*Material suggested:* Squamous epithelial cells from cheek.

N.B. Throughout the processes **2–11** inclusive hold the cover-slip in a nick in a match-stick, and place it tissue downwards in the various liquids.

| *Process* | *Comment* |
|---|---|
| **1** Smear the tissue on a clean cover-slip. | Thinly. See **2**, Method **5**, above. |
| **2** Air-dry by waving the slip in the air. | Do not let the tissue dry completely. |
| **3** Fix in mercuric-acetic (p. 233). (2 min) | Poison – care! Place the cover-slip, tissue downwards, in watch-glass of fixative. |
| **4** Wash in dilute iodine; then in distilled water, followed by 5% sodium thiosulphate solution. (1 min in each) | Gently, or tissue will be lost. To remove mercury compound which would appear as a crystalline deposit under the microscope. |
| **5** Stain in Delafield's haematoxylin (p. 222). (3–10 min) | Dilute the stain about 1 to 3 v/v with distilled water. |
| **6** Differentiate in acid alcohol (p. 186). (Momentarily) | |
| **7** Wash in tap-water. | |
| **8** Counterstain in aqueous eosin Y (p. 212). (30–60 s) | |
| **9** Wash in tap-water. | |
| **10** Dehydrate in alcohol (96%). (1 min) | Although it is usual to up-grade the alcohols more gradually, the dehydration is here done more |

| Process | Comment |
|---|---|
| **11** Dehydrate in alcohol (100%) in covered vessel. (1 min) | quickly because eosin Y washes out very easily in alcohol – especially alcohol (70%). |
| **12** Clear in benzene-phenol (p. 190). (Till transparent) | |
| **13** Mount in D.P.X. (p. 209). | Invert the cover-slip tissue downwards on to a drop of mountant placed ready on the slide. |
| **14** Cover. | |
| **15** Label. | |

## METHOD 16. STAINED SECTIONS

*Material suggested:* Sections of stem of white deadnettle (*Lamium album*); stem of sunflower (*Helianthus annuus*); root of buttercup (*Ranunculus repens*).

| Process | Comment |
|---|---|
| **1** Fix in 'chrom-acetic' (p. 199). (12 h) | |
| **2** Wash in distilled water. | |
| **3** Section (p. 42). | |
| **4** Stain in Baker's 'Haematal 8' haematoxylin (p. 220). (3–10 min) | Use diluted stain and watch progress. |
| **5** Wash in tap water. | |
| **6** "Blue" by rinsing in water made alkaline with a few drops of ammonia. | |
| **7** Rinse in distilled water. | |
| **8** Dehydrate in alcohol (70%).<br>**9** Dehydrate in alcohol (90%).<br>**10** Dehydrate in alcohol (100%).<br>**11** Dehydrate in fresh alcohol (100%) | Purpose is to remove all the water before mounting in a resinous medium with which water will not mix. This is done gradually to prevent shrinkage of tissue. Continue each stage for 2 min. Cover the vessels of absolute (100%) alcohol with another watch-glass to keep out water vapour. |
| **12** Clear in benzene-phenol or xylene-phenol (p. 253). (2 min or *till transparent*) | Purpose is to remove alcohol, and make the tissue more transparent by permeating it with a resin-solvent of higher refractive index. |
| **13** Mount in D.P.X. | This resinous medium seals the preparation and keeps it air-tight. |
| **14** Cover. | |
| **15** Label. | Stick a small white label at one end of the slide. On it write the name of the tissue; the method of staining; the date of preparation; and your initials. |
| **16**. Seal (if desired). | This involves running a ring of cementing material or varnish round the edge of the cover-slip. It is not essential but ensures the permanence of the preparation. |

## METHOD 17. COUNTERSTAINED SECTIONS

*Material suggested:* Sections of stem of white deadnettle (*Lamium album*); stem of sunflower (*Helianthus annuus*); root of buttercup (*Ranunculus repens*).

| | Process | | Comment |
|---|---|---|---|
| 1 | Fix in chrom-acetic (p. 199). | (12 h) | |
| 2 | Wash in distilled water. | | |
| 3 | Section (p. 42). | | |
| 4 | Dehydrate in alcohol (30%). | (2 min) | It is proposed to use an alcoholic stain dissolved in (50%) alcohol. Therefore dehydrate up to this point before staining. |
| 5 | Dehydrate in alcohol (50%). | (2 min) | |
| 6 | Stain in safranin o (p. 244). | (5 min or longer) | This will stain the lignified tissue red. The stain tends to wash out in alcohol and hence 5 min in the stain must be regarded as a minimum. |
| 8 | Dehydrate in alcohol (70%). | (1 min) | |
| 9 | Dehydrate in alcohol (90%). | (1 min) | |
| 10 | Dehydrate in alcohol (100%). | (1 min) | |
| 11 | Counterstain in fast green FCF (in clove oil) (p. 213). | (2 min) | This will stain the cellulose green. |
| 12 | Wash in alcohol (100%) in covered vessel. | (½ min) | |
| 13 | Clear in clove oil. | (2 min) | |
| 14 | Wash in xylene. | (Quickly) | To remove drops of oil. |
| 15 | Mount in D.P.X. | | |
| 16 | Cover. | | |
| 17 | Label. | | |
| 18 | Seal if desired. | | |

Results of staining by this Method: Cellulose → green, i.e. all cells with cellulose walls, e.g. cortical cells of stem and root; medullary cells of stem and root; parenchyma of xylem and phloem; sieve tubes and companion cells in phloem; mesophyllary cells of leaf, including parenchyma and collenchyma. Lignin → red, i.e. fibres; stone cells; pericycle fibres; epidermal tissues opposite the veins in many broad leaves; hypodermal tissues in *Pinus.*

## METHOD 17(a). COUNTERSTAINED SECTIONS

*Material suggested:* Sections of cartilage.

*Note:* It is assumed that the material has been fixed. Bouin's fluid (p. 191), or Zenker's solution (p. 253) are suitable fixatives.

| | Process | | Comment |
|---|---|---|---|
| 1 | Wash the sections in water. | | To remove fixative. |
| 2 | Dehydrate successively in alcohol (30%), (50%), (70%), and (90%). | (2 min. each) | The material must be dehydrated to alcohol (90%) because this is the solvent for Weigert's stain. |
| 3 | Stain in Weigert's stain (p. 216). | (30 min) | Depending on the depth of stain required it may be necessary to stain for a longer period. |
| 4 | Wash in alcohol (95%) | | To remove excess stain. |
| 5 | If necessary, differentiate in acid-alcohol. | (Few min) | Watch under microscope until required contrast of staining is achieved. |
| 6 | Wash in alcohol (70%). | | The sections are brought down to water because water is the solvent for the counterstain. |
| 7 | Wash in distilled water. | | |
| 8 | Stain in van Gieson's stain (p. 218). | (5 min) | |
| 9 | Wash in water. | | |

| Process | Comment |
|---|---|
| **10** Dehydrate successively in alcohol (30%), (50%), (70%), (90%). (2 min each) | |
| **11** Dehydrate in two changes of alcohol (100%). (2 min each) | |
| **12** Clear in xylene. | |
| **13** Mount in D.P.X. | |
| **14** Cover. | |
| **15** Label. | |

Results of staining by this Method:
Collagen fibres → red; elastic fibres → blue-black; matrix → grey-black; other tissues → yellow.

### METHOD 18.

*Material suggested:* Teased portions of striated muscle.

*Note:* It is assumed that the material has been fixed. Bouin's fluid (p. 191), or Zenker's solution (p. 253) are suitable fixatives.

| Process | Comment |
|---|---|
| **1** Wash in distilled water. | To remove fixative. |
| **2** Stain in Heidenhain's (iron) haematoxylin (p. 223). (2 min) | |
| **3** Differentiate in iron alum aq. (p. 187). | Watch under microscope until required contrast in staining is achieved. |
| **4** Wash in distilled water. | |
| **5** Counterstain in van Gieson's stain (p. 218). | |
| **6** Wash in distilled water. | |
| **7** Dehydrate successively in alcohol (30%), (50%), (70%), (90%). (2 min each) | |
| **8** Dehydrate in two changes of alcohol (100%). (2 min each) | |
| **9** Clear in xylene or benzene-phenol. | |
| **10** Mount in D.P.X. | |
| **11** Cover. | |
| **12** Label. | |

### METHOD 19.

*Material suggested:* Unstriated (smooth, plain) muscle from frog's bladder.

| Process* | Comment |
|---|---|
| **1** Cut off a lobe from a fresh frog's bladder (Fig. 5.1a) | |
| **2** Slit up one side (Fig. 5.1b). | |
| **3** Spread out flat (Fig. 5.1c). | |
| **4** Transfer to a slide with the inner side of the bladder uppermost. | |

* With acknowledgements to Professor J. G. Hawkes.

| | *Process* | *Comment* |
|---|---|---|
| **5** | Spread out from the centre, in all directions, with the finger tips. (Fig. 5.1d). | To remove any epithelial cells which would otherwise hide the muscles. |
| **6** | Fix in *weak* Flemming's solution (p. 214). (Overnight) | |
| **7** | Wash thoroughly in gently running tap water. | |
| **8** | Rinse in distilled water. | |
| **9** | Stain in Delafield's haematoxylin (p. 222). (Stock soln. diluted 5 times with distilled water). (5–10 min) | This is a nuclear stain. The slide can be flooded with the stain or placed in a staining tube or jar. Do not overstain. Excess haematoxylin is difficult to remove. |
| **10** | Differentiate in acid-alcohol (p. 186). (Momentarily) | To remove haematoxylin from the cytoplasm which would otherwise assume a purplish-red colour when counterstained with eosin Y. |
| **11** | Wash in tap water, or dilute ammonia (p. 188). (5 min) | To 'blue' the haematoxylin. |
| **12** | Counterstain with eosin Y aq. (p. 212). (30–60s) | |
| **13** | Rinse in tap water. | |
| **14** | Dehydrate in alcohol (96%). (1 min) | Dehydration must be as rapid as possible, otherwise the eosin Y will be washed out. |
| **15** | Dehydrate in alcohol (100%) (1 min) | |
| **16** | Clear in xylene or benzene-phenol. | |
| **17** | Mount in D.P.X. | |
| **18** | Cover. | |
| **19** | Label. | |

Results of staining by this Method:
Cytoplasm of Muscle → pink; Connective tissue fibres → pink; Nuclei → blue.

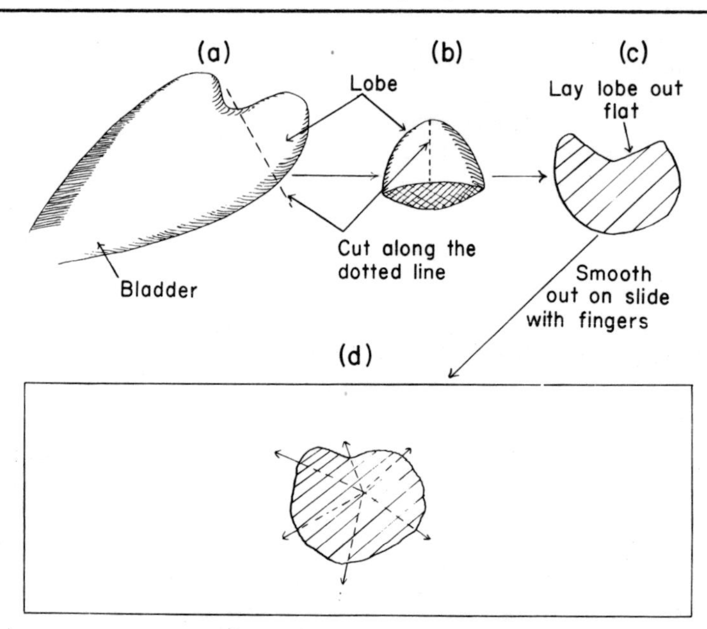


Fig. 5.1 The method of preparing the frog's bladder to demonstrate the smooth muscle and connective tissue fibres.

## C. Permanent Preparations from Wax-Embedded Tissues

### METHOD 20. WAX-EMBEDDING OF TISSUE FOLLOWED BY SECTIONING AND TRIPLE-STAINING* OF SECTIONS

*Material suggested:* Transverse sections of the Earthworm (*Lumbricus* or *Allolobophora* sp.)

*Note:* A standard procedure, using ethyl alcohol as the dehydrating agent is given first – Method **20(A)**, below. If other dehydrating agents are used there will be deviations from this procedure at certain points. These are indicated below with cross-references. Acetone isopropyl alcohol, and *n*-butyl alcohol are cheaper than ethyl alcohol; while 2 ethoxy ethanol reduces the time factor as also does the clearing agent terpineol.

| Process | Comment |
|---|---|
| **1** Kill in alcohol (30%) | |
| **2** Fix in Zenker's solution (p. 253). (minimum 10 h) | Cut the dead worm into pieces no longer than 0.5 cm and wash out any debris from intestine. |
| **3** Wash in running water. (minimum 24 h) | |
| **4** Wash in alcohol (70%) to which iodine has been added (p. 229). (minimum 12 h) | To remove mercuric chloride. If colour disappears from the solution, add more iodine. |

Subsequent processes depend on the dehydrating agent or the clearing agent used.

If ethyl alcohol: proceed to step **5**, below.
If acetone: proceed to Method **20(B)** p. 86.
If isopropyl alcohol: proceed to Method **20(B)** p. 86.
If *n*-butyl alcohol: proceed to Method **20(C)** p. 87.
If 2 ethoxy ethanol: proceed to Method **20(D)** p. 88.
If terpineol is used as the clearing agent: proceed to Method **20(E)** p. 88.

### METHOD 20(A)

*Using ethyl alcohol as the dehydrating agent.*

| Process | Comment |
|---|---|
| **5** Dehydrate in ethyl alcohol (70%). (30 min) | If desired, tissues may remain in 70% alcohol overnight, without harm. |
| **6** Dehydrate in fresh ethyl alcohol (70%). (30 min) | |
| **7** Dehydrate in ethyl alcohol (90%). (6 h) | |
| **8** Dehydrate in ethyl alcohol (100%). (6 h) | |
| **9** Dehydrate in fresh ethyl alcohol (100%) (6 h) | |
| **10** Transfer to pure clearing agent. (24 h) | See note (*b*), p. 53. |
| **11** Transfer to first impregnating mixture,† viz. 50/50 clearing agent/molten paraffin wax. (1 h) | Use wax of m.p. 52°C–56°C and keep in an oven at constant temp. not more than 5°C higher than the m.p. of the wax used (p. 63). |
| **12** Transfer to molten paraffin wax (p. 62). (1 h) | Ditto. |

* Alternative methods of staining to follow process **18** (p. 86) are given under 'Animal Tissue, **6**', page 101.

† If clearing agent was cedar-wood oil, this mixture should consist of equal parts of cedar-wood oil, benzene, and molten paraffin wax.

| Process | Comment |
|---|---|
| **13** Transfer to fresh molten paraffin wax. (1 h) | If benzene or xylene was used for clearing, take care not to let any get into this wax. |
| **14** Embed. (Place the impregnated tissue in a mould of molten wax which is allowed to solidify and then trimmed to a convenient size.) | See p. 63 for detailed instructions. |
| **15** Section. | By a hand-operated or by a mechanical microtome. |
| [**16** Attach sections to slide.] | See p. 43 for detailed instructions. [Omit if loose sections desired. |
| **17** Remove wax from sections with xylene. | |
| **18** Hydrate. | Pass sections through 100, 96,and 70% alcohols. |
| ***19** Stain nuclei in Delafield's or Weigert's haema-toxylin (p. 222). (5 min) | |
| **20** Wash in tap-water. | N.B. If sections are attached to slide, all processes from **17** to **29** inclusive may be carried out by placing the slide, with sections attached, in a tube of suitable size. |
| **21** Stain in Mallory's stain, solution A (p. 232). (Till red; 3–20 min) | |
| **22** Wash in distilled water. | |
| **23** Wash in Mallory's stain, solution B (p. 232). (1 min) | To fix the acid-fuchsin in solution A. |
| **24** Wash in distilled water. | |
| **25** Stain in Mallory's stain, solution C (p. 232). (Till blue; 5–20 min) | For some results of staining, see 'Mallory's Triple Stain' (p. 232). |
| **26** Wash in distilled water. | |
| **27** Dehydrate in alcohol (95%) (industrial methylated spirits). | Any 'milkiness' visible when an alcohol-treated preparation is placed in benzene or xylene is due to moisture and means that dehydration is incomplete. Alternatively, 2 ethoxy ethanol may be used for dehydration in **27** (1 min) after which proceed to **29**. |
| **28** Dehydrate in alcohol (100%). | |
| **29** Clear in benzene-phenol. [See note (*a*), below.] | |
| **30** Mount in D.P.X. | Place the resin on the sections if attached to slide. |
| **31** Cover. | |
| **32** Label. | |
| **33** Seal if desired. | |

*Notes.*

(*a*) Tissues may be kept in storage after process **10** of Method **20(A)** (p. 85); after processes **14, 15**; or (by omission of process **16**) after process **29**, when sections would be stored in benzene.

(*b*) Process **16** may be omitted and the remaining processes up to number **29** carried out with quantities of sections. This will obviate the use of the rather large quantities of reagents necessary to fill the capsules used for carrying the slides to which the sections have been attached.

## METHOD 20(B)

*Using either acetone, or isopropyl alcohol as the dehydrating agent.*

*Note:* isopropyl alcohol is cheaper than ethyl alcohol and is miscible, in all proportions, with water.

*Continuing from process* **4** *of Method* **20** (p. 85):

* Alternative methods of staining are given under 'Animal Tissue', page 101.

| Process | Comment |
| --- | --- |
| 5 Dehydrate in isopropyl alcohol (70%) (p. 52). (30 min) | |
| 6 Dehydrate in fresh isopropyl alcohol (70%). (30 min) | |
| 7 Dehydrate in isopropyl alcohol (95%). (6 h) | |
| 8 Transfer either to isopropyl alcohol, or to acetone. (6 h) | |
| 9 Transfer either to fresh isopropyl alcohol, or to fresh acetone. (6 h) | |
| 10 Transfer either to 50/50 xylene/isopropyl alcohol, or to 50/50 xylene/acetone. (24 h) | Xylene must be used as the clearing agent if this method is used. |
| 11 Transfer either to 75/25 xylene/isopropyl alcohol; or to 75/25 xylene/acetone. (24 h) | |
| 12 Proceed to process **10** of Method **20(A)**, (p. 85). | |

**METHOD 20(C)**

*Using n-butyl alcohol as the dehydrating agent.* *

*Note:* *n*-butyl alcohol is miscible with the higher concentrations of ethyl alcohol; is miscible with and very slightly soluble in water; and is miscible with molten paraffin wax. Hence no clearing agent is required.

*Continuing from process* **4** *of Method* **20** (p. 85):

| Process | | Comment | |
| --- | --- | --- | --- |
| 5 Transfer to this mixture: | | | |
| ethyl alcohol (100%) | 50 ml | | |
| *n*-butyl alcohol | 50 ml | ≡ 30% alcohol. | (1 h) |
| distilled water | 225 ml | | |
| 6 Transfer to this mixture: | | | |
| ethyl alcohol | 50 ml | | |
| *n*-butyl alcohol | 50 ml | ≡ 60% alcohol. | (1 h) |
| distilled water | 62.5 ml | | |
| 7 Transfer to this mixture: | | | |
| ethyl alcohol | 50 ml | | |
| *n*-butyl alcohol | 50 ml | ≡ 80% alcohol. | (2 h) |
| distilled water | 21.9 ml | | |
| 8 Transfer to this mixture: | | | |
| ethyl alcohol | 50 ml | | |
| *n*-butyl alcohol | 50 ml | ≡ 95% alcohol. | (2 h) |
| distilled water | 2.63 ml | | |
| 9 Transfer to *n*-butyl alcohol. | | | (2 h) |
| 10 Transfer to 50/50 *n*-butyl alcohol/paraffin wax. | | This is best done by placing the tissue in fresh *n*-butyl alcohol and adding the wax in shreds, gradually, over of period of 3 h, till the volume of liquid is about doubled. See comment about wax under Method **20(A)**, process **11**, (p. 85). | |

Now proceed to process **12** of Method **20(A)**, (p. 85).

* The author is indebted to E. T. Saunders, M.A., of Bedford Modern School, for a note on this method.

## METHOD 20(D)

*Using 2 ethoxy ethanol as the dehydrating agent.*

*Note:* 2 ethoxy ethanol is miscible with water, with alcohol and with xylene, but it is *not* a solvent for paraffin wax.

Tissue must *not* be in bulky pieces when 2 ethoxy ethanol is used, or distortion and shrinkage will occur.

*Continuing from process* **4** *of Method* **20** (p. 85):

| | *Process* | | *Comment* |
|---|---|---|---|
| **5** | Dehydrate in 2 ethoxy ethanol. | (30 min) | No gradation of strengths is necessary. |
| **6** | Transfer to xylene. | (24 h) | |
| **7** | Transfer to 50/50 xylene/molten paraffin wax. | (1 h) | Method **20(A)**, process **11** (p. 85). |
| **8** | Transfer to molten paraffin wax. | (1 h) | |

Now proceed to process **13** of Method **20(A)**.

## METHOD 20(E)

*Using terpineol as the clearing agent.*†

*Note:* This method has the advantage that terpineol is miscible with alcohol of as low a concentration as (70%) and hence it is not necessary to spend time on dehydration to (100%) alcohol. It is suggested, however, that the beginner should not try to shorten the process unduly, either by transferring from alcohol (70%) to terpineol or by transferring direct from terpineol to paraffin wax, but should, instead, carry out the processes more gradually, as indicated below.

*Continuing from process* **4** *of Method* **20** (p. 85):

| | *Process* | | *Comment* |
|---|---|---|---|
| **5** | Dehydrate in ethyl alcohol (70%) | (30 min) | |
| **6** | Dehydrate in fresh ethyl alcohol (70%). | (30 min) | |
| **7** | Dehydrate in ethyl alcohol (96%). | (6 h) | |
| **8** | Transfer to 50/50 alcohol (96%)/terpineol. (Until the tissue sinks.) | | The word 'transfer' is used advisedly, i.e. do *not* leave the tissue in the containing vessel and simply pour off one liquid and replace it by the next, but have the fresh liquid in another vessel and, using forceps, transfer the tissue from one liquid to the next. A gentle shake will help to free the tissue of unwanted liquid. |
| **9** | Transfer to 33/66 alcohol (96%)/terpineol. | (1 h) | |
| **10** | Transfer to 25/75 alcohol (96%)/terpineol. | (1 h) | |
| **11** | Transfer to pure terpineol, *three* changes. | (1 h each) | |
| **12** | Transfer to a mixture of paraffin wax (m.p. 52–56°C) 10 gm and terpineol 50 ml. | (1 h) | |
| **13** | Transfer to successive changes of pure paraffin wax. | (1 h each) | Until there is no smell of lilac, i.e. until all the terpineol has been replaced. |
| **14** | Proceed to process **14** of Method **20(A)**. | | |

† After A. Wetzel. (1931, *Zeit. f. wiss. Mikr.*, **48**.)

## METHOD 21. WAX-EMBEDDING OF TISSUE FOLLOWED BY SECTIONING, STAINING AND COUNTERSTAINING OF SECTIONS

*Note:* This method is useful for the preparation of quantities of sections of animal material for class work. Modifications necessary when using plant material are given in the Notes (1) at the end of the method.

| | *Process* | *Comment* |
|---|---|---|
| **1** | Fix small pieces of fresh tissue in mercuric-acetic (p. 233). (8 h) | The fixative is poisonous. |
| **2** | Wash in alcohol (96%) containing iodine (p. 229). (12 h) | The iodine removes the mercury precipitate. |
| **3** | Dehydrate in alcohol (100%); 2 changes. (12 h each) | |
| **4** | Clear in benzene-phenol (p. 190). (6 h) | |
| **5** | Impregnate with 50/50 benzene/paraffin wax. (1 h) | |
| **6** | Impregnate with pure paraffin wax. (1 h) | |
| **7** | Transfer to fresh paraffin wax. (1 h) | |
| **8** | Embed in paraffin wax (p. 63). | |
| **9** | Cut sections at 8 μm. If desired, sections may be stored after this process. See Notes 2 (*a*) and (*b*). | |
| **10** | Flatten out and attach about 40 sections to a sheet of thin mica. | See technique of attachment of sections to slide (p. 64). |
| **11** | Remove wax with xylene. | |
| **12** | Hydrate to alcohol (70%). | |
| **13** | Wash in alcohol (70%) containing iodine (p. 229). | |
| **14** | Wash in distilled water. | |
| **15** | Wash in sodium thiosulphate (hypo) (p. 249). | |
| **16** | Wash in distilled water. | |
| **17** | Stain in Delafield's haematoxylin (p. 222) (5 min) | |
| **18** | Wash in *tap* water or *dilute* ammonia solution, followed by a rinse in distilled water. (10 min) | |
| **19** | Stain in eosin Y (aq.) (p. 212). (½ min) | |
| **20** | Dehydrate either, in alcohol (70%), (90%), (96%), (100%). (Each poured on quickly); or, in 2 ethoxy ethanol. (1 min) | Dehydration must be done quickly because eosin Y is rapidly washed out by alcohol (70%) and (90%). One dehydration in 2 ethoxy ethanol is sufficient. |
| **21** | Clear in benzene-phenol. | |
| **22** | Coat with paraffin wax until required for class work. | If desired, store at this stage. |
| **23** | Cut mica into pieces of convenient size and shape for mounting under a cover-slip. | See Note 2 (*c*). |
| **24** | Place mica pieces in xylene. | To remove wax prior to mounting. |
| **25** | Mount the piece of mica bearing the section on a slide in D.P.X. | |
| **26** | Cover. | |
| **27** | Label. | |
| **28** | Seal if desired. | |

*Notes:*

1 This method may also be used for plant material, with suitable alterations. The following are suggested:
  (*a*) In process **1**, fix in alcohol-formalin (p. 187). (12 h)
  (*b*) In process **2**, wash in alcohol (70%) and (90%). (6 h each)
  (*c*) Proceed with processes **3–12** (inclusive).
  (*d*) Omit processes **13–16** (inclusive).
  (*e*) For processes **17–19** (inclusive), substitute any desired staining technique selected from those given on pp. 159–160. A particularly useful one is Method (*b*), p. 159, using safranin o and aniline blue ws.
  (*f*) If *all* the processes of staining Method (*b*) have been carried out (as shown on p. 159), dehydration in process **20** (above) will be in 2 ethoxy ethanol.
  (*g*) Results of staining with safranin o and aniline blue ws: cell nuclei, cutin, lignin, suberin (→ red); cellulose and cytoplasm (→ blue).

2 Sections may be stored as follows:
  (*a*) In ribbons, between sheets of paper, after completion of process **9**. Not a very satisfactory method.
  (*b*) By transference to xylene, after process **9**, if it is *not* desired to proceed with mica mounts.
  (*c*) On mica, after processes **22** or **23**, as indicated above.

## METHOD 22. BULK-STAINING OF TISSUE FOLLOWED BY WAX-EMBEDDING AND SECTIONING

*Note:* This method involves staining the whole piece of tissue before impregnating and embedding. The method is useful if it is not desired to continue operations immediately after staining, because the tissue can be preserved in bulk at a suitable stage in dehydration. Although the method is quicker, staining is definitely less well controlled — there is liability to overstain the tissue at the edges — and at best it must be considered rather rough and ready and it is not recommended for most purposes. It happens to be rather suitable for the tissue suggested below.

*Material suggested:* Sexual organs of *Fucus.*

| | *Process* | | *Comment* |
|---|---|---|---|
| **1** | Fix in osmium tetroxide (1%) (p. 238). | (24 h) | Beware irritant vapour from fixative. |
| **2** | Wash in running water. | (12 h) | |
| **3** | Harden in alcohol (70%). | (24 h) | |
| **4** | Stain in borax carmine (p. 196). | (24 h) | |
| **5** | Differentiate in acid alcohol (p. 186). | (15 min) | |
| **6** | Dehydrate in alcohol (70%). | (1 h) | |
| **7** | Dehydrate in alcohol (100%). | (1 h) | |
| **8** | Clear in 50/50 cedar-wood oil/alcohol.(100%) | (24 h) | |
| **9** | Clear in pure cedar-wood oil. | (24 h) | |
| **10** | Impregnate in 25/25/25: : cedar-wood oil/benzene/paraffin wax . | (1 h) | |
| **11** | Impregnate in molten paraffin wax. | (1 h) | |
| **12** | Impregnate in fresh molten wax. | (1 h) | |
| **13** | Embed in wax (p. 63). | | |
| **14** | Section (p. 64). | | |
| [**15** | Attach sections to slide (p. 43). ] | | See Note. |
| **16** | Remove wax from sections. | | See Note. |
| **17** | Mount in D.P.X. | | |

*Note:* Process **15** may be omitted and the sections treated in quantities in a watch-glass. After process **16** sections may be stored in xylene.

## METHOD 23. WAX-EMBEDDING OF TISSUE FOLLOWED BY SECTIONING AND STAINING OF SECTIONS BY A TYPICAL HISTOCHEMICAL METHOD

Much of microscopical technique is now devoted towards the localization of specific compounds by histochemical staining methods. The technique* given below (for colouring RNA and DNA differentially) is only one of many now available; specialist technical manuals (see Appendix 1, p. 259) should be consulted for details of these.

*Material suggested:* Sections of mammalian pancreas.

| | *Process* | *Comment* |
|---|---|---|
| **1** | Fix small pieces of tissue in Zenker's fluid. (3 h) | This time should not be exceeded. |
| **2** | Wash in running water. (overnight) | |
| **3** | Treat with alcohol (70%) to which iodine has been added (p. 229). (12 h) | |
| **4** | Wash in fresh alcohol (70%). (1 h) | |
| **5** | Dehydrate in 96% alcohol and two changes of 100% alcohol. (1 h in each) | |
| **6** | Transfer to clearing agent. (overnight) | |
| **7** | Embed in paraffin wax. | |
| **8** | Cut sections at 8 μm and attach to slides. | |
| **9** | Remove wax from sections with xylene. | |
| **10** | Hydrate sections in 100% alcohol, 96% alcohol and 70% alcohol containing iodine. (2 min in each) | |
| **11** | Rinse in water. | |
| **12** | Treat sections with 5% sodium thiosulphate solution. (5 min) | To remove all traces of iodine. |
| **13** | Wash in running water. (5 min) | |
| **14** | Stain sections in pyronin/malachite green mixture, buffered to pH 4.8. (20 min) | For composition of this staining solution see p. 24. |
| **15** | Blot sections dry with filter paper. | This step must not be omitted. |
| **16** | Rinse quickly in 0.025% sodium carbonate solution. | |
| **17** | Dip sections momentarily in 96% alcohol. | |
| **18** | Dehydrate in 2 separate lots of 100% alcohol. (2 min altogether) | |
| **19** | Clear sections in xylene. | |
| **20** | Mount in D.P.X. | |

*Note:* Sites containing DNA (i.e. cell nuclei) are coloured blue or blue-green; red or pink areas probably contain RNA. Digestion of a second section must be carried out with crystalline ribonuclease (0.1% in 0.01M phosphate buffer at pH 6.0 and 37 °C for 90 min) after stage **13** above. This digested slide is then rinsed in running water for 5 min and then stained as from stage **14** on. Any material which stains red in the untreated slide but is uncoloured after ribonuclease digestion is to be regarded as being rich in RNA.

* Baker, J. R. and Williams, E. G. M., 1965. *Quart. J. micr. Sci.*, **106**, 3–13.

*Postscript to this Chapter*

It is quite true, as someone unknown to the author has written,* that *'most staining techniques are worked entirely by rule of thumb'*; that *'personal experience counts more than anything else'*; and that *'rules should be regarded lightly – especially rules about length of time in stain – and used as a guide rather than a law'*. Put shortly, this means that the student should observe; should use his common sense; and, once he has gained some experience, should be prepared to experiment and find better ways of doing things. At the same time, it is well to remember that *'a large proportion of the microscopic work done in biological research establishments differs from the 'elementary' work of schools and universities only in the degree of refinement and instrumentation; the methods are basically the same . . . . Furthermore, the vast majority of university graduates . . . . usually have to start from the beginning when they find (often to their dismay) that their research necessitates something more than temporary squashes in lacto-phenol'.*† It would therefore seem worth while to try to become really proficient at carrying out the basic, standard, methods outlined above.

* Instruction sheets issued to zoology students in the University of Cambridge.
† Private communication from Dr. P. W. Talboys. East Malling Research Station.

# 6 Methods for specific material

## Sources and Culture of Material*

Though obviously not strictly a part of micro-technique, it seems essential to have material on which to work, and the writer has sometimes suffered no little inconvenience by not being able to lay his hands on the right material at the right time. As with the rest of the book, the notes on the sources and the culture of material have been culled from various sources. They refer mostly to animal tissue. A friendly acquaintance with a nurseryman (particularly if he be a hot-house specialist) usually paves the way to a ready (and often regular) supply of a wide range of botanical material; and animals often arrive in too great quantity in jam-jars at the hands of junior pupils.

*Information about sources or culture of material, or both, is indicated by the letters* **'S/C'**.

## Preservation of Material*

If it is not convenient to use all one's material at once it may be necessary, or desirable, to preserve it for future use.

If possible, use stoppered vessels for storage. If screw-top vessels are used, smear the threaded portion of the inside of the cap with 'Vaseline'. If corks are used, wax them.

It is, of course, essential to label the vessel. The label should bear the name of the specimen, the date of storage, any special treatment to which it has already been subjected, and the nature of the preservative.

The label may consist simply of pencil-writing on a piece of white paper placed with the specimen in the vessel of preservative. Alternatively, if a gummed label is used on the outside of the vessel, the label should be either waxed over or protected by transparent tape.

*Methods for the preservation of material are indicated by the letter* **'P'**.

## Microscopical Preparations of Specific Material

(i) If a special method is not given for any particular animal, plant, or tissue, one of the general (histological) methods should be used. Those for animal tissue will be found on page 98 ff, and those for plant tissue on page 158 ff.

(ii) Remember that different tissues of the same organism, and the same tissues of different organisms may, and often do, respond differently to the same reagent. If, therefore, the method suggested does not appear to give very satisfactory results in any particular set of circumstances it is best to try a variety of treatments. Let the rule be a guide and not a master. The system of 'trial and error' has often been the basis of the discovery of new and better methods.

* The author is indebted to the Editor of the *School Science Review* for permission to reproduce, in a modified form, some of the information on 'Sources and Culture', and both to him and to Messrs. T. Gerrard & Co., for some of the information on 'Preservation'.

(iii) Unless otherwise stated, the stains suggested are suitable both for temporary and for permanent preparations. Remember that 'rule of thumb' does enter into staining schedules, especially where lengths of time are concerned. Be guided by your growing experience.

(iv) Although ethyl alcohol is usually suggested as the dehydrating agent, it should be understood that any other suitable substance (see pp. 51, 52) may be used, provided the processes are adjusted accordingly.

(v) It is advisable to refer to Chapter 7 in which will be found directions for making up the various fixatives, stains and other reagents, together with notes on the use of some of them.

**Acanthocephalus ranae**

**S/C** (i) In wall of alimentary canal of *Rana*.
(ii) See also the closely related *Echinorhynchus* (p. 124).

*Preparation technique*

1. Kill in chloral hydrate.
2. Fix in formol-acetic-alcohol. (30 min)
3. Wash in alcohol (50%).
4. Stain with borax carmine.
5. Dehydrate in alcohol (70%), (96%), (100%).
6. Clear in clove oil or phenol-xylene.
7. Mount in D.P.X.

**Acarine**

*To find if present in tracheae of honey-bee.*

1. Lay the dead bee, ventral side uppermost, with head pointing forwards, under a hand-lens supported on a suitable stand.
2. Compress the head by means of forceps and insert a needle between the second and third pairs of legs.
3. Draw the head and front legs away from the thorax and expose the thoracic muscles and (sometimes) parts of the tracheal system liable to infestation.
4. Remove the chitinous ring adjacent to the exposed organs and the major portion of the trachea connected to the first pair of spiracles exposed. Or, the whole trachea may be removed.
5. The trachea may now be mounted for temporary examination. After some experience it will be possible to recognize the presence or absence of the parasite by the abnormal or normal appearance of the tracheae as seen under the hand-lens.

**Acidophil Granules**

Stain with haematoxylin and eosin Y (→ red); iron haematoxylin and van Gieson's stain (→ yellow); Mallory's stain (→ yellow to orange).

**Achlya**

**S/C.** See 'Culture Media 3 (*q*) iii' (p. 206).

**Actinosphaerium**

**S/C.** Pond water.

**Adrenal Body**

See 'Suprarenal Body' (p. 174).

**Adrenalin**

See 'Suprarenal Body' (p. 174).

**Agaricus**

(i) See 'Fungi' (p. 130).
(ii) Section gills just before spores turn brownish-black.

**Aleurone Grains (with crystalloids)**

Stain with Eosin Y (alc.).

**Algae**

**S/C.** (i) Culture Collection of Algae and Protozoa, The Botany School, University of Cambridge.
(ii) See 'Culture Media', 3 (pp. 203–208).

**P** (i) Bouin's fluid; formol-acetic-alcohol.

(ii*)

| | | |
|---|---|---|
| Formalin (40%) . . . . . | 5 | ml |
| Potassium chrome alum . . | 10 | g |
| Distilled water . . . . . | 500 | ml |

(iii) *To preserve cell-outline and cell wall:*

| | | |
|---|---|---|
| Potassium acetate (4%) . . | 50 | ml |
| Distilled water . . . . | 50 | ml |

(iv) *To preserve green colour:*
Place the fresh alga in:

* Adapted from *Gerrard's Bulletin*, May 1939. T. Gerrard & Co.

| | | | |
|---|---|---|---|
| (*a*) | Copper acetate (neutral) | 0.2 | g |
| | Lacto-phenol . . . . | 100 | ml |
| or (*b*) | Copper acetate (neutral) | 1 | g |
| | Formaldehyde (40%) . | 0.25 | ml |
| | Distilled water . . . | 99 | ml |
| or (*c*) | Camphor water . . . | 130 | ml |
| | Distilled water . . . | 130 | ml |
| | Acetic acid (glacial) . . | 20 | drops |
| | Mix, and add: | | |
| | Copper acetate . . . | 1 | g |
| | Dissolve, and add: | | |
| | Glycerol . . . . . | 260 | ml |
| | Filter. | | |

*Preparation techniques*

Fix. Chrom-acetic; formalin-alcohol; formal-acetic-alcohol; Bouin's fluid; chrome-osmium (1%).

Stain with anilin blue WS; fast green FSF; Magdala red; phloxine B (the two latter may be counterstained with anilin blue WS – See Chamberlain's method, below), Heidenhain's haematoxylin (mordant with *liquor ferri*).

*Small forms:*

(i) 1 Fix. Formaldehyde (1–2%).
2 Dry on a slide.
3 Wash in distilled water.
4 Mount in glycerol.

(ii) See Methods **1** and **2** (p. 73 ) in Chapter 5.

*Chamberlain's method* *

1 Chrom-acetic.
2 Wash in water.
3 Transfer to glycerol (10%).
4 Wash in alcohol (90%). (Till all glycerol removed)
5 Stain with phloxine B. (12 h)
6 Decant stain and add alcohol (90%). (1 min)
7 Transfer to anilin blue WS. (1 min)
8 Transfer to a clean dish and pour specially *weak* acid alcohol (p. 186 ) on to material. (3–4 s)
9 Decant acid alcohol and wash in alcohol (90%). (3 changes)
10 Dehydrate in alcohol (100%). (5 min)
11 Examine microscopically. If the red colour is too pale – due to too prolonged treatment with acid alcohol – restain in phloxine B (30 min), re-wash in alcohol (95%) and dehydrate again. If the blue is too pale, restain in anilin blue WS, re-wash in alcohol (95%), and dehydrate again.
12 Transfer to Venetian turpentine (10%) (p. 251 ). (In a desiccator. 2 d – or until Venetian turpentine is of the viscosity of glycerol)
13 Mount in Venetian turpentine.
14 Seal.
(Chromatophore → blue; nucleoli → bright red; pyrenoids → bright red.)

* Adapted from Chamberlain, 1932, *Methods in Plant Histology*, and *Stain Technology*, **2**, 1927.

*Methods for delicate specimens:* Useful for those algae and fungi which curl and shrink in xylene as no separate fixation, clearing, or dehydration is required.

(*a*) 1 Place lacto-phenol on slide.
2 Add the object.
3 Warm the slide till the lacto-phenol steams.
4 Stain with anilin blue WS (in lacto-phenol) and keep steaming. (30 s)
5 Transfer to lacto-phenol on slide and remove excess stain by gentle warming. *Examine under microscope during this process to control the differentiation.*
6 Mount in lacto-phenol.
7 Seal with paraffin wax.
8 Add coating of varnish paint to the wax.

(*b*) 1 Fix with formol-acetic-alcohol. (Long immersion)
2 Wash in alcohol (50%) and then in distilled water
3 Stain with anilin blue WS aq.
4 Dehydrate either
(i) to alcohol (100%) (2 changes)
or, cheaper method,
(ii) to industrial methylated spirit (approx. 95%) followed by two changes of iso-propyl alcohol.
5 Mount in Venetian turpentine (10%). (See p. 251).
6 Allow preparation to dry in a desiccator containing soda lime.
7 Seal.

(*c*) 1 Fix with formol-acetic-alcohol. (Long immersion)

**2** Wash in alcohol (50%) and then in distilled water.
**3** Stain with anilin blue WS aq.
**4** Wash in distilled water.
**5** Place either
(i) in glycerol (10%); or,
(ii) in a solution consisting of

| | |
|---|---|
| Distilled water . . . . . . . | 5 ml |
| Industrial methylated spirit . . | 4 ml |
| Glycerol . . . . . . . . . | 1 ml |

**6** Allow the glycerol, or the solution, to concentrate by evaporation at room temperature. (Several d)
**7** Mount in glycerol (p. 219), or glycerol-jelly (p. 220).

See also *Chara* (p. 113), *Cladophora* (p. 119), Desmids (p. 122), Diatoms (p. 122), *Euglena* (p. 127), *Fucus* (p. 129), *Hormidium* (p. 138), *Oedogonium* (p. 153), *Protococcus* (p. 163), *Spirogyra* (p. 171), *Tribonema* (p. 177), *Ulothrix* (p. 177), *Volvox* (p. 178).

### Alimentary Canal

(i) Fix. Do not fix small pieces of the wall but ligature a section, distend with the fixative (if possible by means of a glass syringe) and ligature a segment containing the fixative. Then cut the ligatured segment out and place in fixative [mercuric-formaldehyde or formol-saline (5%)]. After dehydration, the tissue should be embedded in paraffin wax and sectioned at about 8 μm.
(ii) Stain with haematoxylin and eosin; Mallory's.

### Allolobophora

See 'Lumbricus' (p. 144).

### Ammocoetes

See '*Amphioxus*, Whole specimens' (p. 97).

### Amoeba

**S/C**

(i) Dealers. On arrival, allow the tube of culture to stand undisturbed for 1 h. Pipette a small quantity of culture from the *bottom* of the tube and examine under the microscope (low-power objective; light stopped down or, better, with dark-ground).

If the culture is alive, it may be propagated. [See 'Protozoa' (p. 164).] Feed by placing one or two boiled wheat grains in the Petri dish. Do *not* overfeed, because bacteria and infusoria will become too abundant.*

(ii) Surface mud and bottom silt from ditches and ponds. Tie one end of a piece of thread to a cork, and the other end to a small rubber-band which is placed round two cover-slips. Sink the slips to the bottom of the pond. Examine the water film contained between the slips.
(iii) See 'Culture media 3', (pp. 203–208).
(iv) Place chopped *Elodea canadensis* in water and examine surface scum after several days.
(v) *Hay infusion.*

| | |
|---|---|
| Hay (chopped) . . . . . . . | 10 g |
| Distilled water . . . . . . . | 1000 ml |

Steam for ¾ h. Filter. Add a few drops of sodium hydroxide to make filtrate neutral to litmus. Cool. Place a little in a large Petri dish and inoculate with a little soil. Leave for a few days. Once a month add one or two crushed (boiled and dried) wheat grains.

(vi) **1** Prepare a supply of either Chalkley's medium (p. 205), or Pringsheim's solution (p. 206).
**2** Procure a small, shallow, transparent, lidded, plastic dish.
**3** Cover the floor of the dish with the medium containing the organism to such depth (about 2.5 cm) that the floor of the dish can be examined with a hand-lens.
**4** Add not more than six grains of either polished rice (unboiled), or boiled and dried wheat, to the medium.
**5** Place the lid on the dish which should be kept at room temperature (20°–22°C), away from direct light, for about 14–21 d. The less the culture is disturbed, the better.

(vii) *To locate individuals.* †

**1** Place (say) 10 ml of amoeba culture in a Petri dish standing on a black tile or on black paper.
**2** Partly fill the dish with buffered water (see 'Protozoa' **S/C**, p. 164).
**3** Allow the material to settle. The amoebae appear as white opaque bodies among the

* Adapted from *Gerrard's Bulletin*, June 1939. T. Gerrard & Co.
† After '*Protonotes*', T. Gerrard & Co.

debris. Collect individual amoebae by means of a fine pipette and transfer them to a cavity slide.

4 Examine under the microscope arranged with light stopped down by use of the iris diaphragm or, better, with dark-ground illumination.

*Preparation techniques*

(i) See 'Protozoa' (p. 164).
(ii) Kill and fix.

(*a*) Steam, or dry heat, or osmium tetroxide vapour.
(*b*) Cultures may be killed and fixed with Bouin's fluid.

(iii) Large specimens.*

1 Stain with acetic-carmine; acid haemalum (Mayer's); haematoxylin (Delafield's, Ehrlich's or Heidenhain's).
2 Replace stain with distilled water.
3 Add an equal volume of glycerol (20% aq.).
4 Allow the water to evaporate at room temperature. (3–7 d)
5 Replace glycerol with industrial methylated spirit. (5 min)
6 Replace with fresh industrial methylated spirit. (5 min)
7 Replace the spirit with clove oil. (5 min)
8 Mount in D.P.X.

**Amoebocytes**

**S/C** Coelomic fluid and seminal vesicles of the earthworm (*Lumbricus* sp. and *Allolobophora* sp.).

1 Make smears of coelomic fluid or seminal vesicles on slides (p. 79).
2 Stain with Heidenhain's haematoxylin.

**Amphibian Eggs**

See *'Rana'* (p.165).

**Amphioxus**

**P** Alcohol (70%).
*Before dissection.*

1 Place in nitric acid (20%). (2–3 days at room temperature)

* After H. B. Miles. *School Science Review*, **XL**, 140–144, November 1958.

2 Wash thoroughly.

*Preparation techniques*

(i) Fix. Bouin's fluid.
(ii) Nerve cord. Stain in methylene blue.
(iii) Pharynx. Stain in borax carmine.
(iv) Epithelium. Stain in Delafield's haematoxylin.
(v) *Semi-whole mounts.*

1 After treatment as in (i) dissect away one whole side of the animal.
2 Dehydrate.
3 Clear in cedar-wood oil.
4 Either (*a*) Preserve in a tube of cedar-wood oil; or (*b*) Mount in D.P.X.

(vi) *Whole specimens.*

1 Fix in formaldehyde (5%).
2 Stain:
Mayer's hydrochloric acid-carmine 5 ml
Alcohol (70%) . . . . . . . 20 ml
(24–36 h)
3 Rinse in alcohol (70%).
4 Transfer to:
Alcohol (83%) . . . . . . . 97.5 ml
Hydrochloric acid . . . . . . 2.5 ml
(Until the tissue appears light pink against a white background. This will take from 8–12 h. As often as the de-staining bath becomes tinted so that it becomes difficult accurately to judge the colour of the tissue, it must be replaced with fresh solution).
5 Wash in alcohol (83%).
6 Wash in alcohol (95%).
7 Counterstain if desired.
8 If necessary, re-wash in alcohol (95%).
9 Dehydrate in alcohol (100%).
10 Clear in methyl salicylate (oil of wintergreen).
11 Mount in Canada balsam.
[Digestive tube, gill bars, hepatic diverticulum (→ brilliant red); spinal cord (→ reddish-orange); notochord (→ sharp orange); buccal cirri, fin, oral hood, velar tentacles (→ light pink.)]

**Amyloid Substances (plant)**

Stain in Hanstein's fuchsin-violet (→ red).

**Anemone (Sea)**

(i) Kill. Hot Bouin's fluid.
(ii) Store in alcohol (70%).

**Angiosperms**

**S/C** See 'Culture Media 2' (p. 203).

**Animals, Small**

*To macerate and tease.* Chromium trioxide (1%).

**Animal Tissue**

(i) *General Preservative Techniques*

1 Formol-saline (strong) (p. 210). (This also fixes the tissue.) (10–14 d)

2 Either (*a*) Formol-saline (weak) (p. 210). (Permanently)

Or (*b*) 1 Alcohol (30%). (1 d)

2 Alcohol (50%). (1 d)

3 Alcohol (70%) (to which a little glycerol has been added). (Permanently)

(ii) *Class specimens. To preserve from lesson to lesson.*

| | |
|---|---|
| Calcium iodate . . . . . | 2 g |
| Distilled water . . . . . | 2 000 ml |

Warm till dissolved. The above will keep frogs for 6 months; dogfish for 10 days. It is *not* suitable for arthropods.

(iii) *Museum specimens, especially insects.*

Pampel's fluid (see p. 238).

This is recommended by Imms* as an excellent fluid for the preservation of biological specimens, especially insects. It is cheaper than ethyl alcohol, does not harden so much, keeps the tissues in better condition and is non-inflammable. Because of the presence of acetic acid it should clearly not be used for animals having any form of calcareous skeleton.

(iv) *Bulk tissue and pathological specimens (gelatine method).*

(*Permanent and museum mounts.* †)

1 Use fresh tissue, and remove any adherent debris by gentle washing in water. Remove contents of any cavities (intestine, etc.).

2 If possible fix (as below) not later than 10–15 minutes after killing. If delay is unavoidable, wrap the tissue in a dry cloth to absorb moisture.

3 Cut the tissue so that no piece is larger than a 10 cm cube.

4 Fix in the following solution:

| | |
|---|---|
| Potassium acetate . . . . | 30 g |
| Potassium nitrate . . . . | 15 g |
| Formaldehyde (40%) . . . | 200 ml |
| Water . . . . . . . . . | 1000 ml |

See that all cavities are filled and, if necessary, ligature. (12 h usually; brain, blood clots, very large specimens 24–48 h)

5 Immerse in water. (Few min)

6 Immerse in industrial methylated spirit. (To restore colour lost in **4**.) (1–5 h. Watch each specimen and remove when *bright red tint appears.* Prolonged treatment spoils.)

7 If the specimen does not now look very fresh (e.g. kidney, liver, etc.) cut away a thin slice of tissue to expose a fresh surface.

8 Wash of excess alcohol in water.

9 Place in Kaiserling's solution (p. 230). (Days, months, or as a permanent mount.)

(Although this fluid may be used as a permanent mountant, it tends to macerate, and the process should be carried through to completion):

10 Place in permanent storage jars and add melted Kaiserling-gelatine (p. 229).

11 Seal storage jars with pitch. [See 'Sealing Media XV' (p. 247).]

(v) See also *'Rana'* (p. 165).

*Preparation techniques*

(i) *Animal tissue should be fixed before staining.* Formol-saline (p. 215) is a good general fixative, but refer first to 'Fixing' (p. 35) and to the specific tissue required. For very rapid fixation of small pieces of fresh tissue see 'Simple Methods of Fixation, A (*a*)' (p. 37).

(ii) *Small entire objects:*

Treat in quantities in the way recommended in Method **1**, p. 73.

Stain in (*a*) (*Temp.*). Methyl green.

(*b*) (*Perm.*). Borax carmine [see **I** (*a*), p. 99 and Method **12** (p. 78)]; Mayer's alum carmine (not for marine specimens); Mayer's carmalum (not for marine specimens); Mayer's acid haemalum (nuc.); picrocarmine

* A. D. Imms, *Nature*, **144**, 3648, 600, Sept. 30, 1939.

† Adapted from information supplied by the Pathological Department, Cheltenham General Hospital.

(iii) *Fresh tissue:*
Stain in acid fuchsin (diluted 20 times with Ringer's soln.); safranin o; Hofmann's violet; iron-aceto-carmine; safranin o (15 min) and picric-aniline blue WS (*time varies*). (The two latter stain the chromatin); methyl green (temp.).

*General Histology*

N.B. Before starting any method, consult Chapter 7 (p. 183) to find out all you can about the stain, its uses and how it is made up.
To avoid repetition, the final processes of dehydration, clearing, and mounting have not been listed unless special methods are desirable. In any case, details of the process will vary according to the dehydrating agent (ethyl alcohol, or butyl alcohol) in use and reference should be made to the appropriate section on dehydration (p. 51). D.P.X. resin is a satisfactory permanent mountant.
Full details of routine methods are given in Chapter 5, p. 71.

I. SINGLE STAINING

(*a*) *Borax Carmine* (p. 196)
An alcoholic nuclear stain for general use and especially for small, whole animals (p. 78).
**1** Dehydrate tissue up to and including alcohol (50%) (p. 52). If the tissue has been preserved in alcohol (70%) omit this stage and proceed direct to either (i) **2**, or (ii) **2**.
Either (i) *Progressive Method:*
**2** Transfer to stain diluted with alcohol (50%). (Leave till stained sufficiently)
**3** Wash in alcohol (70%).
or (ii) *Retrogressive Method:*
**2** Transfer to stock solution of stain. (Till overstained)
**3** Differentiate in acid alcohol (p. 186).
**4** Wash in alcohol (70%).

(*b*) *Mayer's Acid Haemalum* (p. 220)
An aqueous nuclear stain for sections, small whole animals and bulk tissue. Considered by some authorities to be superior to all other haematoxylins and haematins:
Either (i) *Progressive Method:*
**1** Stain in stock solution of Mayer's acid haemalum diluted to 30% with *distilled* water.
**2** Wash in *tap* water.
or (ii) *Retrogressive Method:*
**1** Stain to excess. (About 5 h for tissue in bulk)
**2** Differentiate in acid alcohol (p. 186).
**3** Transfer to alcohol (50%). (½ h for tissue in bulk)
**4** Transfer to alcohol (30%). (½ h for tissue in bulk)
**5** Wash in tap or alkaline water (p. 188). (1 h for tissue in bulk)

(*c*) *Anderson's Iron Alum Haematoxylin* (p. 222)
A useful nuclear stain for sections. This stain requires a mordant, therefore see page 49.
**1** Stain in Anderson's iron alum haematoxylin. (15 min)
**2** Differentiate in acid alcohol (p. 186).
**3** Rinse in distilled water.
*Note:* Haemoglobin has a great affinity for iron haematoxylin. Do not mistake red blood corpuscles for nuclei.

II. COUNTERSTAINING

(*a*) *Baker's 'Haematal 8'* (p. 220) *counterstained with Biebrich Scarlet* (p. 191)
A blue nuclear stain followed by a pink or red cytoplasmic stain. This is a simple method which is good for general microanatomy.
**1** Bring sections to water.
**2** Stain in Baker's 'Haematal 8'. (2–5 min)
**3** Rinse in tapwater.
**4** 'Blue' if necessary in very dilute ammonia solution (p. 188).
**5** Rinse in distilled water.
**6** Counterstain in 0.2% aq. Biebrich scarlet. (c. 1 min)
**7** Rinse in water.
**8** Dehydrate quickly in 70%, 96% and absolute alcohols.
**9** Clear in xylene and mount in D.P.X.
*Note:* Material fixed in Carnoy's fluid works well, as does material fixed for 3–6 h in Zenker's fluid.

(*b*) *Delafield's Haematoxylin* (p. 222) *counterstained with Eosin Y aq.* (p. 211)
An aqueous nuclear stain counterstained with an aqueous plasma stain, for general use and especially for sections.
See Method **19** from process **6** onwards (p. 84).

*Results of Staining, Methods* (*a*) *and* (*b*) *above.*

Basiphil structures (e.g. nuclei, areas of cytoplasm rich in ribonucleoprotein) . . . . . blue

Acidophil structures (e.g. cytoplasm, collagen and elastic fibres, decalcified bone matrix, erythrocytes, keratin and stratum lucidum of skin, muscle fibres etc.) . . . . pink or red

(*c*) *Anderson's Iron Alum Haematoxylin* (p. 222) *counterstained with Eosin Y aq.* (p. 211)

**1–3** As I (*c*)**1–3** on p. 99.
**4** Counterstain in eosin Y aq. (c.1 min)
**5** Wash in distilled water.
**6** Dehydrate in alcohol (96%). (1 min)
**7** Dehydrate in alcohol (100%). (1 min)
**8** Clear in xylene and mount in D.P.X.

(*d*) *Anderson's Iron Alum Haematoxylin* (p. 222) *counterstained with van Gieson's stain* (p. 218)

**1–3** As I (*c*)**1–3** (p. 99). Staining in haematoxylin must be prolonged [see (*g*) **1**, below].
**4** Counterstain in van Gieson's stain. (½–5 min)
**5** Wash quickly in distilled water.
**6** Dehydrate, clear and mount.

*Note:* Should the tissue be too deeply counterstained, excess red may be removed by water and excess yellow by alcohol.

*Results of Staining*

| | |
|---|---|
| Nuclei . . . . . . . . . . . . | black |
| Collagen fibres . . . . . . . . | red |
| Cytoplasm, elastic fibres, muscle, erythrocytes . . . . . . . . . | yellow |

(*e*) *Borax Carmine* (p. 196) *counterstained with Eosin Y alc.* (p. 212)

**1** Overstain in borax carmine.
**2** Wash in alcohol (70%).
**3** Differentiate in acid alcohol (p. 186).
**4** Wash in alcohol (70%).
**5** Counterstain in eosin Y alc.
**6** Dehydrate in alcohol (96%). (1 min)
**7** Dehydrate in alcohol (100%). (1 min)
**8** Clear in xylene and mount in D.P.X.

(*f*) *Eosin Y aq.* (p. 212) *counterstained with Borrel's Methylene Blue* (p. 234)

**1** Dilute some Borrel's methylene blue to 1 in 4 with distilled water.
**2** In separate vessels warm some diluted methylene blue, and some eosin Y aq., both to 60°C.
**3** Place the sections in a dish and pour the warm eosin Y on them. (2 min)
**4** Transfer sections to another dish and pour on the warm methylene blue. (1 min)
**5** Differentiate in tap water. (Till excess stain removed)
**6** Differentiate in alcohol (70%) examining frequently under low power.
**7** Transfer to alcohol (100%). (2 min)

(*g*) *Delafield's Haematoxylin* (p. 222) *counterstained with van Gieson's stain* (p. 218).

**1** *Stain* in Delafield's haematoxylin diluted to 1 in 5 with *distilled* water. (At least 15 min. Otherwise the haematoxylin may be washed out by the picric acid contained in van Gieson's stain.)
**2** Rinse in tap water or alkaline water (p. 188). (To blue the stain)
**3** Counterstain in van Gieson's stain. (7–10 min)
**4** Blot dry.
**5** Transfer to alcohol (100%). (As short a time as possible)
**6** Clear in xylene and mount in D.P.X.

(*h*) *Ehrlich's Haematoxylin* (p. 222) *counterstained with Eosin Y aq.* (p. 212)

**1** Stain in stock solution of Ehrlich's haematoxylin. (5 min–24 h)
**2** Differentiate in acid alcohol (p. 186).
**3** Wash in tap water and 'blue' if necessary.
**4** Counterstain in eosin Y aq, (1 min)
**5** Wash in water. (2 min)
**6** Dehydrate in alcohol (96%). (1 min)
**7** Dehydrate in alcohol (100%). (1 min)
**8** Clear in xylene and mount in D.P.X.

(*i*) *Heidenhain's Haematoxylin* (p. 223) *counterstained with Eosin Y aq.* (p. 212)

Useful for cytological work.

**1** Place in iron alum (2% aq.) (p. 187), or *liquor ferri* (p. 231).
[½–12 h according to fixative used. Material fixed in Bouin, Carnoy, formaldehyde and mercuric-formaldehyde requires a short time (1 h) in the mordant: algae fixed in formol-acetic-alcohol should be mordanted in *liquor ferri* for about 4 h.]
**2** Wash with distilled water.
**3** Stain in Heidenhain's haematoxylin. (For as long as the tissue was in the mordant)
**4** Rinse in distilled water.

**5** Differentiate in iron alum (2% aq.) or in *liquor ferri* (if this was used for mordanting) and then dip in *distilled* water. Repeat.
(Until, on watching under the lower power of the microscope, the colour is removed from almost all but the nuclei)
**6** Immerse in running tap water. (½ h)
**7** Counterstain in eosin Y aq. (2 min)
**8** Wash in water.
**9** Dehydrate in alcohol (96%). (1 min)
**10** Dehydrate in alcohol (100%). (1 min)
**11** Clear in xylene and mount in D.P.X.

(*j*) *Weigert's Stain* (*Basic Fuchsin-Phenol*) (p. 216) *counterstained with van Gieson's stain* (p. 218)

**1** Drain all water from loose sections, or xylene from sections attached to slide.
**2** Rinse in alcohol (100%).
**3** Rinse in alcohol (96%).
**4** Stain in Weigert's stain. (½–1 h in a closed vessel)
This stain must *not* be poured on the slide.
**5** Differentiate in acid alcohol (p. 186). (1 min)
**6** Rinse in distilled water. (Quickly)
**7** Counterstain in van Gieson's stain. (½–5 min)
**8** Wash quickly in distilled water.
**9** Dehydrate quickly, clear and mount in D.P.X.

*Note:* Should the tissue be too deeply counterstained, excess red may be removed by water and excess yellow by alcohol.

[Collagen fibres (→ red, against a yellow ground); elastic fibres (→ blue-black); epithelia (→ yellow); muscle (→ yellow.]

(*k*) *Weigert's Iron Haematoxylin* (p. 222) *counterstained with van Gieson's stain* (p. 218)

**1** Hydrate sections (p. 65): alcohol (100%), (90%), distilled water. (1 min each)
**2** Stain in Weigert's iron haematoxylin. (10–15 min in the cold)
**3** Wash off excess stain in tap water. (Thoroughly)
**4** Stain in Gieson's stain. (2 min)
**5** Differentiate and dehydrate in ethanol (*very quickly* otherwise de-staining will be excessive).
**6** Clear in xylene and mount in D.P.X.

[Collagen fibres (→ red, against a yellow background); connective tissue (→ red); cytoplasm (→ yellow); elastic fibres (→ blue-black); epithelia (→ yellow); keratinized tissue (→ bright yellow); muscle (→ yellow); nuclei (→ bluish-black).]

(*l*) *Ehrlich's Haematoxylin* (p. 222) *counterstained with Eosin Y alc.* (p. 212)

A useful method for bulk staining.

**1** Stain in 1 part of stock solution of Ehrlich's haematoxylin diluted with 2 parts of acetic acid (2%).
**2** Transfer to fresh, diluted stain.
**3** Rinse in *distilled* water.
**4** Differentiate in acid alcohol (p. 186).
**5** Wash in running tap or alkaline water (p. 188).
**6** Dehydrate up to and including alcohol (75%).
**7** Counterstain in eosin Y alc. (6 h)
**8** Wash in alcohol (96%).
**9** Dehydrate in alcohol (100%).

## III. DOUBLE STAINING

(*a*) *Picro-Carmine* (p. 197)

An aqueous nuclear double stain for general use and small whole animals.

Either (i) *Progressive Method:*

**1** Stain (stain diluted to 50% with distilled water). (Leave till sufficiently stained)
**2** Wash in distilled water.
**3** Dehydrate successively in alcohol (70%), (90%), (100%), clear in xylene and mount in D.P.X.

or (ii) *Retrogressive Method:*

**1** Stain in stock solution of stain. (Till overstained)
**2** Dehydrate to alcohol (70%).
**3** Differentiate in acid alcohol (p. 186), controlling process by microscopical examination.
**4** Wash in alcohol (70%).
**5** Dehydrate successively in alcohol (90%), (100%). (2 min each)
**6** Clear in xylene and mount D.P.X.

(*b*) *Mann's Double Stain* (p. 233).

A good double stain for sections.

**1** Fix tissue in Mann's fixative (p. 232).
**2** Stain sections in Mann's stain. (24 h)
**3** Wash in water.
**4** Dehydrate in alcohol (70%), (90%), (100%). (2 min each)
**5** Place in this solution:
Alcohol (100%) . . . . . . . 50 ml
Sodium hydroxide [1% in alcohol (100%)] . . . . . . . . 4 drops
(Till sections are red)
**6** Wash quickly in alcohol (100%).
**7** Hydrate to water (p. 65). (2 min to remove excess blue)

8 Transfer to water slightly acidified with acetic acid. (Sections become blue and no more stain comes out.)

9 Dehydrate.

[Nuclei (→ blue); Connective tissue fibres (Collagen) (→ blue); Mucus-containing cells (→ blue); Basiphil cell-granules (→ blue); Erythrocytes (→ red); Oxyphil cell-granules (→ red).]

IV. TRIPLE STAINING

(*a*) *Mallory's Triple Stain* (p. 232)

A good stain for routine work with sections of material *which has previously been fixed in Zenker's solution and dehydrated in alcohol.*

(i) **1** Stain in solution A. (Till bright red; 3–20 min)
**2** Wash in distilled water.
**3** Wash in solution B. [To fix the fuchsin and prevent decolorization (1 min).]
**4** Wash in distilled water. (Thoroughly)
**5** Stain in solution C. (Till blue; 5–20 min)
**6** Wash in distilled water.
**7** Dehydrate rapidly.
**8** Clear in xylene and mount in D.P.X.

(ii) *Brilmyer's Modification.*
**1** Stain Delafield's haematoxylin. (5 min)
**2** Wash in tap water.
**3** Follow **1–7** in (i) above.

*Results of Staining*

| | |
|---|---|
| Acidophil substances (e.g. erythrocytes, some cell inclusion granules) | yellow to orange |
| Cytoplasm | pink to red |
| Collagen fibres, bone, cartilage matrix | blue |
| Nuclei, muscle, elastic fibres, keratin | red |

**Annelids**

(i) Fix. Chrom-acetic. (12 h)
(ii) See also 'Hirudo' (p. 138), and 'Lumbricus' (p. 144).

**Anodon**

**S/C**

(i) Dealers.
(ii) From the floor of ponds and canals.
(iii) On arrival from a dealer, keep in running water in a dark place. May be kept in larger aquaria.

**P** Formaldehyde (10%), after inserting wood plug between valves of shell.

(i) *To kill.*
(*a*) Plunge into boiling water. (1 min)
(*b*) Put a wooden peg between the shells, and place in formaldehyde (10%).

(ii) *Gill lamellae.*
(*a*) The best sections are cut from embedded material, but quite good sections can, with care, be hand-cut from tissue held in a piece of carrot. Cut both horizontal/longitudinal, and vertical/transverse sections.
(*b*) Stain in Delafield's haematoxylin.

*Glochidium.*

**1** Treat in quantities as suggested in Method **12** (p. 78).
**2** Stain in borax carmine.
**3** Clear in (*a*) lactophenol,
or (*b*) In a solution consisting of

| | |
|---|---|
| Phenol | 20 g |
| Glycerol | 40 ml |
| Distilled water | 40 ml |

Allow to evaporate at room temperature to half its original volume.

**4** Mount in (*a*) After **3**(*a*) in lactophenol, or (*b*) after **3**(*b*) in glycerol (p. 219).

**Anopheles**

**S/C**

(i) *Eggs and Larvae:* Collect from the surface of ponds, water butts, etc., by towing a bolting-silk tow-net, attached to a bottle, across the surface.
(ii) *Adults:* Caught at rest by placing over them a specimen tube with a piece of chloroform-soaked cotton wool at the bottom. See 'Killing Bottle iii' (p. 230).

**Anthers**

See 'Chromosomes 2(*b*)' (p. 119), and 'Pollen Grains' (p. 161).

**Aphis**

**S/C**

Obtainable almost universally as ecto-parasites on plants in gardens in summer (unless particular steps have been taken to remove eggs, young and adults) especially on broad beans (black aphis), roses (green aphis), black currants (green aphis). In winter adults may sometimes be found hibernating just below ground level alongside the stems of their host-plants; eggs may be found on the stems of many fruit trees and on the stems of the spindle tree (*Euonymus*) which is the alternative (winter) host of the black aphis of beans.

*Preparation techniques*

*Whole mounts*

(i) **1** Prick the abdomen of the aphis with a needle.
**2** Boil in potassium hydroxide (dil. aq.) until clear.
**3** Wash in distilled water.
**4** Mount in de Faure's Fluid or glycerol jelly.

(ii) **1** Heat the aphides in alcohol (70%) on a water-bath. (30 min)
**2** Transfer to lactic acid (70%). Heat on a water-bath. (20–30 min)
**3** Clear in phenol (95%).
**4** Drain off excess phenol.
**5** Mount in Berlese's fluid.
**6** Seal with gold size.
**7** When dry, seal with Canada balsam or D.P.X.

*Head, mandibles, maxillae.*

**1** Place the insect, back downwards, in a drop of water on a slide.
**2** Hold in position with a needle placed against abdomen.
**3** If labium happens to be lying posteriorly along the abdomen, ease it upwards and anteriorly.
**4** Cut off head at junction with thorax.
**5** Separate the mouth parts so that they will be displayed to the best advantage.
*Either,*
**6a** For temp. mount: Lactic acid (dorsal side uppermost) *or*
**6b** Transfer to glycerol/alcohol [i(*a*) **3** (ii) (p. 58).] (Several h)
**7** Mount dorsal side uppermost, in glycerol.
**8** Ring with glycerol-jelly, after first removing any surplus glycerol from edges of cover-slip by means of small pieces of filter-paper rolled into a pointed spill.
**9** Seal when glycerol-jelly has set.

**Apis. (Honey Bee)**

*Preparation techniques*

(i) *Body Hairs.* Mount in glycerol.
(ii) *Acarine in tracheae.* See '*Acarine*' (p. 94).
(iii) *Mouth Parts*
**1** Boil in potassium hydroxide aq. (CARE. Gently. 1 min)
**2** Wash in distilled water.
**3** Dehydrate in 2 ethoxy ethanol.
**4** Clear in xylene.
**5** Mount in D.P.X.

**Aquatic and Marine Animals (Small)**

(i) *To kill.*
(*a*) Allow the live specimen to expand in water; sprinkle menthol on the surface. Touch the specimen gently with a glass rod to test the degree of narcotization. The process is slow.
(*b*) Vapour of acetic acid (glacial), or osmium tetroxide.
(*c*) *Specially useful for whelks and other molluscs.*
Carefully run soda-water from a syphon down the slide of the vessel of water containing the animals.
(*d*) *Specially useful for ascidians, Balanus, sponges.*
Chloral hydrate (0.1%).
(*e*) *Coelenterates and polyzoa.* See pp. 119 and 163.
When dead, quickly remove to strong formol-saline.

(ii) *Preparation technique*
(*a*) *General treatment.*
Deal with quantities as suggested in Method **12** (p. 78).
(*b*) Stain in borax carmine.

**Arcella**

**S/C** From duckweed on pond surfaces.

**Arenicola**

(i) *Kill.* Alcohol (70%).
(ii) *Fix.* Formaldehyde (10%).

**P** Formaldehyde (10%).

**Artemia**

*To display general features of Crustacean organization.*

Inject with methylene blue in saline.

**Arthropods (Small Terrestrial and Aerial)**

(i) *To kill.* See 'Killing Bottle' (p. 230).
(ii) *Preparation technique.*
 **1** Kill and clear in Berlese's fluid (p. 190).
 **2** Mount in Berlese's fluid.
 **3** Dry off in oven.
 **4** Seal.
(iii) See also 'Aphis' (p. 102), 'Crustacea' (p. 121), and 'Insects' (p. 140).

**Ascaris**

**S/C**
(i) Dealers.
(ii) Abattoirs — take a vessel of formaldehyde (5%), and also try to keep live ones for a short time in warm saline (0.6%) in a vacuum flask.

Preserve in Formaldehyde (2%), or alcohol (70%).

*Preparation techniques*
(i) See 'Nematodes' (p. 150).
(ii) (*a*) *Section.* By embedding in wax. First roughen cuticle and make it wax-permeable by treating specimen with potassium hydroxide (5% aq.). (Several h)
 (*b*) Stain in Mallory's stain.

**Ascomycetes**

**S/C** See 'Culture Media 3' (p. 203).

**Ascophanus**

**S/C** See 'Culture Media 3' (p. 203).

**Aspidium**

To macerate the stele.* .

| | |
|---|---|
| Sodium hydroxide | 2.5 g |
| Water | 100 ml |

Macerate for 1 month and wash in running water for not less than 24 h.

**Astacus**

**S/C**
(i) Dealers.
(ii) Catch at night, in nets in streams in limestone districts.
(iii) On arrival after a journey in damp grass, place the animals in a shallow vessel and half cover with water. This enables them to exclude air from gill covers gradually.
(iv) May be kept in an aquarium with a stony bottom.

Preserve in Alcohol (70%).

*Preparation techniques*
(i) *To kill.* Plunge into boiling water. (10 s)
(ii) *Fix.* Alcohol (70%).
(iii) *Small appendages.* First boil in potassium hydroxide (5% aq.). (Few min)
(iv) *Eye.* Use a fresh crayfish.
 (*a*) *To see crystalline cones.* Mount sections in potassium hydroxide (5% aq.).
 (*b*) *To see rods.* Tease out with osmium tetroxide (1%).

**Astasia longa**

**S/C** See 'Culture Media 3' (p. 203).

**Asterias**

**S/C**
(i) Dealers.
(ii) Rock pools.
(iii) Fishermen.
(iv) Keeping in sea-water tanks not easy, except by experienced aquarists. Feed on live shell-fish.

**P** Formaldehyde (5%). First open dorsal surface of each arm.

*Preparation techniques*
(i) *Kill.* Formaldehyde (5%).
(ii) *Fix.* Formaldehyde (10%).
(iii) *Sections.* (*T.S. arm; T.S. disc; H.S. disc.*)
 **1** Decalcify in:

| | |
|---|---|
| Alcohol (70%) | 99 ml |
| Hydrochloric acid | 1 ml |

 **2** Embed in paraffin and section at 10 $\mu$m.
 **3** Stain in Mallory's stain or borax carmine.

**Atax ypsilophorous**

**S/C** In mantle cavity of *Anodon.*

*Preparation techniques*
**1** Kill in alcohol (30%).
**2** Mount in Berlese's fluid.

* Adapted from *Gerrard's Bulletin*, May 1939. T. Gerrard & Co.

**Autobasidiomycetes**

*To show clamp connections.* *

Stain: Methylene blue (1%) is preferable to lacto phenol/anilin blue WS.

**Bacteria**

**S/C**

(i) *Bacteria of Medical Importance:* National Collection of Type Cultures, Central Public Health Laboratory, Colindale Avenue, London, N.W.9.

(ii) *Bacteria of Milk and Milk Products:* National Collection of Dairy Organisms, National Institute for Research in Dairying, Shinfield, Reading, Berkshire.

(iii) *Bacteria Pathogenic to Plants:* National Collection of Plant Pathogenic Bacteria, Plant Pathology Laboratory, Milton Road, Harpenden, Hertfordshire.

(iv) *General Type Cultures:* Torrey Research Institute, Aberdeen.

(v) See 'Culture Media 3' (pp. 203 – 208).

(vi) *To culture in the dark.* † Use a plaster-of-Paris box with a plaster lid, either moistened from the outside from time-to-time, or placed in a shallow reservoir of water.

(vii) Because of its large size, *Sarcina lutea* is a useful bacterium with which to acquire a technique. It is a yellow Gram +ve type, sensitive to penicillin. Also useful is *Chromobacterium prodigidiosum* which is a red Gram –ve type, sensitive to streptomycin. Both types are obtainable from the Commonwealth Mycological Institute, Ferry Lane, Kew, Richmond, Surrey.

*Preparation techniques*

*General notes:*

(*a*) Absolutely clean, grease-free, sterilized slides, cover-slips, needles and forceps are essential. See 'Glass-ware, to clean' (p. 218).

(*b*) Bacterial films are best made on the slide. The general tendency is to make them too dense. A good guide is, that the bacteria should be invisible in the wet film and become visible only as the film dries.

(*c*) Films and smears are made by using a sterilized wire, 26 gauge (nichrome, platinum, or the basal wires from an old electric-light bulb – the base of which provides a useful mount) with a small loop (2 mm diam.) at one end, to spread a drop of culture over an area rather less than that of a cover-slip.

(*d*) Films are conveniently dried by waving the slide in the air, and the organism fixed by passing the slide, face downwards, through a bunsen flame, twice.

(*e*) Slides are processed either by placing a small quantity of the reagent on the slide, or by standing the slide in a slotted glass staining jar, or in a wide specimen tube containing the reagent. After treatment any excess reagent is drained off. The treated slide is finally dried thoroughly, but carefully, either with filter-paper or over a flame.

Stains: Basic fuchsin (aq.); Bismarck brown Y; phenol-fuchsin (especially for cilia and flagella); phenol-methylene blue; crystal violet; Loeffler's methylene blue.

*Temporary preparations*

(i) **1** Place a drop of infusion containing bacteria on a slide.
**2** Film and allow to dry in the air.
**3** Add a drop of very dilute methylene blue to the film.
**4** Cover with a No. 1 cover-slip.
**5** Press gently with a clean filter-paper.

(ii) **1** As stages **1–3**, above.
**4** Drain off excess stain on to a filter-paper.
**5** Add a drop of glycerol to the film.
**6** Cover with a No. 1 cover-slip.

(iii) So-called temporary preparations can, in fact, be kept for some months if, after staining, the excess stain is washed off with distilled water and the slide is dried over a flame. The slides must be stored in a dust-free atmosphere. When required for examination the immersion oil is placed direct on the film.

(iv) *To Observe Motility.*
Make a hanging-drop culture (p. 208). The drop should be small, otherwise focusing will be difficult.

(v) *In Zooglea Stage.*
Stain in iodine, to distinguish protoplasm, which stains, from gelatinous material, which does not stain.

(vi) See also Methods **1** and **2** (p. 73).

* From information kindly supplied by Dr. M. J. Cole, University of Aston in Birmingham.

† After Strasburger, 1930, *Handbook of Practical Botany* (English Edition), Allen & Unwin.

*Permanent preparations*

See note on mounting, under 'Blood' (p. 109)

(i) *To differentiate between Gram +ve bacteria (i.e. those forming a complex with crystal violet/iodine) and Gram −ve bacteria (i.e. those forming no complex*). In using this method it is necessary to have some controls in the form of Gram +ve and Gram −ve types. These are: *Gram* +ve, *Escherichia coli* (*Bacterium coli*) and Gram −ve, *Staphylococcus aureus.*

1 Fix the *dried* film by passing it through a flame, face downwards.
2 Stain in a mixture of:

| | |
|---|---|
| Crystal violet (1% aq.) . . . . . . | 30 ml |
| Sodium bicarbonate (5% aq.) . . . | 8 ml |

(5 min)

3 Wash off the stain with Gram's iodine and cover with fresh Gram's iodine (p. 229). (2 min)
4 Drain off the iodine.
5 Transfer to alcohol (100%). (Till no more colour is lost. But note that if this treatment is too prolonged a weak Gram +ve type can give a Gram −ve result.)
6 Wash in water.
7 Transfer to Ziehl's phenol-fuchsin (0.1% aq.). (½ min)
8 Transfer to tap water.
9 Dry thoroughly with filter-paper.
10 Mount in D.P.X. and cover with a No. 1 cover-slip.

*Note:* If desired, the un-covered film may be examined by placing immersion oil directly on it. Slides of films without cover-slips remain useful for some weeks.

(ii)

1 Smear a film of culture on slide with a sterilized needle.
2 Wave slide in air to dry.
3 Kill and fix by warming over a flame.
4 Stain in basic fuchsin aq. or other stain from selection p. 105. (5 min)
   Correctly stained slide should be almost colourless to naked eye.
5 Wash in distilled water.
6 Dry over a flame.
7 Mount in D.P.X.
8 Cover with a No. 1 cover-slip.

(iii) *'Negative' staining for Bacteria*

1 Mix culture with Indian ink ('Pelican' brand).
2 Smear mixture on a slide, thinly.
3 Dry in the air.
4 Mount in D.P.X.
   The Bacteria will appear unstained, in an opaque matrix.

(iv) *Bacteria in tissues.*

(*a*) *Jensen's Method.*

1 Stain in Jensen's picro-carmine (p. 197). (Overnight at 37°C)
2 Wash in tap-water, thoroughly.
3 Stain in methyl violet 2B (1% aq. freshly filtered). (3 min)
4 Wash in tap water.
5 Stain again in Jensen's picro-carmine. (5 min)
6 Decolorize with picric-anilin (p. 189). (To a uniform yellow tint. Distribute the anilin evenly by blotting it on to the slide.)
7 Wash in xylene, *carefully.*
8 Mount in D.P.X.

(*b*) *Weigert's Method.* (*Also suitable for fibrin.*)

1 Stain in lithium carmine (p. 197). (1–5 min)
2 Differentiate in acid alcohol. (Several h)
3 Wash in distilled water.
4 Dry off with filter-paper.
5 Stain in anilin-methyl violet 2B (p. 234). (20–30 s)
6 Drain stain off slide. Blot off with filter-paper.
7 Transfer to Gram's iodine. (20–30 s)
8 Drain iodine off slide. Blot off with filter-paper.
9 Differentiate in anilin-xylene (p. 190). (Until the stain begins to leave the nuclei and the ground colour is red.)
10 Mount in D.P.X.
   [Gram + ve bacteria (→ darkish blue); fibrin (→ glistening blue); nuclei (→ red).]

(*c*) *Ziehl-Neelson Method for Tubercle Bacilli.*

1 Bring sections attached to slides through xylene, alcohol (100%), methylated spirit, to water.
2 Place a small quantity of Ziehl's phenol-fuchsin in a test-tube and bring it to the boil.
3 Flood the slide with the boiling stain and leave. (5 min)
4 Decolourize by dipping in sulphuric acid (25% aq.) and then in industrial methylated spirit (70%), *alternately.* (Until sections are colourless, or almost so.)
5 Wash in distilled water.

6 Counterstain in Delafield's haematoxylin. (1 min)
7 Wash in tap water.
8 Dehydrate in industrial methylated spirit.
9 Dehydrate in alcohol (100%).
10 Clear in xylene.
11 Mount in D.P.X.
[Tubercle bacilli (→ pink); remainder (→ blue).]

(*d*) *Ziehl-Neelson Method for Tubercle Bacilli in Sputum.*
1 Make a smear of sputum as in 'Blood' (p. 108).
2 Fix by very gentle heat over a gentle flame.
3 Cool.
4 Flood the slide with Ziehl's phenol-basic fuchsin.
5 Warm over gentle flame. (Until liquid steams)
6 Drain off excess fluid.
7 Wash in distilled water.
8 Flood the slide with acid alcohol [5% of hydrochloric acid (conc.) in alcohol (70%)].
9 Drain off the acid alcohol.
10 Flood again with fresh acid alcohol. (10–15 min)
11 Wash in distilled water.
12 Counterstain with malachite green (or methylene blue). (1 min)
13 Wash in distilled water.
14 Drain off the water.
15 Stand the slide on end to dry in the air.
[Tubercle bacilli → pink; remainder → green (or blue).]

(*e*) See also the Drew-Murray method for connective tissue, 'Connective Tissue' (p. 120).

(v) *Bacterial Spores.*

(*a*) *Quick Method.*
1 Make a dried film.
2 Stain in malachite green (1%) and heat to steaming but do not let film dry on heating. (2–3 min)
3 Wash in tap water. (Until washings are colourless)
4 Stain in safranin o (0.5% aq.).
5 Wash in water. (Quickly)
6 Dry with filter-paper or by passing through a flame.
[Spores (→ green); vegetative parts, i.e. rest of bacterial body (→ red).]

(*b*) *Slow Method* (1 h).
1 Make a dried film.
2 Stain in Ehrlich's anilin-water-fuchsin (p. 216), or Ziehl's phenol-fuchsin (at 60°C) (p. 217). (1 h)
(This uniformly stains spores and protoplasm.)
3 Wash in acid alcohol.
4 Counterstain with methylene blue (aq. or alc.).
5 Wash in water.
6 Dry with filter paper or by passing through a flame. (Spores → red; vegetative parts → dark blue.)

**Balantidum**

**S/C** In bladder of *Rana*.

**Balanus**

**P** Formaldehyde (10%).

*Preparation techniques*
(i) *Kill and fix.* Formaldehyde (10%).
(ii) See 'Aquatic and Marine Organisms' (p. 103).

**Barnacle**

See 'Balanus'.

**Basidiomycetes**

**S/C** See 'Culture Media 3' (p. 203).

**Basiphil Granules**

Stains: Haematoxylin and eosin Y (→ blue); iron haematoxylin and van Gieson's stain (→ black); Mallory's stain (→ red).

**Bdelloura**

See 'Amphioxus, whole specimens' (p. 97).

**Bean Cotyledon**

See 'Cotyledon' (p. 121).

**Bean Root Tip**

See Method **13** (p. 79) and 'Chromosomes 1 (*a*)' (p. 115).

**Bladder**

*Unstriated muscle fibres.* See Method **19** (p. 83).

## Blood

Grease-free slides and cover-slips are essential. (See 'Glassware — to clean', p. 218.)

*Preparation techniques*

(i)

1 To obtain a drop of human blood hold the alcohol-sterilized ball of the middle or third finger against the thumb and jab the ball with a sterilized straight triangular No. 3 or No. 4 surgeon's needle.* *Do not squeeze the flesh.* Alternatively, an automatic blood-sampler, as supplied by P. K. Dutt (p. 264), may be used. It is both cheap and effective.
2 Place *small* drop of blood on clean cover-slip. Do this by placing the cover-slip on the freshly exposed blood. Do not allow the slip to touch the skin.
3 Dilute with sodium chloride solution (0.6% aq.).
4 Invert the slip on a clean slide and examine.
5 To show nuclei of erythrocytes in frog blood, and leucocytes in frog and mammalian blood, irrigate with acetic acid (1%).
6 If the examination is prolonged, ring the slide with Vaseline.

(ii) *ortho-Toluidine test for blood stains*†

*Note:* The solutions used should be kept in dropping bottles at 0°C, and it is important that, in carrying out the test, the dropping bottles should not be allowed to touch the filter-paper.

1 *Either* (*a*) rub the stain to be tested, *lightly*, with a dry 4 cm diam. filter-paper;
*or* (*b*) place a fragment of the material to be tested on a dry 4 cm diam. filter-paper.
2 Add a few drops of a solution of *ortho*-toluidine in acetic acid (see p. 251) to the filter paper. Leave for 5 s.
*Note:* if any colour develops at this stage, the presence of direct oxidizing agents is indicated, and *the test must be interpreted with caution.*
3 Add a few drops of hydrogen peroxide (see p. 228). If blood is present an *intense blue* stain will appear *immediately.*
*Note:* The colour, and the speed of the reaction, are characteristic. Weak colours, colours not appearing immediately, and minute blue dots on the filter paper are all to be ignored.

(iii) *Precipitin test for blood origin* (*whether human or non-human*).

1 Immerse some of the blood stain in saline solution, for a few hours.
2 Filter.
3 Allow about 12 mm column of the liquid to be drawn up into a *clean* capillary tube.
4 Allow a similar volume of 'rabbit anti-human serum' to be drawn into the other end of the tube, so that the two liquids mix.
If the blood is human blood, a white precipitate or 'colour' slowly forms.
5 It is essential to carry out the following controls:
(*a*) Will the given 'rabbit anti-human serum' precipitate from *known* human blood?
(*b*) Will the saline extract of the blood stain fail to give a reaction with normal rabbit serum?
(*c*) Will both the 'rabbit anti-human serum' and the saline extract of the blood stain fail to react with the saline alone?

(iv) *Preparation of a blood smear*

1 Obtain the required glassware and reagents and place them ready on the bench.
2 Jab the ball of the middle or third finger with a lancet to obtain a drop of blood (see details above, Method i).
3 Touch the fresh drop of blood onto the end of a clean slide, lying on the bench. Do *not* let the surface of the skin touch the slide.
4 Hold the edge of the end of another slide so that it stands diagonally across the lower slide, inclined at an angle of about 60° to it, in such a way that the drop of blood occupies the acute angle between the two slides (see Fig. 6.1).
5 *Push* the upper slide along the lower slide so that the blood is *dragged* behind the moving slide (see Fig. 6.2, p. 109).
*Note:* The diagonal position of the upper slide across the lower slide must be such that when the blood is dragged along, the smear will

* Needles obtainable from Messrs. Albert Browne Ltd., Chancery Street, Leicester.

† The author is indebted to W. E. Montgomery, Ph.D., D.I.C., for information about this test which may be regarded as having superseded the leuco-malachite green test. For further details see L. C. Nickolls, *The Scientific Investigation of Crime*, 1956. Butterworth. Note, however, that *ortho*-toluidine has been substituted for benzidine in this test, since benzidine has been found to have carcinogenic properties.

*not* reach the edges of the lower slide, otherwise the distribution of leucocytes will be unequal.

6 Wave the slide in the air to dry the smear and stain by method of choice (e.g. Leishman's, Giemsa's, Wright's etc.).

(v) *Staining a blood smear*

*Note:* When using Giemsa's, Leishman's, or Wright's stains, stained preparations are best washed first with stain diluted with distilled water buffered to pH 6.6–6.8 for Giemsa's and Leishman's stains, or pH 6.5 for Wright's stain, and then differentiated in similarly buffered distilled water. (See 'Buffer Solutions', p. 191 ff.)

1 Make a blood film as described above.
2 Place 5 drops of Leishman's stain on the blood film. (The methyl alcohol in the stain fixes the tissue.) (Leave for 1 min)
3 Add 5 drops of distilled water buffered to pH 6.6–6.8 and rock the slide to mix well with the stain. (Leave for 5 min)

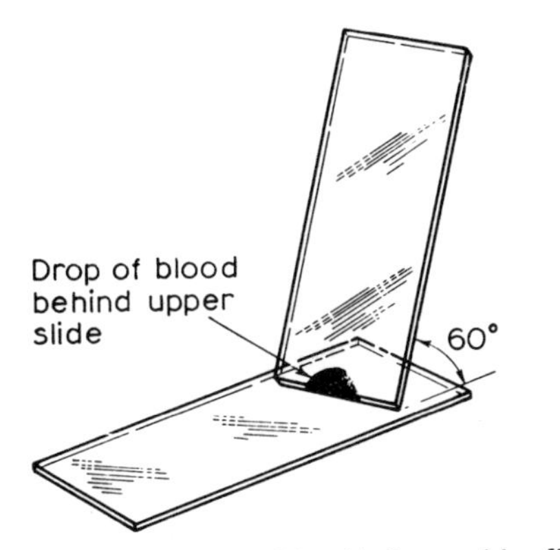


Fig. 6.1 Position of slides and blood before making film.

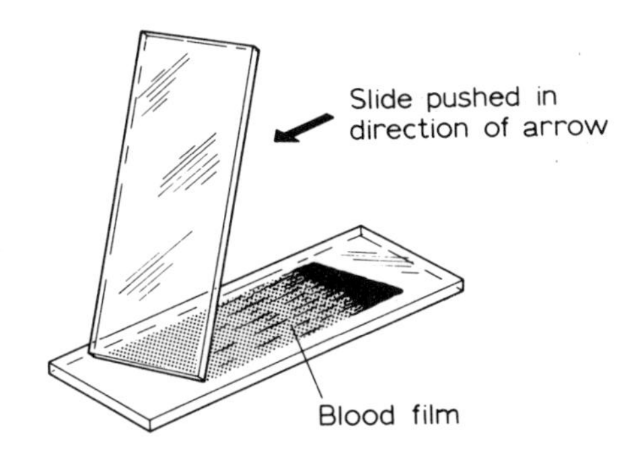


Fig. 6.2 Position of slides after completion of blood film.

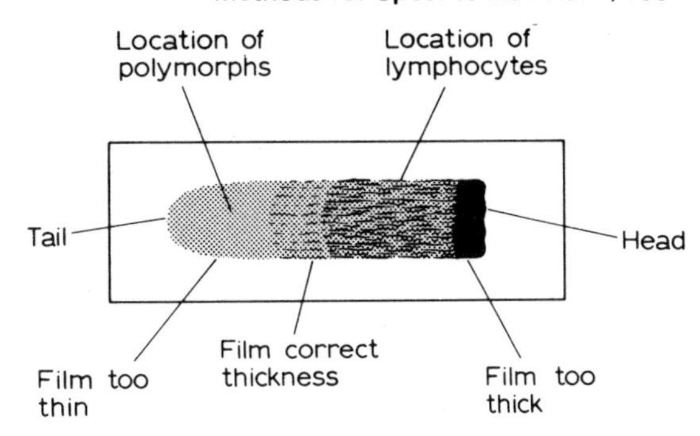


Fig. 6.3 A well-made blood film, with the location of the leucocytes.

4 Place the slide in a wide specimen tube containing 50 ml of buffered distilled water to which a few drops of Leishman's stain have been added. (Leave till the film becomes rosy pink, usually c. 30 s)
5 Drain the slide and lean against a bottle with the film side *downwards* to dry.
6 Mount in D.P.X. and cover if desired.

*Note:* If stained blood films are to be examined with an oil immersion lens, it is not necessary to mount them. A drop of oil may be added directly to the dry, stained film.

*Staining reactions*

Erythrocytes → pink
Basiphil granules → purple
leucocyte nuclei → blue/purple
lymphocyte cytoplasm → bluish
eosinophil granules → red
platelets → pink → purple
neutrophil granules → purple.

*Note:* As an alternative to step 4 above, the slide may be washed in a stream of buffered water (from a polythene squeeze bottle) until the smear is red in colour. This usually takes about 30 seconds; be careful not to wash for too long or nuclear colour is lost.

(vi) *Crossmon's technique for staining red blood cells in sections.* *

1 Fix material in 10% formalin in 0.85% NaCl. (48 h)
2 Wash in several changes of 70% alc.
3 Dehydrate, impregnate in paraffin wax and cut sections at 5 μm. Attach them to slides.
4 Dewax sections and bring to water.

* Crossmon, G. 1940. Stain Technology, 15, 155.

5 Stain in the following mixture: (1–5 min)

| | |
|---|---|
| Chromotrope 2R | 0.25 g |
| Glacial acetic acid | 1 ml |
| Distilled water | 100 ml |

6 Rinse sections four or five times in distilled water.
7 Differentiate in fresh 5% phosphotungstic acid in 95% alcohol. Agitate sections occasionally in this medium and leave until all tissue elements are decolorized except red cells. This may take many minutes.
8 Stain in the following mixture: (2–4 min)

| | |
|---|---|
| Methyl blue. . . . . . . . . . | 0.5 g |
| Glacial acetic acid . . . . . . | 1 ml |
| Distilled water . . . . . . . . | 100 ml |

9 Rinse in distilled water.
10 Transfer to 2% acetic acid. (15–60 s)
11 Absolute ethyl alcohol – 2 changes. (c.1 min in all)
12 Clear in xylene and mount in D.P.X.
(Erythrocytes → red; basiphilic elements → blue.)

*Note:* If desired a nuclear stain of Weigert's iron haematoxylin may be added between stages **4** and **5** and stages **8–10** omitted.

(vii) *Blood Parasites.*
(*a*) As Method (v) above.
(*b*) *Malaria parasite.*

(1)
1 Prepare a blood film according to the method suggested in (iv) above.
2 Fix the film in methyl alcohol. (2 min)
3 Dry by waving in the air.
4 Stain with Giemsa's stain diluted. (Two drops of stain to 2 ml of distilled water.) (1 h)
5 Rinse in distilled water buffered to pH 7.2.
6 Dry between hard (fluff-free) filter-paper.

*Note:* If, on preliminary examination, it is found that there are very few parasites in the sample, repeat the preparation with a larger sample of blood as in (2), below.

(2)
1 Prepare a blood film from a larger drop of blood (about 0.5 $mm^3$). Spread the drop of blood out, until it is sufficiently transparent, by dragging it with the end edge of another slide (held at an angle of 60° to the horizontal) with a circular motion.
2 Dry the film at 37°C.
3 Without prior fixation, stain in Field's stain A (p. 214). (3 s)
4 Transfer to phosphate buffer solution (p. 192). (5 s)
5 Stain in Field's stain B (p. 214). (2 s)
6 Wash in distilled water. (Quickly)
7 Drain off excess water.
8 Dry in air by standing the slide vertically.

**Blood Counts**

See 'Haemocytometer' (pp. 223–227).

**Blood-forming Tissues**

1 Bring sections attached to slides through xylene, alcohols to water.
2 Remove excess water by blotting with filter-paper.
3 Stain in Leishman's stain (ii) (p. 231). (Until tissue is deep blue)
4 Decolorize in acetic acid (0.66% aq.). (Until only the nuclei are blue)
5 Wash in distilled water.
6 Dehydrate *rapidly* in alcohol (90%) and (100%).
7 Mount in D.P.X.

**Blood Vessels**

Fix in formol saline. Small vessels may be dissected out and stretched on filter paper which is then immersed in the fixative.
Embed in paraffin and section.
Stain in haematoxylin and van Gieson's.
The internal elastic lamina of small arteries or the elastic fibres in the tunica media of large arteries are well shown by staining the sections with Verhoeff's technique for elastic fibres (p. 252) or by staining with orcein (p. 238).

**Bodo**

S/C Culture in an infusion of putrid fish.

**Bone**

*Preparation techniques*

(i)
1 Fix thin slices in formol-saline.
2 Decalcify (see p. 210).
3 Wash out decalcifying medium.
4 Usual processes leading to embedding and sectioning.
5 Stains: Haematoxylin and eosin Y (→ pink); iron-haematoxylin and van Gieson's (→ black); Mallory's (→ blue).
6 Dehydrate, clear and mount in D.P.X.

(ii) *Ground sections (to show lamellae, lacunae and canaliculi).*

1 Cut segments about 0.5 cm square and 1 mm thick with a small saw from a piece of dried bone.
2 Cover a slide with natural Canada Balsam (*not* the solution in xylene) and heat over a small flame till the balsam melts.
3 Place four or six segments of bone onto the slide and heat till the balsam bubbles. With a pair of forceps press each piece of bone well into contact with the slide and allow to cool. *Note:* the balsam sometimes ignites during this stage, but the flame may be extinguished quickly by blowing on it.
4 Pour a pool of water onto the centre of a sheet of 6 mm thick plate glass about 15 cm square and add some 100 mesh 'Carborundum' powder to make a thin cream.
5 Invert the slide with its pieces of bone and rub on the glass with a circular motion. Carry on, replenishing abrasive and water as necessary, until the slices of bone have been ground to a uniform thinness.
6 Wash off the abrasive with running water from the glass and the slide and replace with successively finer grades of 'Carborundum' and then 'Aloxite' powders. The final polishing may be done with jewellers rouge or ceric oxide. Do not use much pressure in the final polishing stages and do not allow to dry.
7 Prepare another balsamed slide; heat both slides and when the ground sections are free, transfer to the new slide with the polished side in contact with the glass. Press firmly and allow to cool.
8 Repeat the grinding and polishing process until the sections are thin enough. This is best judged by the increasing transparency of the section.
9 Wash well under a tap after each stage of polishing finishing with a very through wash.
10 If the sections are very thin at the conclusion of the grinding and polishing they may be removed from the carrier slide by dissolving the balsam in benzene, washed in 2 or 3 changes of clean benzene, allowed to dry and mounted dry. The cover should be sealed by gold size and finished by varnishing.

If the sections are on the thick side, then it is better to melt them off the carrier slide and remount in fresh balsam, melted by heat, on a fresh slide. When the cover-slip has been added it should be held in place with a clip or a weight until the balsam has hardened.

(iii) *Dawson's method for whole mounts.* * *(To stain the skeleton but not the flesh.)*

1 Fix in alcohol (95%). (Several weeks: until complete penetration has ensued)
2 Transfer to acetone. (Time will depend on size of object — not less than 14 d)
3 Transfer to alcohol (95%). (Time will depend on size of object — not less than 14 d)
4 Macerate in potassium hydroxide (2%). (Until bones show through flesh clearly)
5 Stain with alizarin red S. (Until bones thoroughly stained)
6 Clear in Moll's solution (p. 236). (Until flesh transparent)
7 Transfer to glycerol (50% aq.).
8 Transfer to glycerol (pure). (2 washings.) ( = preserving agent)

**Bone Marrow (from rib)**

(i)

1 Make a smear of bone marrow (on a slide or cover-slip).
   by either
   (*a*) squeezing a piece of rib with the forceps until the marrow exudes, and then using the method shown in Fig. 6.6, p. 152;
   or
   (*b*) splitting the rib and smearing the slide (or cover-slip) on the marrow *in one direction only.*
2 Wave in the air to dry.
3 Proceed as for blood films iv (p. 108 ff).

(ii) *For glycogen in marrow.* Use the P.A.S. technique (p. 112).

**Brain**

*Preservative fluids*

(i) Muller's fluid (p. 236).
(ii) Formaldehyde (5%).
(iii) Chrome alum . . . . . . . . . 2.5 g
Copper acetate . . . . . . . . . 5.0 g
Acetic acid (glacial) . . . . . . . 5.0 ml

* With acknowledgements to R. W. Bateman, B.Sc.

Formaldehyde (4%) . . . . . . . 10.0 ml
Water . . . . . . . . . . . . . 77.5 ml

Boil the chrome alum in the water and allow it to dissolve. Remove from the flame and add the copper acetate (powder) and the acetic acid. Stir well. Cool. Add the formaldehyde. The tissue can be regarded as preserved in 14 d.

**'Brown Bodies'**

**S/C** In coelom of earthworm (*Lumbricus* sp. and *Allolobophora* sp.). More common in the segments near the posterior end.

*Preparation techniques*

(i) **1** Place in a drop of saline (0.75% aq.) on a slide.
**2** Cover with a cover-slip and squash very gently.

(ii) See 'Amoebocytes' (p. 97).

**Bryozoa**

See 'Polyzoa' (p. 163).

**Bundle Ends**

To distinguish venation. See 'Leaf' (p. 142).

**Buttercup**

See 'Ranunculus' (p. 166).

**Capillaries**

*To see in the finger.*
Place a drop of cedar-wood oil on the skin above the nail-bed of the 4th digit. Place the finger on microscope stage and view under low power by direct light from a small spot light, such as a low voltage bulb. A motor cycle spot lamp held in a retort stand and supplied by a low voltage transformer acts as a cheap substitute.

**Carbohydrates**

(i) These are detected by the violet-red colour developed upon the addition of

| | |
|---|---|
| α napthol (20% alc.) | 1 drop |
| conc. sulphuric acid | 2 drops. |

This mixture must be freshly prepared.

(ii) *Periodic acid/Schiff reaction.*

**1** Bring paraffin sections through xylene, and alcohols to water.
**2** Oxidise in 1% periodic acid solution. (8 min)
**3** Wash in running water. (1 min)
**4** Schiff's reagent (p. 245). (20 min)
**5** Sulphurous acid (p. 250), 3 changes. (2 min in each)
**6** Wash in running water. (3 min)
**7** Counterstain nuclei, if desired, in Mayer's haemalum. (c.10 min)
**8** Wash in dilute ammonia solution to blue the section.
**9** Wash in running water. (1 min)
**10** Dehydrate through the alcohols, clear in xylene and mount in D.P.X.

*Result:* Substances containing the vicinal glycol group, —C(H)(OH)—C(H)(OH)—, i.e. most carbohydrates, are stained red. If glycogen is suspected, then a diastase or ptyalin incubation control must be done (see glycogen p. 136).

See also cellulose p. 113.

**Cartilage**

*Preparation techniques*

(i) *Fix.* Formol-saline.

(ii) Stains: *Weigert's stain and van Gieson's (collagen fibres → red, elastic fibres → blue-black, matrix → grey black); *Mallory's (collagen fibres → blue, elastic fibres → red, matrix → blue); *haematoxylin and eosin Y (collagen fibres → pale pink, elastic fibres → bright pink, matrix → slate blue); methyl green (nuclei and intercellular matrix → green); orcein and van Gieson's [elastic fibres (nuclei → blue), (cytoplasm → brownish-pink); connective tissue → red].

(iii) See Method **17** (p. 82) and 'Animal Tissue, II (*j*)' (p. 101).

(iv) *van Wijhe's method for whole mounts.*† (*To stain the skeleton but not the flesh.*)

**1** *Fix.* Alcohol (70%). (Until complete penetration)
**2** Stains: Toluidine blue o, or thionin, or new methylene blue N. (3 weeks)
**3** Transfer to 0.1% HCl in 70% alcohol. (Till no more stain removed)
**4** Dehydrate in alcohol (70%).

* Adapted, by permission, from Hartridge and Haynes, 1936, *Histology for Medical Students*, The University Press, Oxford.

† With acknowledgements to R. W. Bateman, B.Sc.

5 Dehydrate in alcohol (90%).
6 Dehydrate in alcohol (100%). (Several washes)
7 Transfer to benzene. *Spalteholtz clearing method.*
8 Clear in methyl salicylate (oil of wintergreen).
(= preserving agent).

*Times will vary with size of object but in any case will probably be not less than* 14 *d*.
(Cartilage → blue; other tissues unstained.) It is possible to clear and preserve in cedar-wood oil. Small pieces may be mounted in Canada balsam.

*Notes:*
(i) The composition of the staining solution is

| | |
|---|---|
| 70% alcohol | 100 ml |
| Hydrochloric acid (conc) | 0.1 ml |
| Toluidine blue | 0.1 g |

(ii) Material fixed in picric acid is *not* suitable; well washed mercuric-fixed embryos are best.
(iii) The differentiation in acid alcohol will require several changes of reagent and may take from 1–2 weeks for a small (2 cm) larva of *Triturus* to 3–6 months for a rabbit embryo several inches long.
(iv) Ensure that the specimen is completely dehydrated before mounting.

**Cell Outlines**

*To demonstrate intercellular matrix (cement substance)*.
See 'Epithelia iv' (p. 126).

**Cellulose**

**S/C** Well seen in date stone. Soak for 24 h in water and scrape off endosperm with heel of razor.

*Preparation techniques*
Stains: Schulze's soln. (specific stain) (→ blue-violet) [reaction quicker by a few min treatment with potassium hydroxide (5%) to remove fats beforehand]; Congo red (→ red; then + dil. hydrochloric acid → blue); iodine (→ faint yellow-brown); iodine + sulphuric acid (approx. 40%) (→ blue); iodine + zinc chloride (→ blue).

Delafield's haematoxylin (→ purple); anilin blue WS; fast green FSF; (all counterstained with safranin O); acid fuchsin; Mayer's carmalum; (both counterstained with iodine green); Hanstein's fuchsin violet (→ pale violet); exylene-eosin Y (→ red); xylene-erythrosin bluish (→ red).

**Cell Wall Stratification**

Stain: Hanstein's fuchsin violet (→ pale violet).

**Cell Walls (Unliginified)**

Stains: Delafield's haematoxylin (counterstain with aq. eosin Y); Heidenhain's haematoxylin (→ light blue). See also 'Cellulose' (above).

**Ceratium**

**S/C** Marine plankton.

**Cereus pedunculatus**

*Mesentery.*

1 Remove sufficient whole and undamaged mesenteries from the animal.
2 Wash alc. (50%). (2–3 min)
3 Wash alc. (70%). (2–3 min)
4 Stain: chlorazol black. (About 5 min)
5 Wash alc. (90%). (20 min or longer)
6 Dehydrate alc. (100%). (2 min)
7 Dehydrate alc. (100%). (2 min)
8 Clear in xylene.
9 Mount in Canada balsam. Support cover-slip as suggested on pp. 58–59.

**Cestodes**

See 'Dipylidium' (p. 123) and 'Taenia' (p. 174).

**Chara**

(i) Stain in iodine and basic fuchsin.
(ii) See also 'Algae' (p. 94) and 'Cladophora' (p. 119).

**Chick Embryo**

For the beginner it is useful to commence with an egg incubated for 60 hours.

(i) *Entire embryo:*
1 Place the egg in a dish of warm sodium chloride soln. (0·6% aq.).
2 Chip the shell away.
3 Cut round the embryo with scissors.
4 Slide the embryo off into the saline.
5 Wash off the yolk.
6 Shake off the vitelline membrane.

**7** Transfer embryo to a cover-slip (this prevents curling).
**8** Fix in Bouin's fluid diluted with 50% of its own volume of distilled water. (Small—1 h. Large—12 h)
**9** Wash in alcohol (50%), (70%). (Twice in each)
**10** Stain in borax carmine (3—4 h); or Mayer's alcoholic cochineal (refer to p. 200) by the method suggested for *'Amphioxus, vi* whole specimens' (p. 97).
**11** Dehydrate from alcohol (70%).
**12** Clear in clove oil. (Overnight)
**13** Pass quickly through xylene.
**14** Mount in D.P.X. (See pp. 57, 58 for mounting thick specimens.)

(ii) *Sections:*

**1** As (i) up to and including **13** above.
**2** Remove from cover-slip and transfer to bath of pure wax at 50°C. (30 min)
**3** Embed in wax (see p. 62 *et seq.*).
**4** Cut sections 10μm—12μm thick (see p. 43 *et seq.*).
**5** Attach sections to slide (see p. 64).
**6** Remove wax from sections (see p. 65).
**7** Mount in D.P.X.

### Chilomonas paramecium

**S/C** See 'Culture Media 3' (pp. 203—208).

### Chironomus

**S/C** Larvae are the 'blood-worms', found in ponds.

*Salivary glands (for chromosomes)*
See 'Chromosomes, 1 (*b*) (vi)' (p. 117).

### Chitin

(i) Stains: Picric acid, aq. or alc. (→ yellow); picro-clove oil.
(ii) *To identify in fungus.* *

**1** Cut fungus into small pieces.
**2** Boil with dilute potassium hydroxide.
**3** Boil with dilute sulphuric acid.
**4** Transfer to alcohol (70%).
**5** Transfer to ether.

* After Strasburger, 1930. *Text-Book of Practical Botany,* Allen and Unwin.

**6** Decant ether, and dry the white residue: it is chitin.

### Chlamydomonas

**S/C**

(i) Rain-water butts in spring.
(ii) *Chlamydomonas pulsatilla:* See 'Culture Media 3 (p. 203).

*To demonstrate flagella.* *
Stain in anilin blue ws-lacto-phenol.

### Chloride Ions

Stain in silver nitrate 0·5% aq. soln.

### Chlorococcales

**S/C** See 'Culture Media 3' (pp. 203—208).

### Chloroplasts

Stain in fuchsin-violet (Hanstein's).

### Chromatin

*Staining techniques*

(i) *Animal.*
(*a*) *General.*
Delafield's haematoxylin (purple).
(*b*) *In fresh tissue.*†
Safranin o and anilin blue ws—picric; iron-acetic-carmine.
(*c*) *In blood parasites.*
Leishman's stain (→ ruby red).
(ii) *Plant*
Safranin o (→ red).
(iii) See also 'Chromosomes' (below).

### Chromatophores

(i) Stain in acid fuchsin.
(ii) See 'Macromysis' (p. 146).

### Chromosomes‡

*Note:* (i) 'Squash' and 'smear' techniques are rapid methods for obtaining temporary and

* With acknowledgements to Dr M. J. Cole, University of Aston in Birmingham.
† *Science Master's Book, Part II.* London, John Murray.
‡ With acknowledgements to Dr. B. John, Department of Genetics, University of Birmingham, for various suggestions in this section and for the notes on the identification of chromosomes.

permanent preparations of chromosomes. The 'squash technique' may be used for harder tissues that may require some degree of maceration. The 'smear technique' may be used for soft tissues. The 'wax embedding technique' is necessarily longer, but remains useful when preparations of quality or in quantity are desired.

(ii) It is suggested that of the techniques and materials given below, Methods 1 (*a*) (i); 1 (*a*) (ii); and 1 (*b*), will be found the most rewarding as far as the elementary student is concerned.

1 *MITOSIS*

(*a*) SQUASH TECHNIQUES

*Suggested material: Root-tip meristem of Crocus balanae var. Zwanenberg.*

S/C

1 Obtain corms from Walter Blum, Leavesden, Watford, Herts. Place orders in June/July.
2 Plant the corms in early September, either out-of-doors, or indoors in a box of potting compost or vermiculite.
3 Allow to grow for 4–5 weeks, or until the roots are of suitable length, i.e., from 2.5 cm–3.8 cm long, when they are ready for use.
4 Choose roots of suitable length (about 2.5 cm–3.5 cm) and cut the root tips about 6 mm from the apex.
5 Place the fresh root tips in *either*, α-bromonaphthalene (1–2 h); *or* β-hydroxyquinoline (1–2 h); *or* colchicine (1–2 h); *or* paradichlorbenzene (1–4 h). See Chap. 7 for details.
*Note:* (i) This treatment causes shrinkage and inhibits clumping of the chromosomes.
(ii) These substances are in aqueous solution. *It is essential that any air should be removed from the root tips* and both this pretreatment and subsequent fixation are best carried out by placing the root tips in small tubes of solution placed under a filter-pump. The removal of air takes about 2 h.
6 Fix in Clarke's fluid. (15 min at least)
7 If kept cool, roots may be preserved in Clarke's fluid and will remain workable for several months.

*Preparation technique*

*Method* (i)

*Fixation followed by the Feulgen technique, with counterstaining if desired.*

1 If fresh roots are used, fix in Clarke's fluid. (15 min at least)
If roots preserved as above are used, proceed to:
2 Warm the roots in hydrochloric acid (N/1) on a water-bath at 60°C, to effect hydrolysis. (6 min)
*Note:* The hydrolysis frees the aldehyde groups of the nucleic acid. They then combine with the fuchsin-sulphurous acid of Schiff's reagent, with resultant staining of the DNA of the chromosomes. The hydrochloric acid also dissolves the middle lamella of plant tissue, with resultant loosening of the cells.
3 Transfer the root tips to Schiff's reagent [see formula (p. 245)], *in the dark.* (1–3 h)
*Note:* (i) The mitotically-active region containing DNA (→ pink).
(ii) *Use only the deeply stained region for making the preparation.*
(iii) Feulgen-stained root tips will not keep for long. If placed in a refrigerator they will keep overnight.
4 Place small pieces of densely stained tissue on a slide, *either*
(*a*) in acetic acid (45% aq.); *or*
(*b*) if it is desired to give a stronger and more durable stain and to show up the cell surface and cytoplasm, in orcein-acetic (p. 238).
5 Separate the cells and spread them evenly in a single layer by tapping the slide with the point of a needle, or with a blunt metal or bone spatula.
Remove any large pieces of tissue. It is a help if this can be done under a dissecting microscope.
6 Warm *gently* over a small flame to help to flatten out and spread the cells. Do NOT boil. Place the slide on the back of the hand to test for 'gentle warmth' (about 50°C). If necessary, repeat the tapping and warming processes.
7 Cover with a cover-slip.
8 Make a squash by covering the cover-slip with filter-paper and pressing it *vertically*, gently, but firmly and evenly, with the thumb. Avoid sideways pressure.
*Note:* Temporary preparations may be examined at this stage.
If a permanent preparation is required, proceed to:

9 Have ready three smearing dishes—Petri dishes wide enough to carry a slide. In each, place two small pieces of glass rod, each long enough to allow a slide to rest on them. In one dish place just sufficient Clarke's fluid to cover the rods. In the other two dishes place alcohol (100%) in like quantity. Keep these dishes covered.

10 Invert the prepared slide in the dish of Clarke's fluid. Leave it until the cover-slip drops off. (Up to 10 min)

*Note:* It is important to remember which are the prepared sides of slide and cover-slip.

11 Transfer slide and cover-slip to one of the dishes of alcohol for dehydration of the tissue. Keep the dish covered. (1 min)

12 Quickly transfer slide and cover-slip to the second dish of alcohol. Keep the dish covered. (1 min)

13 Mount in 'Euparal'. (Preferable to synthetic resin, to avoid shrinkage.)

14 Cover with the cover-slip.

15 Blot off any excess liquid with a filter-paper applied with light pressure.

*Note:* In *Crocus balanae* there are three pairs of homologous, often metacentric, chromosomes; $2n = 6$. The pairs can be distinguished at metaphase and anaphase. Pair I has a secondary (nucleolar) constriction just beyond the centrosome. Pairs II and III have no such constriction, but can be distinguished from one another by the marked difference in the length of their short arm.

*Method* (ii)

*Combined fixation and staining with lacmoid-acetic.*

1 Place the fresh root tips in a mixture of:

| | |
|---|---|
| Hydrochloric acid (N/1) . . . . | 1 ml |
| Lacmoid-acetic (p. 230) . . . . | 10 ml |

in a watch-glass. Warm (about 50°C) but do NOT boil. Allow to cool. Repeat the heating and cooling processes 2—3 times, after which, leave for 10 min.

2 Transfer to lacmoid-acetic (1 drop) on a slide.

3 Separate the cells by tapping.

4 Cover with a cover-slip.

5 Warm.

6 Squash.

*Note:* Temporary preparations may be examined at this stage.

If permanent preparations are required proceed to processes **9—15**, above, of method (i).

*Method* (iii)

*Fixation followed by staining with carmine-acetic, or orcein-acetic.* *

*Suggested material:* Root tips of *Allium cepa* (as an alternative to Crocus balanae).

1 Cut off actively growing root tips, about 0.5 cm—1 cm long, and transfer them to Clarke's fluid. (1—24 h)

2 Transfer to:

| | |
|---|---|
| Alcohol (100%) . . . . . | 100 ml |
| Hydrochloric acid . . . . | 10 ml |

(5—6 min)

3 Transfer to one or two drops of carmine-acetic (p. 193) or orcein-acetic (p. 238) on a slide. Mash up the root tip with steel needles. (15—20 min)

If necessary, add more stain to replace that lost by evaporation.

4 Cover with a large cover-slip.

5 Squash gently, but vertically, with a piece of filter-paper until the cells are separated as seen under the low power of the microscope (e.g. eye-piece x 10; 16 mm objective).

6 Warm gently over a low flame. Do NOT boil. Allow to cool. Continue intermittent warming and cooling until the desired contrast is obtained.

[7 Temporary preparations may be examined at this stage. They may be sealed by running molten paraffin wax (applied by means of a hot brass wire) round the edges of the cover-slip.

*Note:* Staining will improve after a few days.]

If permanent preparations are required later, proceed to:

8 Carefully remove the wax seal, if this has been applied.

9 Invert the preparation in a dish containing two short pieces of glass rod to support the slide, and sufficient Clarke's fluid to cover the slide. Leave until the cover-slip falls off. (Few min—overnight)

9 Transfer slide and cover-slip to alcohol (100%). (Two changes)

10 Recombine slide and cover-slip in 'Euparal'.

* After *Progress Report* 36, Flatters and Garnett.

(*b*) SMEAR TECHNIQUES

*Fixation followed by staining, or combined fixation and staining with orcein-acetic.*

*Method* (iv)

*Suggested material:* Young embryos of *Schistocerca gregaria* (Desert Locust).

**S/C**

Obtain 3–6 day embryos from the Anti-Locust Centre, 1 Prince's Gate, Kensington, London, S.W.7.

**P**

1 Place the eggs in insect saline [See 'Saline Solutions 1 (iii) (p. 245)].
2 Puncture the eggs with a sharp needle to allow embryos to flow out. Embryos are white and transparent. Yolk is yellow.
3 If desired, fix and preserve the embryos in Clarke's fluid.

*Preparation techniques*

1 With the aid of a thin, flat scalpel make a smear of the material (fresh or preserved) in orcein-acetic (1 drop) on a slide (see Fig. 6.6, p. 152).
2 Warm gently. Do NOT boil.
3 Cover with a cover-slip.
*Note:* Temporary preparations may be examined at this stage.
If permanent preparations are required proceed to Method (i), processes **9–15** (p. 116).

*Note:* In *Schistocerca gregaria* $2n = 23$. All the chromosomes are acrocentric, i.e. they have their centromeres so near one end that the chromosomes appear to be one-armed structures. There are 11 pairs of homologous autosomes (graded in length from 'long' to 'short') and a single X chromosome in the male, as opposed to XX in the female.

*Method* (*v*)

*Suggested material:* Testis of 3rd or 4th instar larvae of *Schistocerca gregaria* (Desert locust) or *Chorthippus* sp. (Grasshopper).

**S/C**

*Schistocerca gregaria,* as above.

*Chorthippus* sp., hedgerows and grass-land in summer. Suppliers.

**P**

1 Place the insect in insect saline [see 'Saline Solutions 1 (iii)' (p. 245)].
2 Make a median longitudinal incision through the abdominal segments.
*Note:* The testis lies in the anterior one-third of the abdomen. The follicles of the testis are banana-shaped.
3 With the aid of forceps, remove the testis.
4 Transfer the testis to insect saline.
5 With sharp needles, carefully pick away the fat-body which invests the individual follicles.
6 Fix and preserve the follicles in Clarke's fluid. They will keep for many months.

*Preparation techniques*

Follow Method (iv) above, processes **1–3** for temporary preparations; add Method (i) processes **9–15** for permanent mounts.

*Note:* (i) For details about chromosomes of *Schistocerca gregaria* see the note following Method (iv).

(ii) In *Chorthippus* $2n = 17$. There are 8 pairs of homologous chromosomes of which 3 are metacentric and of length varying from 'medium' to 'long', and 5 are acro-centric and of length varying from 'short' to 'medium'. The X (male) chromosome is acrocentric and of 'medium' length.

*Method* (vi)

*Suggested material:* Salivary glands of *Drosophila melanogaster.*

**S/C**

(i) Use large, well-nourished larvae on the point of pupation. Obtainable from suppliers.

(ii) See also 'Drosophila **S/C** ii and iii' (p. 124).

*Preparation technique*

1 Place the larva in a little insect saline (p. 245) on a slide.
2 Hold the body of the larva on the slide by pressure from a needle.
3 With another needle in the other hand remove the head.
4 If the salivary glands do not ooze out when the pressure of the needles is released, dissect them out carefully and clear away as much of the debris as possible.
5 Transfer the salivary gland to orcein-acetic (which will both fix and stain the tissue) on a slide. (10 min)
6 Place a cover-slip on the tissue.

7 Press the cover-slip hard, but vertically, downwards, with filter-paper. *There must be no sideways movement.*
8 Warm *gently.* The degree of warmth is related to the degree of staining.
9 Examine under the microscope. If the preparation appears worth preserving, proceed to:
10 Place the slide, face downwards, on two pieces of glass rod in a Petri dish containing alcohol (50%). (30 min–12 h)
This loosens the cover-slip from the slide. The cover-slip will fall away, carrying most of the tissue with it.
11 Counterstain in fast green FCF (0.5%) in 2 ethoxy ethanol.
This is conveniently done by holding the cover-slip in forceps and gently rinsing it in the counterstain contained in a wide specimen tube.
12 Drain off excess stain.
13 Dehydrate and remove excess stain in 2 ethoxy ethanol.
14 Drain off excess 2 ethoxy ethanol and clear in xylene.
15 Mount in 'Euparal'.

(*c*) WAX EMBEDDING TECHNIQUE

*Note:* (i) Animal tissue should not be in pieces greater than 3 mm in any direction.

Plant tissue should not be in pieces greater than 4–6 mm in any direction.

(ii) Suitable fixatives:

For animal material, San Felice's fluid (p. 245), La Cour's 2BD (p. 201).

For plant material, La Cour's 2BE (p. 201).

(iii) Up to the stage of embedding, the operations may be carried out in small glass tubes.

*Method* (vii)

1 Fix under a filter-pump. Air is removed from tissue in about 2 h. (24 h)
2 Wash in tepid distilled water. (3–4 changes over 1 h)
3 After La Cour's fixatives, bleach in:
Alcohol (80%). . . . . . . . . . 80 ml
Hydrogen peroxide (20 vols. soln.) . . 20 ml
(4–12 h)
This removes any dark colouration caused by the staining of any fatty materials by the osmium tetroxide in the fixative.
4 Dehydrate successively in alcohol (50%), (70%), (90%). (3 h each)
5 Dehydrate in alcohol (100%). (12 h)
6 Clear in alcohol (100%)/chloroform parts by volume–(50/50). ($1\frac{1}{2}$ h)
7 Clear in pure chloroform. ($1\frac{1}{2}$ h)
8 Impregnate with paraffin wax (m.p. 50°C). The total time for impregnation should not exceed 4 h.
9 Embed.
10 Cut sections at 15 $\mu$m to 20 $\mu$m.
*Note:* If root tips are used they should be cut truly longitudinally and the orientation of the wax block should be checked by examining the sections, and adjusted if necessary.
11 Attach sections to slide.
12 Dissolve off wax in xylene.
13 Wash in alcohol (100%). (2 min)
14 Wash in alcohol (90%). (2 min)
15 Wash in distilled water. (2 min)
*Note:* (i) Sections attached to slides are not harmed by being brought direct from alcohol (90%) to water.
16 Stain sections in crystal violet (1% aq.). (15 min)
17 Rinse in distilled water.
18 Transfer to iodine solution (1% in 2% aq. potassium iodide solution). (1 min)
19 Rinse in distilled water.
20 Dehydrate in fresh 70%, 90% and absolute alcohol. (*10 sec* in each).
21 Dehydrate in a second lot of fresh absolute alcohol. (1 min)
22 Clear in xylene and mount in D.P.X.
Chromatin and chromosomes are stained blue/violet; everything else unstained. If a section is understained this can be corrected with another slide by *either* lengthening stage **16** *or* shortening stage **21**. If a section is overstained, with crystal violet in the cytoplasm, the reverse applies.

2 *MEIOSIS*

(*a*) *Suggested material:* Testis of adult *Schistocerca gregaria* (Desert locust); or *Chorthippus* sp. (Grasshopper).

*Preparation techniques*

*Method* (iv) above, (p. 117) or Method (vii) above.

*Note:* For details about chromosomes in: *Schistocerca gregaria,* see note following Method (iv) p. 117.

*Chorthippus* sp., see Note (ii) following Method (v) p. 117.

(*b*) *Suggested material:* Pollen mother cells from anthers.

**S/C**

The source will depend on what flowers are available at any given time of the year.

The anthers should be cut from the flower when still translucent and when they have grown about one-third of their full length.

**P**

Preserve in Clarke's fluid.

*Preparation technique*

The method used is the 'squash technique'.

There is no guarantee that any particular anther will be at the desired state of development. A temporary mount should, therefore, be made first and examined before time is spent on making a permanent preparation.

1 Crush an anther on a slide with the aid of a flat, wooden or bone scalpel handle.
2 Flood the slide with carmine-acetic (p. 193).
3 Tease out the material with *steel* needles, and remove remains of anther wall. (Until the colour changes to bluish-red)
4 Warm *gently* over a flame. (Few s)
5 Examine for the desired stages of meiosis.
*Note:* The preparation may be made semi-permanent at this stage by covering with a cover-slip and sealing with wax.

*Permanent preparations*

Assuming that the desired stage of meiosis has been found in a temporary mount:

1 Prepare a Petri dish by placing in it two short pieces of glass rod (to support a slide) and adding just sufficient Clarke's fluid to cover a slide when it is laid on the rods.
2 Crush an anther on a slide as in above.
3 Quickly invert the slide and lower it, with a precisely vertical movement, into the dish of fluid. (2 min)
4 Add a drop of carmine-acetic to the slide and tease the material with *steel* needles. (Until the colour changes to bluish-red)
5 Remove any debris. Preferably work under a dissecting microscope.
6 Warm *very gently* over a flame, to help to flatten the cells. Do NOT allow to boil.
7 Invert the slide, as before, in Clarke's fluid. (2 min)
8 Transfer the slide to alcohol (100%). (2 min)
9 Transfer to fresh alcohol (100%). (2 min)
10 Mount in 'Euparal' and cover with a cover-slip.
11 Label.
12 After 1–2 days apply very gentle pressure to the cover-slip to squeeze the cell contents flat. Clean the slide with alcohol.
13 Store carmine-acetic–stained slides in the dark.

**Cilia**

Stains: Phenol-fuchsin; iodine.

**Cladocera**

**S/C**

(i) See 'Culture Media 3' (p. 203).
(ii) See 'Daphnia' (p. 122).

*Preparation technique*

See 'Daphnia' (p. 122).

**Cladophora**

**S/C** *To obtain swarm spores:* *

Take from rapidly running water and lay in 12 mm depth of water in a shallow vessel. (Overnight)

*Preparation techniques*

(*a*) *Fix.* Chrom-acetic (24 h); chromic acid (1%) (24 h); chrom-osmium-acetic ($\frac{1}{2}$ h); osmium tetroxide (1%) (24 h); picric acid (sat. aq.) (24 h).

(*b*) Stain: Alum-carmine.

**Cockroach**

See 'Periplaneta' (p. 156).

**Coelenterates**

**P** Quickly transfer to strong formol-saline.

*Preparation techniques*

(i) *To kill.*

Allow the live specimen to expand in water. Add crystals of magnesium sulphate from time

* After Strasburger, 1930, *Handbook of Practical Botany* (English edition), Allen and Unwin.

to time. Do not allow the crystals to drop on the specimen. Test state of narcotization with a glass rod. The process is slow. See also 'Hydra' (p. 138).

(ii) *General treatment of small specimens.* Deal with quantities in the way recommended in Method 12 (p. 78).

(iii) *Mounting small specimens.*

(*a*) *Specimens with tentacles* (e.g. *Hydractinia; Tubularia; etc.*).

1 Place drop of mountant on the slide.
2 Push the specimen along the slide, tentacles first, into the mountant to ensure displaying to full advantage.

(*b*) *Medusae.* See 'Obelia, ii' (p. 153). Do not use pressure on the cover-slip.

(iv) See also 'Cereus pedunculatus' (p. 113), 'Hydra' (p. 138), 'Hydractinia' (p. 139), 'Obelia' (p. 153), 'Pleurobranchia' (p. 161).

**Collagen (White) Fibres**

See 'Cartilage' (p. 112) and 'Connective Tissue' (below).

**Colpidium**

S/C See 'Culture Media 3' (p. 203).

**Columba**

S/C
(i) Dealers.
(ii) Fishmongers.
*Live specimens:* kill with chloroform vapour.

**Connective Tissue**

(i) *Fixatives* Formol-saline; Bouin's fluid; mercuric-formaldehyde.

(ii) *Suitable stains*

(*a*) *Collagen* (*white*) *fibres*

Eosin Y aq.; van Gieson (→ red); Mann's (→ blue); Masson (→ green). See also 'Animal Tissue II(b)' p. 98 and 'Cartilage' p. 112.

(*b*) *Elastic* (*yellow*) *fibres*

Weigert's stain (→ blue-black); orcein (→ red/brown); Verhoeff's technique (→ black).

*Note:* In preparations stained with haematoxylin and eosin, Goldstein* has shown that elastic fibres fluoresce strongly and can be clearly visualized in this way. For details see his original article.

(iii) *Drew-Murray Method.*

*Also suitable for bacteria and organisms in tissues.*

1 Stain in van Gieson's stain (p. 218). (1–3 min)
2 Wash in distilled water.
3 Stain in Nile blue sulphate (2% aq.), [(*b*), (p. 237)], or toluidine blue o (ii, p. 251). (2–24 h
4 Wash in distilled water. (Several changes until the washing water is pale blue)
5 Stain in van Gieson's stain, again. (1–5 min)
6 Wash in distilled water. (Several changes until the washing water is pale yellow)
7 Dehydrate with alcohol (100%). (Rapidly, by putting the alcohol on the slide from a dropping bottle)
8 Clear in xylene. (Not more than 1 min)
9 Differentiate in clove oil. (5 min–several h)
10 Pass through xylene to remove clove oil.
11 Mount in D.P.X.

[Bacteria (→ blue); collagen (→ red); erythrocytes (→ orange-yellow); keratin (→ orange-yellow); nuclear chromatin (→ transparent blue); mast cell granules (→ almost black).]

(iv) *Reticulin Fibrils* (*Wilder's Method*).

If sections are paraffin-embedded and attached to slides the paraffin must first be removed with xylene; the xylene removed with alcohol (100%), and the sections hydrated to water.

1 Place in phosphomolybdic acid (10% aq.) (p. 240). (1 min)
2 Rinse in distilled water. (1 min)
3 Place in uranium nitrate (1% aq.) (p. 252). (5 s)
4 Rinse in distilled water. (1 min)
5 Place in silver diaminohydroxide (p. 248). (1 min)
6 Rinse in alcohol (95%). (Quickly)
7 Place in special reducing solution (p. 243). (1 min)
8 Rinse in tap water. (1 min)
9 Place in gold chloride (0.2% aq.) (Merck's reagent), (p. 220). (Until sections go grey)
10 Place in sodium thiosulphate (5% aq.). (1 min)
11 If desired, counterstain in van Gieson's stain.
12 Dehydrate to alcohol (100%).
13 Clear in xylene.
14 Mount in D.P.X.

* Goldstein D. J. 'The fluorescence of elastic fibres stained with eosin and excited by visible light' Histochemical Journal, **I**, 187–198, 1969.

*Note:* Material for this method is best fixed in either Zenker's fluid or in a mercuric/dichromate/ formaldehyde mixture.

(v) *Masson's Trichrome method for collagen fibres.*

This is also good for general microanatomy.

1 Bring thin (5μm) paraffin sections attached to slides to water, through xylene and alcohols.
2 Stain nuclei in Hansen's haematoxylin (p. 223). (3–4 min)
3 Wash in running water. (15 min)
4 Stain cytoplasm of cells in 0.1% xylidene red in 1% acetic acid. (5 min)
5 Rinse in distilled water.
6 Treat sections with phosphomolybdic acid, (freshly prepared 1% aq. soln) for 5 min.
7 Rinse.
8 Stain in 2% Light green SF in 2% acetic acid until collagen is green but cytoplasm of cells retains the red colour. This will vary but may be from 5 s to 15 s.
9 Pass quickly through alcohols.
10 Xylene; mount in D.P.X.

Chromatin of nuclei → black; cytoplasm → red; mucin and collagen fibres → green.

*Note:* Thin sections are needed to obtain good results. Material fixed in Zenker's fluid is very suitable.

(vi) *Verhoeff's stain for elastic fibres*

1 Bring paraffin sections attached to slides to water through xylene and alcohols.
2 Stain in Verhoeff's stain, p. 252. (10–20 min)
3 Rinse in water.
4 Place in 2% ferric chloride solution till differentiated. (2–10 s)
5 Wash in running water. (several minutes)
6 95% alcohol. (till no more iodine comes away from the section)
7 Absolute alcohol; xylene; mount in D.P.X.

Elastic fibres → black.

*Note:* If counterstaining is required then a 2% solution of eosin Y will be suitable.

The differentiation at stage **4** must be controlled under the microscope.

**Coprinus**

**S/C** See 'Culture Media) 3' (p. 203).

**Copromonas**

**S/C** Large intestine of *Rana.*

**Cork**

See 'Suberin' (p. 173).

**Cotyledon**

*For food stores.* Refer to the various substances under their names in this chapter.

Mount in glycerol jelly.

**Crayfish**

See 'Astacus' (p. 104).

**Crustacea**

(i) *To display general features of organization.* Inject *Artemia* with methylene blue in saline.

(ii) *Preparation Techniques*

(*a*) See 'Animal Tissue Preparation techniques, ii' (p. 98).

Carry out the processes with a quantity of specimens in the way recommended in Method 12 (p. 78).

(*b*)

1 Kill and fix in Bouin's fluid, or mercuric-acetic, or alcohol (30%).
2 Wash in alcohol (50%) 3–4 times [no washing if alcohol (30%) is used to fix].
3 Dehydrate in alcohol (70%).
4 Stain in borax carmine.
5 Wash in alcohol (70%).
6 Dehydrate in alcohol (90% and 100%).
7 Clear in clove oil.
8 Stain in picro-clove oil (chitin → yellow or brown).
9 Wash in clove oil.
10 Pass through xylene.
11 Mount in D.P.X.

*Note:* **4–5** may be omitted and dehydration after **3** then carried to alcohol (100%).

(*c*) See also 'Macromysis' (p. 146); and 'Amphioxus Whole Specimens' (p. 97).

**Cryptobia helicis***

**S/C** Parasitic in the spermatheca of *Helix* sp.

*Preparation technique*

1 Make smears of contents of spermatheca of *Helix* sp. on a slide or cover-slip.

* After P. M. Nolan and J. N. R. Grainger, *School Science Review.* **XXXIX,** 139, 486, June 1958.

2 Fix in Schaudinn's fluid.
3 Stain in Heidenhain's iron haematoxylin.
4 Usual processes of dehydrating, clearing and mounting.

**Ctenophores**

See 'Pleurobrachia' (p. 161).

**Culex**

See 'Anopheles' (p. 102).

**Cutin**

*Staining reactions*

Iodine + sulphuric acid (50%) (→ yellow-brown) (similarly for suberin); nascent indophenol blue (mixture of a-naphthol and dimethylparaphenylene-diamine) (→ deep violet) (similarly for suberin); Nile blue sulphate (→ blue) (useful for delicate specimens); phloroglucin + hydrochloric acid (conc.) (→ deep pink) (similarly for suberin); Schulze's soln. (→ yellow-brown); Sudan III (heat sections on slide until alcohol boils) (→ red).

*Stains for permanent mounts*

Safranin O (→ pink); Sudan black B; Sudan III (slow); Sudan IV (5% alc.).

**Cyclops**

**S/C**
(i) See 'Culture Media 3' (p. 203).
(ii) See 'Daphnia'

*Preparation techniques*
(i) See 'Crustacea ii' (p. 121).
(ii) See Method 12 (p. 78).
See also 'Amphioxus vi' (p. 97).

**Cytoplasm**

*Staining reactions*

Haematoxylin and eosin Y (→ pink); acid fuchsin (→ red); iron haematoxylin and van Gieson's (→ yellow); Mallory's (→ pink to red); Masson (→ pink to red); Leishman's (→ bluish).

**Daphnia**

**S/C**
(i) Dealers.
(ii) Dredge from semi-stagnant ponds in a very fine mesh net.
(iii) See 'Culture Media 3' (pp. 203–208).
(iv) Boil 20 wheat grains in 1 litre of water. Cool. Inoculate with *Daphnia.* Add fresh boiled grains *once a month* and subculture *once in three months.*
(v) Mix together small quantities of horse-dung, rabbit-droppings, scrapings of green algae from surface soil, and surface soil. Dilute with about 10 vols. of rain water or distilled water. A mixed culture of organisms results after about 1 week. Add a few ml of the stirred-up mixture to the *Daphnia* culture occasionally.*

*Preparation techniques*
(i) See 'Crustacea ii' (p. 121).
(ii) See Method 12 (p. 78).

**Dendrocoelum**

*Fix.* Formaldehyde (5%).
Stain in Mayer's hydrochloric acid-carmine.
[Digestive system (→ deep purplish-red to orange); reproductive system (→ brilliant crimson).]

**Dentine**

See 'Teeth' (p. 175).

**Dermis**

See 'Connective Tissue' (p. 120).

**Desmids**

(i) *To preserve green colour.*
See 'Algae **P** iv' (p. 94).
(ii) Stain in Leishman's stain.

**Dextrin**

With iodine solution (→ brown colour).

**Dextrose**

See 'Sugars. Tests For, (*b*) Dextrose' (p.173).

**Diatoms**

**S/C** See 'Culture Media 3' (pp. 203–208).

* After Scourfield, 'Note on the Feeding of *Daphnia*'. *Quekett Magazine,* 1944, from information kindly supplied by Miss Grace B. Hilbert.

*Preparation techniques*

*Method* (i)*

Have ready the following:

(a) Grease-free sides and cover-slips prepared either by the method given under 'Glassware – to clean' (p. 218) or by rubbing them with a green ink-eraser until the water remains evenly all over the glass when the slide is held on edge to drain off the water.

(b) A fine-pointed pipette fitted with a rubber bulb.

(c) A bristle, as thick as a fine sewing needle and such as may be obtained from a good-quality hairbrush. The bristle should be sealed, by means of sealing-wax, into a small hole drilled in the end of a piece of brass wire, No. 12 B.W.G., heated over a non-luminous flame. For convenience of revolving, the other end of the wire should be twisted into a knob.

(d) Some adhesive, e.g.:

glycerol-egg albumen or

glycerol-dextrin (best for large slides and does not dry).

For delicate specimens, either adhesive should be diluted with an equal volume of distilled water.

**1** Place the material containing the diatoms in a vessel of distilled water.

**2** By means of a pipette collect water containing diatoms and spread them over a slide cleaned as above.

**3** Remove excess water with pipette held at one corner of the tilted slide.

**4** Dry off remaining water at room temperature

**5** Prepare a slide with adhesive by rubbing a drop of adhesive over the slide with the tip of the clean finger. Wipe off repeatedly till only a trace of adhesive remains.

**6** Place the spread slide of diatoms on the microscope stage, focus the required diatom and pick it up on the tip of the bristle. If it does not instantly adhere, dip the tip of the bristle in a little adhesive.

**7** Inspect the diatom for cleanliness. If it is not clean, breathe on a clean slide and rub the diatom (on the end of the bristle) in the moisture from the breath. If this is inadequate, use a drop of distilled water.

**8** Have the slide covered with the film of adhesive ready on the stage of another microscope. Lower the diatom on to the adhesive. Saucer-shaped diatoms should be mounted with the rim on the slide, i.e. so that the convex side is towards the objective.

**9** Heat the slide for 5 min (fairly high temp.) to drive off the glycerol and harden the dextrin or egg albumen.

**10** Cool the slide. Clear the diatoms by adding a drop of benzene or xylene.

**11** Apply a drop of mountant ['Micrex' or 'Styrax' are best see (ii) **8**, below] to be mounted diatom and cover with a clean slip. If necessary, raise the cover-slip by a suitable device [see 'Mounting' (pp. 58, 59)].

**12** Heat quickly to drive off benzene (or xylene).

**13** Seal if desired.

*Note:* If it is found that the hand trembles too much to mount accurately, the mounted bristle may be clamped to the microscope tube and moved up and down by means of the focusing rack. The diatom is then positioned by lateral movements of the slide made by hand.

*Method* (ii)

*Bause's Method*

**1** Fix in formol-acetic alcohol. (A long time).

**2** Wash in water.

**3** Stain in Heidenhain's haematoxylin.

**4** Transfer to glycerol (10%) and allow this solution to concentrate in air at room temperature.

**5** Transfer to pure glycerol.

**6** Transfer to Venetian turpentine (see p. 251).

**7** Transfer to xylene (to remove Venetian turpentine).

**8** Mount in Canada balsam (or in 'Micrex' or in 'Styrax', both of which, being of greater refractive index, give greater transparency).

**9** Cover.

**10** Seal.

**Dipylidium Proglottides**

**P**

Alcohol (70%).

*Whole mount preparation technique*

**1** From alcohol (70%) transfer to Mayer's acid haemalum. (Until red – 30 min)

**2** Wash alcohol (70%)

* Adapted, by permission, from Messrs. Watson's *Microscope Record.*

3 Differentiate in acid alcohol. (Watch carefully)
4 Blue in alkaline alcohol.
5 Dehydrate in alcohol (90%).
6 Dehydrate in alcohol (100%); use two separate lots of alcohol.
7 Clear in xylene.
8 Mount in D.P.X.
9 Cover with a raised cover-slip.

**Discomycetes**

**S/C**

See 'Culture Media 3'(p. 203).

**Distomum**

See 'Fasciola hepatica' (p. 127).

**Doris**

(i) *Kill.* Drown in water.
(ii) *Fix and preserve.* Alcohol (70%).

**Drosophila**

**S/C**

(i) Suppliers of live zoological material.
(ii) Culture media.*

(*a*) Maize meal . . . . . . . . 400 ml
Raw sugar (= unrefined sugar molasses) . . . . . . . 100 ml
Treacle . . . . . . . . . . 100 ml

Thoroughly mix the above. Next have ready,
Water (boiling) . . . . . . 500 ml
and
Agar-agar (powder) . . . . . . 10 g

Add about 30 ml of boiling water to the agar, and boil. Proceed to add a further 30 ml of boiling water, and boil the whole again, and so on till all the water is added.

Next add the meal-sugar-treacle mixture to the agar solution. Stir thoroughly. Heat until the mixture begins to stiffen (about 1 min). Add,
Cold water . . . . . . . . 100 ml

Stir thoroughly. Pour into *sterilized* bottles or specimen tubes to about 4 cm depth. Add to each vessel,
Yeast suspension . . . about 0·25 ml

To allow gases to escape, remove a little of the medium from the side of the bottle. Place a piece of absorbent tissue paper (toilet paper) in the vessel. Plug with cotton wool and re-sterilize. (See 'Glassware 4, To sterilize', p. 219).

(*b*) Agar-agar (powder) . . . . . 3.5 g
Bananas (skinned) . . . . . 3

Mix the agar and bananas thoroughly. Add,
Water . . . . . . . . . . 850 ml

Boil and stir thoroughly. As in (*a*), above, place in vessel, add yeast suspension, toilet paper, and plug.

(*c*) Agar-agar (powdered) . . . . 30 g
Water . . . . . . . . . . .1000 ml

Boil the water and agar and then add corn-flower, until the mixture is of the consistency of porridge.

Then add:
Black Treacle . . . . . . . 7 g

*Note:* To prevent growth of moulds on above culture media, add:
Nipagin M,* to every 1000 ml of medium, . . . . . . . . . . . . 1·5 g

Culture the flies at 25°C.

For suggested experiments see G. Pugh Smith, *School Science Review,* XVIII, 70, 260, December 1936 and P. G. Fothergill, *Biology,* V, 1, 14, Summer Term, 1939; also Demerec, M. and Kaufman, B. P., 7th Edn., *Drosophila Guide,* (1961) Carnegie Inst., Washington, USA.

*Preparation of salivary glands of larva* (*for chromosomes*);

See 'Chromosomes Method vi' (p. 117).

**Earthworm**

See 'Lumbricus' (p. 144).

**Echinorhyncus**

**S/C**

Encysted forms as egg-shaped orange bodies on gut of *Astacus.*

*Preparation technique*

See 'Acanthocephalus ranae' (p. 94).

**Echinus**

*Kill and fix.* Formaldehyde (10%)

Preserve in Formaldehyde (8%), after puncturing the test (shell).

* Suggested by Dr. Pugh Smith.

* Obtainable from T. Gerrard & Co.

*Preparation techniques*

*Ova.* Treat in quantities in a tube as recommended in Method **12** (p. 78). Processes **3** and **4** (below) may be omitted if desired.

**1** Fix in formaldehyde (3%). (2 min)
**2** Wash in alcohol (50%). (2 min)
**3** Stain in borax-carmine. (2 min)
**4** Differentiate in acid alcohol.]
**5** Dehydrate in alcohol (70%).
**6** Dehydrate in alcohol (90%). (3 min)
**7** Dehydrate in alcohol (95%). (3 min)
**8** Transfer to mixture.
Alcohol (100%) . . 3 vols.
'Euparal Essence' . 1 vol. (Up to 15 min)
**9** Transfer to mixture
Alcohol (100%) . . 2 vols.
'Euparal Essence' . 2 vols. (Up to 15 min)
**10** Transfer to mixture
Alcohol (100%) . . 1 vol.
'Euparal Essence' . 3 vols. (Up to 15 min)
**11** Transfer to 'Euparal Essence'. (Up to 15 min)
**12** Mount in 'Euparal'.

*Pluteus larvae.*

Treat quantities in a tube as recommended in Method **12** (p. 78).

**1** Fix in mercuric chloride (cold satd. aq. soln.) (2–3 min)
**2** Wash in distilled water.
**3** Stain in very dilute Mayer's alcoholic cochineal (p. 200).
*Note:* The staining solution should be barely tinted. (12–24 h, with intermittent examination under the microscope.)
**6** Dehydrate in alcohol (70%). (2 min)
**7** Dehydrate in alcohol (90%). (2 min)
**8** Dehydrate in alcohol (100%). (2 min)
**9** Have ready a tube which can be corked and into which the following have been introduced in the order stated:
1st. A layer of 'Celloidin' (20% stock soln., p. 200).
2nd. An equal volume of 'Celloidin'-clove oil (p. 200).
3rd. An equal volume of clove oil.
4th. An equal volume of alcohol (100%).
**10** Clear the larvae* by placing them in the alcohol layer (top most) in the tube. Cork the tube. (Leave till larvae sink to the bottom of the tube)
**11** Pipette off the supernatant layers of liquid.
**12** Pour the larvae into a clean, grease-free watch-glass, standing on a piece of black paper.
**13** In the centre of an absolutely clean and grease-free slide, and within the area of a cover-slip, place several *very minute* drops of 'Celloidin'-clove oil (p. 200). Each drop will serve to position one larva on the slide.
**14** Fashion a paper lifter by making a sharp fold down the centre of a narrow strip of moderately stiff paper.
**15** Using the tip of the paper lifter, remove one larva from the watch-glass.
**16** Invert the paper lifter and lower its tip, with the larva on the lower side, on to one of the 'Celloidin'-clove oil drops.
**17** Repeat **15** and **16** until all the drops are occupied
**18** By means of a pipette, very gently flood the area of the slide neighbouring the drops with chloroform. This hardens the 'Celloidin'.
**19** Drain off any excess chloroform.
**20** Place a drop of synthetic resin mountant in the centre of the 'drop area'.
**21** Gently lower a cover-slip into position.

* Boycott's method.D. P. Wilson, *Journal of the Royal Microscopical Society*, **LIII**, 1933.

**Elastic Fibres**

*Preparation techniques*

*For-wax embedded sections attached to slides.*

(*a*)
**1** Remove wax with xylene.
**2** Remove xylene with alcohol (100%).
**3** Stain in orcein (p. 238). (At 37°C for 2 h)
**4** Wash in alcohol (90%).
**5** Differentiate in acid alcohol.
**6** Dehydrate in alcohol (90%) and (100%).
**7** Clear in xylene.
**8** Mount in D.P.X.
[Elastic fibres (→ brown to dark red).]

(b) See also Verhoeff's method 'Connective Tissue' p. 121.

**Embryo Plants**

**S/C**

(i) Select a plant of Shepherd's Purse (*Capsella bursa-pastoris*) from which the petals have just fallen. Dissect out the ovules from a young fruit on a slide.

(ii) Place some seeds of *Capsella bursa-pastoris* on moist filter-paper in a Petri dish and allow them to begin to germinate.

*Preparation techniques*

(i)

1 Place either ovules from **S/C** i, or *very young developing* seeds from **S/C** ii (above), on a slide.
2 Add potassium hydroxide (5% aq.). (Few min)
3 Drain off the potassium hydroxide and add distilled water.
4 Cover with a cover-slip and press *gently*.

*Note:* The young embryo shows (*a*) suspensor with large basal cell; (*b*) the embryo cell. Later embryos show stages in the development of the embryo. A chronological series of ovules may be taken from successively older developing fruits.

(ii)

1 Dissect out ovules as in **S/C** i (above).
2 Stain and clear fast green FCF in Amann's medium (lactophenol) (see iv, p. 188).
3 Mount in glycerol-jelly.
4 Seal.

See note under (i) above.

**Enamel**

See 'Teeth' (p. 175).

**Endodermis (of root)**

*Preparation techniques*

(i) *Casparian strip.*

1 Soak tissue in phloroglucin (p. 239).
2 Add hydrochloric acid (conc.).
[Casparian strip and lignified tissue (→ red).]

(ii) *Further development of endodermis.*

1 Wash sections in potassium hydroxide (N/10).
2 Wash in distilled water.
3 Stain in Sudan III.
4 Pour off excess stain.
5 Stain in iodine.
6 Pour off excess iodine.
7 Add zinc chloride (aq.).

This treatment demonstrates the original cellulose wall, the suberin lamella and the inner cellulose wall.

**Endothelium**

See 'Epithelia'.

**Epichloë**

Treat as under 'Peronosporaceae' (p. 156).

**Epidermis of Frog**

See 'Epithelia'.

**Epidermis of Leaf (Fresh)**

See 'Leaf methods' (pp. 142, 143).

**Epithelia**

*To prevent curling.* Stretch thin epithelia over a glass tube (and tie on), or stretch over a cover-slip.

*Fix.* Weak formol-saline.

*Suitable stains.* Delafield's haematoxylin; crystal violet; methylene blue; van Gieson's (→ yellow).

(i) *Squamous epithelium.*

See Methods **5** and **6** (p. 75); and **15** (p. 80).

(ii) *To show intercellular matrix in fresh pavement epithelium.*

1 Place in silver nitrate (0.5%). (5 min)
2 Rinse in distilled water.
3 Expose to sunlight.
4 Mount in glycerol.

(iii) *To show nuclei in squamous epithelium* (e.g. *epithelium inside cheek*).

Stain in iodine or examine under dark ground or phase contrast.

(iv) *To show cell outlines in frog mesentery.* *

1 Open up a fresh frog and remove a large coil of the intestine.
2 Pin the coil to a cork ring so that the mesentery is stretched out taut across the ring (Fig. 6.4).

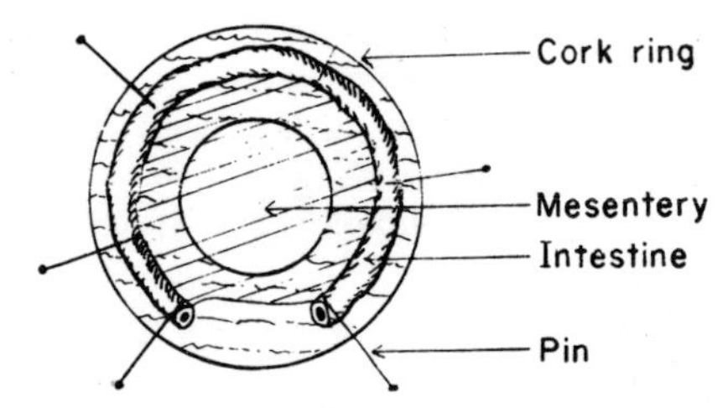


Fig. 6.4 Method of stretching frog mesentery on a cork ring.

3 Rinse with sodium nitrate (1.5% aq.) (to remove surface chlorides).

* From Prof. J. G. Hawkes, Sc.D., University of Birmingham.

4 In the dark, immerse in silver nitrate (0.5% aq.). (5–20 min)
5 In the dark, rinse in distilled water.
6 Either (a) expose to sunlight (to reduce silver nitrate) or (b) immerse in amidol (1%), and wash in distilled water. (5 min: not too long, or tissue blackens)
7 Cut out a section of the now stiff mesentery.
8 Dehydrate.
9 Clear in xylene.
10 Mount in D.P.X.

*Note:* Carry out processes in watch-glasses and agitate frequently.

**Eremothecium Ashbyi**

**S/C**

See 'Culture Media 3' (p. 203).

**Erythrocytes**

See 'Blood' (p. 108 ff).

**Eudorina**

**S/C**

See 'Culture Media 3' (p. 203).

**Euglena**

**S/C**

(i) Dealers. On arrival, allow the tube of culture to stand undisturbed for 1 hour. Pipette a small quantity of culture from the *surface* of the liquid, and examine under the microscope (low-power objective, light stopped down).
If the culture is alive, it may be propagated. [See 'Protozoa' (p. 164).] Feed by placing one or two boiled rice grains in the Petri dish. Do *not* overfeed. Keep in a light place. For further culture: add about 60 boiled rice grains to a glass jar (15 cm x 10 cm x 5 cm) three parts full of distilled water. When a scum has formed on the surface, add the culture of *Euglena*. Keep in a light place.*
(ii) Examine green-topped stagnant ponds and ditches, especially those connected with heaps of farm-yard manure.
(iii) Culture media.

| | | |
|---|---|---|
| (a) | Peptone | 0.5 g |
| | Glucose | 0.5 g |
| | Citric acid | 0.2 g |
| | Magnesium sulphate | 0.02 g |
| | Potassium phosphate | 0·05 g |
| | Water | 100 ml |
| (*b*) | Ammonium sulphate | 0.2 g |
| | Potassium phosphate | 0.2 g |
| | Magnesium sulphate | 0.1 g |
| | Ferrous sulphate | Trace |
| | Tap-water | 200 ml |

(iv) See also 'Culture Media 3' (pp. 203–208).

*Preparation techniques*

(i) See 'Protozoa' (p. 164), but difficult by ordinary methods; best treated as for delicate algae. See 'Algae', methods for delicate specimens (p. 95).
(ii) Mount direct in Berlese's fluid or glycerol-jelly, unless a method for algae is being used.
(iii) *To see flagellum.*
Irrigate under cover-slip with very dilute iodine.

**Eurotium**

**S/C**

(i) Place a piece of dry, stale bread under a bell-jar.
(ii) Prune agar (p. 204).

**Eye**

(i) *Crayfish.*
See 'Astacus (iv)' (p. 104).
(ii) *Vertebrate.*
Fix in Muller's fluid before preserving in alcohol (70%).

Owing to the complicated structure of this organ it is not a useful subject for beginners. More advanced workers should refer to Carleton, *Histological Technique,* University Press, Oxford. Some workers have obtained good results from embedding the whole organ in 'Celloidin' as this keeps the various parts of the organ *in situ.*

**Fasciola hepatica (Liver Fluke)**

**S/C**

(i) Dealers.

* Adapted from *Gerrard's Bulletin,* June 1939. T. Gerrard & Co.

(ii) Abattoirs.

**P**

Formaldehyde (5%).

*Preparation techniques*

See 'Planaria' (p. 157) and 'Taenia' (p. 174).

*Fix.* Alcohol (70%). Press between two slides tied together with cotton.

(i) *To show excretory and alimentary system.*

1. Inject a dilute medium (see 'Injection Fluid', p. 228) through body wall at posterior end with a fine hard-glass pipette.
2. Harden in alcohol (90%). Keep pressed between slides.
3. Dehydrate.
4. Clear in clove oil or xylene (Several weeks)
5. Mount in D.P.X.

(ii) *Sections*

(*a*) Quite thin sections of hardened specimens can be cut with a razor, free-hand, if the specimen is held between two pieces of carrot or expanded polystyrene (p. 241).

(*b*) Stain in Delafield's haematoxylin; or Mallory's stain.

(iii) *Whole mounts.*

(*a*) Use the method suggested for *Taenia*, p. 174, ignoring those parts concerned with the segments of *Taenia*, but exercising the greatest care in the matters of bleaching and thorough dehydration.

(*b*) See also, 'Amphioxus Whole Specimens' (p. 97). [Ovary (→ red); testes and vasa efferentia (→ light red); digestive system, shell gland, vitelline ducts (→ delicate pink); parenchyma (→ colourless).]

## Fat and Oils (Lipids)

On filter-paper they give a translucent mark that does not disappear on drying.

*Suitable stains*

Nile blue sulphate; Sudan black (a specific stain for neutral fats); Sudan IV.

*Preparation techniques*

*In animal tissue*

Method (*a*) will show unmasked fats but not masked fats. If sections are required they must be produced by the freezing method (p. 68 *et seq.*).

(*a*)*

1. Tease tissue in a small quantity of saline on the slide.
2. Fix in formaldehyde vapour (40%). ($\frac{1}{2}$–1 min)
3. Flood slide with alcohol (50%). (3 min)
4. Stain in Sudan IV in a covered Petri dish.
5. Wash in alcohol (50%).
6. Mount in glycerol (50%); or glycerol-jelly. (Fat globules (→ red).)

(*b*) *For material fixed in formol-saline and sectioned on the freezing microtome.*

*Method 1*

1. Wash sections in tap water thoroughly.
2. Rinse in alcohol (70%). (Quickly)
3. Stain in Sudan IV. (20 min–12 h depending on the extent to which fat is dispersed)
4. Rinse in alcohol (70%). (Quickly)
5. Wash thoroughly in distilled water.
6. Stain in Mayer's haemalum. (Lightly, 3 min)
7. Blue thoroughly in tap water.
8. Mount in Farrants' medium or glycerol-jelly.
9. Seal.

[fats (→ bright red).]

*Method 2*

1. Wash sections in tap water thoroughly.
2. Stain in Nile blue sulphate. (30 min at 40°C; or 20 min to 24 h in the cold)
3. Wash in tap water.
4. Differentiate in acetic acid (2% aq.). (Watch carefully. 1 min)
5. Wash thoroughly in tap water. (1–2 h)
6. Mount in Farrants' medium or glycerol-jelly.
7. Seal.

[fats (→ reddish); fatty acids (→ blue); phosphatides (→ dark blue) ]

*In plant tissue.*

Suitable stains: Alkanet (→ red); nascent indophenol blue (a mixture of $\alpha$-naphthol and dimethyl paraphenylene-diamine) fats (→ deep blue); Sudan black B (→ black); Sudan III [0.1% in alcohol (70%) + an equal volume of glycerol] warm till the alcohol boils (→ red).

## Feather

*Preparation technique*

1. Place in alcohol (100%). (Few min)

* After Carleton, 1957, *Histological Technique*, University Press, Oxford.

2 De-alcoholize in benzene-phenol.
3 Mount in D.P.X.

### Fern

*Prothalli.*
**S/C**
(i) On damp walls, or on soil of flower-pots in fern houses.
(ii) *Scrub clean a small flower-pot (internal diameter across top 6.35 cm; size known to horticulturists as '72's', or 'thumbs'), fill it with sphagnum moss and sterilize the whole in boiling water. Allow to cool. Invert the flower-pot and contents in a vessel of rain-water so that the water level is about one-third the way up the sides of the inverted pot. Crush some sporangia by rolling them with a wooden roller and sprinkle the material over the exposed surface of the pot. Cover the whole with a bell-jar. Keep at room temperature.

### Fibres (Textile and Vegetable)

*Preparation technique*
1 Dehydrate to alcohol (90%).
2 Clear in terpineol.
3 Mount in D.P.X. (or in 'Euparal' which, being of lower refractive index, enhances visibility).

### Fibrin

Use the Weigert method for bacteria, 'Bacteria' (p. 106).

### Fish

See also 'Scyllium' (p. 169).
*Kill and fix.* Formaldehyde (10%).

*Preparation techniques for Scales.*
(*a*)
1 Wash and dehydrate to alcohol (100%).
2 Clear in cedar-wood oil.
3 Pass quickly through xylene.
4 Mount in D.P.X.
(*b*)
1 Mount direct in glycerol-jelly.
2 Seal.

* Suggested by N. C. Peacock, M. A., Colorado Academy, Denver, Colorado, U.S.A.

### Flagella

Stains: Phenol-fuchsin; iodine.

### Flower Primordia

See 'Leaf vii' (p. 142).

### Flowers, cut

*To delay decay when standing in water.*
Chlorhexidine . . . . . . . . . . 95 g
Distilled water . . . . . . . . . 5 ml
To every 500 ml of water in which the cut stems are standing, *Add:*
Chlorhexidine soln. 5% aq. (as above) . 1 ml

### Flustra

See 'Polyzoa' (p. 163).

### Fresh-Water Mussel

See 'Anodon' (p. 102).

### Frog

See 'Rana' (p. 165).

### Frog-Bladder

See Method **19** (p. 83).

### Frog-Spawn

See 'Rana' (p. 165).

### Frozen Sections

See p. 68.

### Fucus

*Preparation techniques*
(i) See 'Plant tissue' (p. 158).
(ii) *Sexual organs.*
(*a*) *To cause to empty.*
1 Hang the plant in air. (6 h)
2 Replace in sea water. (6 h)
3 Repeat **1** and **2**. (Until empty)
(*b*) *Fix.* Osmium tetroxide (1%); bromine vapour; boiling water.

(*c*) *Harden.* Alcohol (70%).
(*d*) Stain sections in: Crystal violet; Delafield's haematoxylin; borax carmine.
(*e*) *Clear.* Clove oil.
(*f*) Mount in D.P.X.
(*g*) *Wax-embedded Sections.* See Method **22.**

**Fungi**

**S/C**

(i) *Fungi and yeasts pathogenic to man and animals:* Sub-Department of Medical Mycology, London School of Hygiene and Tropical Medicine, Keppel Street, Gower Street, London, W.C.1.
(ii) *Fungi* (*other than animal pathogens and wood-rotting fungi*): Commonwealth Mycological Institute, Collection of Fungus Cultures, Ferry Lane, Kew, Surrey.
(iii) *Fungi* (*wood rotting*): Forest Products Research Laboratory, Princes Risborough, Aylesbury, Bucks.
(iv) *Yeasts* (*other than pathogens*): National Collection of Yeast Cultures, Brewing Industry Research Foundation, Lyttel Hall, Nutfield, Redhill, Surrey.
(v) *Useful types for culture:*
(*a*) *Eurotium* (p. 127); *Mucor* (p. 149); *Penicillium* (p. 155); *Phytophthora* (p. 157); *Pythium* (p. 165); Yeast (p. 180).
(*b*) Saprophytes generally, and some plant parasites. Use potato agar (p. 204).
(*c*) Coprophilous species. Use Dung agar (p. 204).
(vi) *Slide cultures.*
For micro-fungi, e.g. *Aspergillus, Mucor, Penicillium, Rhizopus* (especially good for the 'stolons' and 'root-like' parts).

1 Sterilize slides and cover-slips by dipping in alcohol and passing through a flame.
2 Spread a slide, thinly, with a suitable agar medium (p. 203 ff).
3 Inoculate the medium on the slide.
4 Place the slide(s) in a clean slotted staining-jar containing a little water.
5 Incubate at 25°C for 2 d, or at room temperature (say 20°C) for 3 d.
During this time spores will grow to maturity.

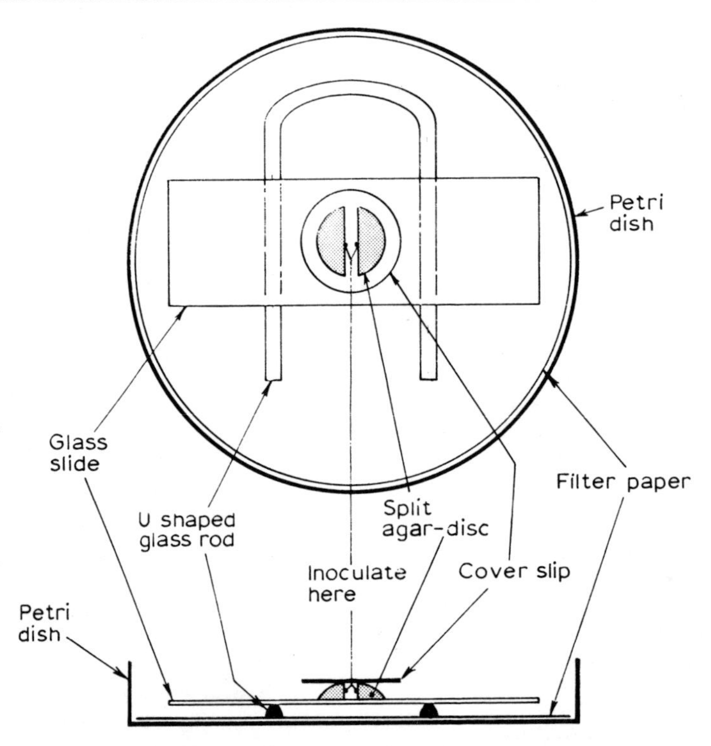


Fig. 6.5 Arrangement of split agar disc on slide in a Petri dish.

*Note:* The slides may be examined under the microscope, as they are, with little prospect of desiccation of the naked film

(vii) *Split agar-disc culture and permanent preparation.* *

*Note:* All processes must be carried out aseptically. Glassware should be dipped in alcohol and flamed.

1 Support a slide on a U-shaped rod in a Petri dish containing a filter paper in the bottom (see Figure 6.5, p. 130).
2 Put a large drop of molten agar in the centre of the slide. Allow to cool.
3 Autoclave.
4 Cut across one diameter of the agar disc and push the two halves about 3 mm–4 mm or more apart.
5 Using sterilized forceps, lay a flamed and cooled 22 mm diam. cover-slip on the two pieces of agar.
6 Using an inoculating wire, transfer some fungus spores to the two vertical inner faces bordering the split agar-disc (see Fig. 6.5).
7 Flood the filter-paper with glycerol (20% aq.) to prevent drying.
8 Cover the Petri dish.
9 Incubate at 20°C to 25°C.
10 When the fungus has grown sufficiently remove the slide from the dish. Remove the cover-slip from the agar. Carefully scrape away the two half-discs of agar and discard them.
11 Mount in a drop of aniline blue ws–lacto-phenol.
12 Cover.
13 Seal if desired.

(viii) *Cover-slip method for culture and permanent preparations.* †

1 By means of asphalt varnish fix two narrow strips of filter-paper parallel to each other, and rather less than the width of a square cover-slip apart, near the centre of a slide. Allow to dry.
2 By means of asphalt varnish, fix a square cover-slip on the two strips of filter paper.
3 By means of a pipette, half fill the cavity between slide and cover-slip with warm fungus-culture medium. [For temporary preparations use nutrient agar (p. 204) substituting 15 g gelatine for agar; for semi-permanent preparations use potato agar (p. 204).]
4 Clean the slide and cover-slip.
5 Seal one end of the cavity with asphalt varnish.
6 By means of a sterilized platinum wire, introduce the fungus, through the open end of the cavity, on to the culture medium.
7 Incubate at room temperature in a covered Petri dish. (2 d)
8 When incubation is complete, introduce a drop of aniline blue ws–lacto-phenol (p. 189) which both fixes and stains.
9 Seal the open end of the cavity with asphalt varnish.

(ix) *Hyphal tips – To isolate single specimens.* *

The method followed is similar to that suggested for isolating single spores, q.v. below, with modifications as indicated.

1 Prepare a dish of agar as indicated for the spore isolation process below.
2 At scattered points on the agar place very small pieces (say 1 mm$^3$) of the fungus culture.
3 Cover the dish and incubate for 12–48 h.
4 During this period make frequent examinations of this sub-culture under the microscope to locate the initial (and usually sparse) hyphae growing from the inocula.
5 Select a well grown single hypha; adjust its position under the microscope so that its tip is in the field of view.
6 Swing the modified La Rue cutter† (with its cutter previously sterilized – see x below) into position and cut the disc bearing the hypha tip.
7 Use a sterilized needle to lift off the upper portion of the agar disc and take the greatest care to avoid dragging away any other hyphae that may be growing in the lower part of the disc.
8 Transfer the upper portion of the disc to a microscope slide for examination; or sub-culture if desired.

(x) *Spores – to isolate single specimens.* *

*Note:* For this purpose a modified La Rue cutter is required.† This is a device which screws into the rotating nose-piece of a microscope in

* With acknowledgement to F. G. B. Jones, Brunel University.

† After J. F. Shillito, 1932. *Science Masters' Book, Part III,* Series III. London, John Murray.

* Adapted from W. G. Keyworth, 1959. *Transactions of the British Mycological Society* **42**, (1), 53.

† Modified La Rue cutters are obtainable from I. Saint, 50 Clarendon Avenue, Leamington Spa, Warwickshire.

place of one of the objectives and which can be sterilized before use.

1 Pour molten agar (plain, filtered, 3%) to a depth of about 3 mm in a Petri dish.
2 By means of a bent glass rod, spread the spores over the surface of the still-molten agar.
3 Allow the agar to gel.
4 Sterilize the tip of the cutter by sliding the cylinder of the cutter from the body and passing the tip through a bunsen flame or by dipping it in alcohol and burning off *all* the alcohol.
5 Replace the cylinder in the body.
6 Locate a well-separated single spore thorugh an objective giving suitable magnification.
7 Swing the modified La Rue cutter into position, instead of the objective.
8 Rack the cutter down on to the dish when it will cut a disc of agar carrying the required spore.
9 Transfer the disc to a microscope slide by means of a sterilized needle.

(xi) See also 'Culture Media' 3 (*a*) (pp. 203–205).

**P** Store in Calberla's fluid (p. 193).

*Preparation techniques*

(i) *Fresh specimens.* *

(*a*) *Free-growing.*
Examine by reflected light (p. 7) with a 25 mm or 16 mm objective.

(*b*) *Growing on agar.*
Place a block of agar on the slide. Examine as above. To obtain a lateral view, cut a thick slice of agar and lay it on its side on the slide.

(ii) *Spores.* Examine in water.

(iii) *Specimens containing air.* *
Either (*a*)
1 Dip in alcohol (70%) or 90%) to remove air.
2 Wash in water.
3 Mount in water, or in dilute glycerol.
or (*b*)
Mount direct in acetic acid (glacial).

(iv) *Moist specimens: asci.* *
Mount direct in water, or in dilute glycerol.

* Adapted from Gwynne-Vaughan and Barnes, 1937, *The Structure and Development of the Fungi*, Cambridge, University Press.

(*v*) *Hyphae in host plant – vital staining.* *
For this purpose trypan blue in lacto-phenol (iii, p. 251) is preferable to anilin blue ws in lacto-phenol.

1 Bleach and clear leaves of host plant by placing them in a gas jar (with a cover) and introducing chlorine gas (from a gas cylinder) (CARE). (A few moments)
*Special note:* This process MUST BE CARRIED OUT IN THE OPEN AIR and the greatest care exercised during the operation. It is best carried out under supervision *and both operator and supervisor should wear, at least, a primitive respirator, e.g. an absorbent pad soaked in sodium carbonate aq.*
2 When bleaching is complete transfer the leaves *at once* to a suitable vessel and evacuate all gases under a suction pump.
3 Transfer the leaves to trypan blue in lacto-phenol and leave them over-night.
(Fungal hyphae → blue.)

*Permanent Preparations.*

*Note:* It is essential to fix and (unless the fixative contains alcohol) to remove air from the tissue as soon as the specimen is collected. Best results are generally obtained by collecting in the afternoon. Material should be cut in pieces not bigger than 0.5 cm in any direction.†

(vi) *Hand-sections of fleshy fungi for general characters and habit: loose hyphae: hyphae and fructifications.*

1 Either, fix in acetic-alcohol (15–30 min) and wash in alcohol (90%), or (95%) (2–3 h) and omit **3** (below).
or, fix in alcohol (70%), and wash thoroughly in water;
or, fix in chrom-acetic, and wash in running water (6–12 h).
2 Section if necessary.
3 Dehydrate in alcohol (30%) and (50%).
4 Transfer to a mixture of

| | | |
|---|---|---|
| | Glycerol (pure) | 1 part |
| *either* | Erythrosin bluish (aq.) | 1 part |
| *or* | Anilin blue WS (aq.) | 1 part |

(Few minutes)

* Adapted from Gwynne-Vaughan and Barnes, 1937. *The Structure and Development of the Fungi,* Cambridge, University Press.

† Suggested by R. B. Maude, National Vegetable Research Station, Wellesbourne, Warwickshire.

**5** Wash in glycerol (50% aq.) to remove excess stain.
**6** Transfer to fresh glycerol (50% aq.) and allow to concentrate in the air.
**7** Mount in glycerol-jelly (p. 220).
[If the specimen is on agar, cut away all but a thin slice of agar. On transference to warm glycerol-jelly the agar will melt, and the specimen will clear.]

(vii)
**1** Fix in alcohol (70%).
**2** Wash in water.
**3** Section if necessary.
**4** Stain in either crystal violet, or Ziehl's phenol-fuchsin.
**5** Wash in distilled water.
**6** Transfer either to glycerol (10%), or to a solution consisting of

| | |
|---|---|
| Distilled water | 5 g |
| Industrial spirit [= alcohol (95%)] | 4 g |
| Glycerol | 1 g |

**7** Allow the glycerol, or the solution, to concentrate by evaporation at room temperature. (Several d)
**8** Mount in pure glycerol or glycerol-jelly.

(viii)
**1–3**, as **1–3** Method vii (above).
**4–5**, as **6–7** Method vii (above).
**6** Stain and mount by placing in glycerol-jelly containing safranin o. (The stain passes into the fungus in the course of a week.)

(ix) *For alcohol-preserved fungi:*
**1** Stain in erythrosin-glycerol (p. 212).
**2–4**, as **6–8** Method vii (above).

(x) *Wax-embedded sections for detail work, e.g. cytology, spores, spore-mother cells.* *
*Note:* Material may be stored in Calberla's fluid after process **9**.
Unless nuclear detail is required, processes **4**, **6**, and **8** are to be omitted.
Unless the material is delicate, processes **12** and **14** are to be omitted.
**1** Fix in Flemming's fluid (stock solution diluted to 50% with distilled water).
**2** Wash in running water. (6–12 h)
**3** Dehydrate in alcohol (20%). (1 h)
[**4** Dehydrate in alcohol (30%). (3 h)]
**5** Dehydrate in alcohol (40%). (3 h)
[**6** Dehydrate in alcohol (50%). (3 h)]
**7** Dehydrate in alcohol (60%). (3 h)
[**8** Dehydrate in alcohol (70%). (3 h)]
**9** Dehydrate in alcohol (80%). (3 h)
**10** Dehydrate in alcohol (90%). (3 h)
**11** Dehydrate in alcohol (100%). (3 h)
[**12** Transfer to mixture of
Alcohol (100%) . . . . 75%
Chloroform . . . . . 25% (3 h)]
**13** Transfer to mixture of
Alcohol (100%) . . . . 50%
Chloroform . . . . . 50% (3 h)
[**14** Transfer to mixture of
Alcohol (100%) . . . . 25%
Chloroform . . . . . 75% (3 h)]
**15** Transfer to chloroform in an uncorked capsule (2 cm diam. x 3 cm long). Add a few shavings of paraffin wax (m.p. 52°C) and keep at room temperature. (3 h)
**16** Place the capsule *on* the oven, and as the chloroform evaporates, add further paraffin wax from time to time. (3 h)
**17** Place the capsule *in* the oven (53°C). (20 min)
**18** Transfer contents of capsule to warm watch-glass in the oven, to allow all the chloroform to evaporate. (Approx. 10 min)
**19** Warm a solid watch glass in the oven; smear the inside thinly and evenly with glycerol; fill it with fresh molten paraffin wax; using warmed forceps, transfer the impregnated material to the wax, for embedding. While the wax is still molten, insert a slip of paper with the name and treatment of the tissue written on the protruding part.
**20** Solidify the paraffin wax quickly. Hold the vessel on a dish of water; blow on the surface to form a skin; finally immerse the vessel in cold water. If the inside of the vessel has been carefully coated with glycerol the block will float out of it. If it does not, it must be cut out round the edges.
**21** Cut sections at 10μm to 15 μm.
**22** Attach sections to slide (p. 64).
(For detail work be careful to keep the sections in sequence.)
**23** Remove wax from sections (p. 65).
**24** Wash off xylene with alcohol (100%).
**25** Wash in alcohol (90%).
**26** Transfer to distilled water.

*See footnote† on preceding page.

[Sections *attached to the slide* will not be harmed by transference from alcohol (90%) to water.]

**27** Stain according to one of the following methods:

*Either,*

(*a*) *For general work: and for parasitic fungi in host tissue.* See also xi (p. 135).]

**28** Stain either in safranin o or in methylene blue aq. (5 min)
**29** Wash in distilled water. (2 min)
**30** Dehydrate in industrial spirit [= alcohol (95% approx.)]. (2 min)
**31** Dehydrate in alcohol (100%). (2 min)
**32** Counterstain either in fast freen FCF (in clove oil) (watch under microscope until safranin o remains only in nuclei and in lignified walls of host), or in erythrosin bluish (satd. soln. in clove oil).
*Note:* The methylene blue and erythrosin bluish combination is useful if the host's tissues are very resinous.
**33** Wash in xylene.
**34** Mount in D.P.X.

[Results with safranin o and fast green FCF: hyphae (→ green); cellulose walls of host (→ green); nuclei (→ red); lignified walls of host (→ red). Results with methylene blue and erythrosin bluish: hyphae (→ red); cellulose walls of host (→ red); nuclei (→ blue); lignified walls of host (→ blue).]

*Or,*

(*b*) *For general work, especially with dense storage substances.*

**28** Stain in crystal violet (aq.) (10 min)
**29** Wash in water.
**30** Dehydrate in industrial spirit [= alcohol (95% approx.).] (Rapidly)
**31** Dehydrate in alcohol (100%). (Rapidly)
**32** Counterstain in fast green FCF (in clove oil).
**33** Wash in xylene.
**34** Mount in D.P.X.

[Chromatin (→ purple); cellulose walls (→ green); cytoplasm (→ almost colourless).]

*Or,*

(*c*) *For general cytological characters:* Heidenhain's haematoxylin counterstained with fast green FCF or erythrosin bluish, or orange G.

**28** Mordant in iron alum. (20 min–2 h)
**29** Wash in distilled water.
**30** Stain in Heidenhain's haematoxylin. (1–24 h)
**31** Wash thoroughly in distilled water.
**32** Differentiate rapidly, under the microscope, in a Petri dish containing iron alum (2%–8% in distilled water) to which 3–4 drops of acetic acid (glacial) have been added.
**33** Wash in distilled water.
**34** Wash in running tap water to remove acidity. (5 min)
**35** Dehydrate in industrial spirit [= alcohol (95% approx.).].
**36** Dehydrate in alcohol (100%).
**37** Counterstain either in fast green FCF, in clove oil; or in erythrosin bluish, in clove oil; or in orange G, in clove oil.
**38** Wash in xylene.
**39** Mount in D.P.X.

*Or,*

(*d*) *Newton's crystal violet method for general cytology.*

**28** Stain sections in crystal violet (1% aq.) which has previously been boiled and filtered. (4–7 min according to nature of material)
**29** Wash in distilled water. (Several *quick* changes)
**30** Place in alcohol (80%) containing 1% iodine and 1% potassium iodide. (30 s)
**31** Dehydrate alcohol (90%) and (100%), both containing iodine as in **30**. (Quickly)
**32** Dehydrate alcohol (100%). (Quickly)
**33** Clear and differentiate in clove oil.
**34** Pass *quickly* through xylene to remove adherent clove oil.
**35** Mount in D.P.X.

*Or,*

(*e*) *Flemming's triple stain for general cytology.*

**28** Mordant in iodine. (5 min)
**29** Stain in crystal violet. (15 min)
**30** Wash alcohol (50%). (Quickly)
**31** Stain in safranin o. (5 min)
**32** Dehydrate in industrial spirit [= alcohol 95% approx.)]. (Rapidly)
**33** Dehydrate in alcohol (100%). (Rapidly)
**34** Wash in a mixture of 50/50 : : xylene/alcohol (100%). (Rapidly)
**35** Examine under the microscope.
(Destaining is complete when chromosomes are red and spindle fibres are violet.)
**36** Transfer to clove oil.
**37** Stain in orange G in clove oil. (1 min)

**38** Wash off excess stain in fresh clove oil.
**39** Wash in xylene.
**40** Mount in D.P.X.
[Chromosomes (→ red); spindle fibres (→ violet); surrounding plasma (→ orange).]

(xi) *Parasitic hyphae in host plant.*
(*a*) *In non-lignified plant tissues.*
Dring's modification of the Periodic Acid-Schiff (PAS) Method.*
This is one of the few methods that will result in the staining of the fungus cell wall (as distinct from staining the cytoplasm) and is particularly useful for the study of rust diseases.
**1** Fix material in Navashin's Fluid (p. 237) or F.A.A. (p. 215).
**2** Embed, section, remove wax, and dehydrate by the usual methods.
**3** Immerse in periodic acid (p. 239).
(2–5 min, unless the tissue is to be counterstained at **10** (below), when immersion in periodic acid *must not exceed* 3 min)
**4** Wash in running tap water. (10 min)
**5** Immerse in Schiff's reagent (5 min)
(The reaction will be complete at the end of this time although the tissue will appear colourless or only slightly pink)
**6** Transfer to potassium metabisulphite (p. 241). (5 min)
**7** Transfer to fresh potassium metabisulphite. (5 min)
**8** Wash in running tap water. (10 min)
(During this time the colour develops)
**9** Dehydrate to alcohol (70%).
[**10** If desired, counterstain in light green SF yellowish (in alcohol 90%).
(Until maximum differentiation is obtained)]
**11** Dehydrate in alcohol (90%).
**12** Dehydrate in alcohol (100%).
**13** Transfer to fresh alcohol (100%).
**14** Clear.
**15** Mount.
[Carbohydrates (→ magenta); fungus mycelium, host cuticle and parts of phloem (→ pink, to red, to purple, to magenta); host cellulose (→ hardly stained unless counterstained with light green SF yellowish, when → green); host lignin (→ hardly stained).]

* From information supplied by Dr. D. M. Dring of the Royal Botanic Gardens, Kew. Dr. Dring suggests (private communication) that martius yellow might well be used as a counterstain instead of light green SF yellowish.

*Godwin's method.* *

**1** Place section on slide in a drop of Amann's medium (lacto-phenol) (formula ii, p. 188).
**2** Heat over a bunsen flame.
(Few seconds, till Amann's medium fumes)
**3** Transfer section to anilin blue ws in Amann's medium lactophenol [special formula (*f*), p. 189].
**4** Warm again on the slide.
**5** Transfer to Amann's medium, and heat and examine alternately. (To remove excess stain)
**6** Mount in fresh Amann's medium.
**7** Cover.
**8** Seal.

*Durand's method.* †

**1** Stain sections deeply in Delafield's haematoxylin.
**2** 'Blue' in alkaline water.
**3** Wash in alcohol (95%).
**4** Dehydrate in alcohol (100%).
**5** Clear in carbol-turpentine.
**6** Stain sections eosin Y [1.5% in alcohol (95%)]. (5–10 min)
**7** Place sections on slide.
**8** Remove excess stain with filter-paper.
**9** Wash thoroughly phenol-turpentine (*not* alcohol). (Use a pipette for this process.)
**10** Wash xylene.
**11** Mount in D.P.X.
[Host's tissues (→ blue); parasitic hyphae (→ red).]

See also 'Hymenomycetes' (p. 140), 'Peronosporaceae' (p. 156), 'Rusts' (p. 168), and 'Stereum purpureum' (p. 172).

(xii) *Hyphae in wood sections.* ‡ §
This method is of particular value for the study of vascular pathogens in plants and for timber-rotting fungi. It is entirely satisfactory for all plant anatomical studies.
**1** Stain sections in safranin O (1% aq.). (10–15 min)
**2** Wash in distilled water.
**3** Stain picro-anilin blue WS [(ii, p. 189)]. (5–10 s)
**4** Wash thoroughly in distilled water.

* With acknowledgements to Dr. H. Godwin.
† After E. J. Durand, *Phytopathologist,* I, p. 129, quoted by Strasburger, 1930, *Handbook of Practical Botany* (English edn.), Allen and Unwin.
‡ After Cartwright; adapted from information supplied by Dr. P. W. Talboys, East Malling Research Station, Kent.
§ Very thin sections of wood are best cut with a *very sharp* plane.

5 Transfer to alcohol (96%) and wash *very* thoroughly.
(Until no more safranin diffuses out from the sections).
*Note:* Process **5** – *thorough* washing in alcohol (96%) – is the most important part of the differentiation and is the key to success. Patience must be exercised and the process carried out completely.
6 Wash in alcohol (100%).
7 Clear in xylene.
8 Mount in D.P.X.

[Fungal hyphae (→ blue); cellulose (→ blue); lignified tissue (→ red).]

(xiii) *Vital staining.*
Follow Method v, p. 132. After process **3** mount in fresh lacto-phenol, cover and seal.

(xiv) *Structures with food supplies** (e.g. *Pyronema* oogonia):
1 Fix in Merkel's fluid.
2 Wash in running water. (6–12 h)
3 Proceed as from process **3** of (x) above (p. 133).

(xv) *Very minute objects:*
*Note:* Handling during dehydration and impregnation is undesirable.
1 Fix and wash as (x) above, processes **1** and **2** (p. 133).
2 Transfer to glycerol (10% aq.) and allow to concentrate to pure glycerol in a desiccator. Test purity by adding a drop of pure glycerol.
3 Wash thoroughly in alcohol (100%).
4 Transfer to a capsule containing a mixture of
Alcohol (100%) . . . . . . . 90 parts
Cedar-wood oil . . . . . . . 10 parts
5 Allow the alcohol to evaporate at room temperature. (Till only the oil remains)
6 Add shavings of paraffin wax (m.p. 52°C) at room temperature. (3 h)
7 Place the capsule *on* the oven and add more paraffin wax from time to time. (3 h)
8 Place the capsule *in* the oven (53°C). (20 min)
9 Transfer to pure paraffin wax in oven. (5 min)
10 Transfer to fresh pure paraffin wax in oven. (5 min)
(Changes are to ensure that no cedar-wood oil is carried into the embedding wax.)
11 Proceed as from process **19** of (x) above (p. 133).

(xv) *Delicate specimens:*
See 'Algae' (p. 95).

See also 'Agaricus' (p. 94), 'Autobasidiomycetes' (p. 105), 'Mucor' (p. 149), 'Penicillium' (p. 155), 'Yeast' (p. 180).

**Glochidium**

See 'Anodon' (p. 102).

**Glucose**

See 'Sugar, Tests For, (*b*) Dextrose' (p. 173).

**Glycogen**

For temporary preparations, stain with iodine
(i) To preseve the stain in permanent preparations, after staining with iodine, treat with potassium acetate (aq. satd.). Seal cover-slip with gold size.
(ii) *Best's carmine method for wax-embedded sections.*
1 Float sections on to slide with alcohol.
2 Dry in oven (37°C). (Overnight)
3 Remove wax with xylene.
4 Wash off xylene with alcohol (100%).
5 Dip in 'Celloidin' (1%).
6 Drain and allow to dry.
7 Transfer to alcohol (80%).
8 Wash in distilled water.
9 Stain in Carazzi's haematoxylin.
10 Wash in tap water.
11 Stain in Best's carmine (p. 196).
12 Differentiate in Best's differentiator (p. 191). (Till no more stain removed)
13 Dehydrate in alcohol (90%).
14 Dehydrate in xylene-acetone (p. 252).
15 Clear in xylene.
16 Mount in D.P.X.
(iii) *Periodic acid/Schiff technique, with diastase controls.*
This technique is suitable for paraffin wax sections attached to slides or for blood or bone marrow films.

* Adapted from Gwynne-Vaughan and Barnes, 1937, *The Structure and Development of the Fungi,* Cambridge, University Press.

Full details are given in the section on Carbohydrates (p. 112). In order to demonstrate the presence of glycogen, a control slide must be incubated in a solution of malt diastase before the PAS procedure and stained at the same time as the experimental material.

1 Bring section through xylene and alcohols to water.
2 Incubate in a 1% aq. solution of malt diastase. (1 hr 37°C)
3 Rinse in running water. (1 min)
4 To stage **2** of the PAS technique (p. 112).

Material which is coloured red in the experimental slide but is *absent* or *unstained,* in the slide incubated in diastase before the PAS technique, is glycogen.

### Golgi Bodies

(i) *Modified Cajal's method for animal tissue.*

1 Cut tissue in pieces not more than 5 mm thick (preferably less).
2 Fix (within 3 hours of death) in Cajal's fixative (de Fano's modification) (p. 193). (3–8 h)
3 Rinse in distilled water.
4 Transfer to silver nitrate at room temperature. [Solution ii (β) (p. 248).] (36 h)
5 Wash twice in distilled water. (Rapidly)
6 Reduce in hydroquinone. [i (p. 228).] (9–12 h)
7 Wash in running water. (5 min)
8 Dehydrate in alcohol (70%), (90%), (100%). (Not more than 2 h each)
9 Clear in cedar-wood oil.
10 Impregnate and embed (p. 62 ff.).
11 Cut sections at 4 μm.
12 Fix sections to slide (p. 64).
13 Remove wax with xylene (p. 65).
14 Wash in alcohol (100%). (Rapidly)

*Either,*

(*a*)

15 Clear in xylene.
16 Mount in D.P.X.

*Or,*

(*b*)

15 Hydrate in alcohol (95%).
16 Hydrate in distilled water.
17 Tone sections in gold chloride toning solution (p. 220). (Watch under microscope, 5–10 min: cytoplasm from yellowish → grey)
18 Wash in running water.
19 If desired, counterstain in Delafield's haematoxylin.
20 'Blue' in tap water.
21 Dehydrate in alcohol (95%), (Rapidly)
22 Dehydrate in alcohol (100%). (Rapidly)
23 Clear in cedar-wood oil. (Rapidly)
24 Mount in D.P.X.

[Cytoplasm → yellow-brown (if untoned), or → grey (if toned); Golgi bodies → black (network or rodlets); Mitochondria → impregnated golden-brown.]

(ii) *Kolatchev's method.* *

1 Fix tissue in Meve's solution (p. 236). (24 h)
2 Wash in running water. (5 h)
3 Place tissue in 2% aq. osmium tetroxide solution at 35–37°C. (4 days)
4 Wash in running water. (1 h)
5 Dehydrate and embed in paraffin.
6 Section at 5 μm and attach sections to slides.
7 Dewax in xylene, wash in absolute alcohol, pass through fresh xylene and mount in D.P.X.

The Golgi body appears black.

*Note:* a suitable tissue for practice is the middle part of the epididymis of the mouse.

### Gonionemus

Stain in Mayer's hydrochloric acid-carmine.

### Gonium pectorale

S/C
See 'Culture Media 3' (p. 203).

### Gums

(i) Stain in basic fuchsin (→ red).
See also 'Pectic substances' (p. 155).

### Haemopis (Horse Leech)

S/C
See under 'Hirudo' (p. 138).

* Zoology, University of Oxford.

**Haemosiderin**

See 'Iron' (p. 141).

**Hair**

See 'Skin' (p. 170).

**Hanging-Drop Cultures**

See 'Culture Media 4' (p. 208).

**Hay Infusions**

**S/C**
See 'Culture Media 3' (p. 203).
See Methods **1** and **2** (p. 73).

**Heart**

See 'Blood Vessels' (p. 110).

**Helianthus**

See Methods **9** (p. 76); **10** (p. 77); **16** (p. 81); and **17** (p. 81).

**Helix**

**S/C**
(i) Dealers.
(ii) *H. aspersa* in damp places in gardens. Hibernate in groups at the bases of dry garden walls under shelter.
*H. pomatia* collected locally, particularly in the Cotswolds. Supply with fresh cabbage leaves and moisture.

*Preservation techniques*
*To kill.*
(*a*) *To obtain in an expanded condition.*
Either, place in a screw-top bottle brimful of tepid, boiled water to which a little nicotine has been added through the medium of a cigarette 'stub', and screw down the top; Or, *place in a beaker of cold water, heat gently till expanded, then heat quickly (without cooling) for 1 min.
(*b*) Place in mercuric chloride (sat. aq.) (Poison). ($\frac{1}{2}$ h)
When dead wash under running water very thoroughly.

* *Gerrard's Bulletin*, May 1939, T. Gerrard & Co.

(i) Inject formaldehyde (20%) through the dorsal surface of the foot of a distended snail.
(ii) Formaldehyde (4%).
(iii) Inject, with and preserve in,*

| | |
|---|---|
| Alcohol (100%) | 60 ml |
| Formaldehyde | 0.5 ml |
| Water | 39.5 ml |

*To remove mucus.*
When dead, wash in alchol (50%).

*Suitable stains*

*Radula and jaw plate.*
Delafield's haematoxylin.
*Salivary gland.*
Borax carmine.
*Nerve collar.*
Borax carmine; mount under cover-slip raised on glass ledges.

**Hirudo (Medicinal Leech)**

**S/C**
(i) Dealers – purchase alive.
Feed at intervals of 2–3 months with raw flesh.
*Kill for dissection.* Chloroform vapour, or alcohol (30%).
*Fix and preserve.* Alcohol (60%).
*For sectioning.*
(*a*) *Narcotize.* Two menthol crystals placed on limited water surface. (Till immobile)
(*b*) *Fix.* Bouin's fluid. (18 h)
(*c*) Stains: Mallory's; Delafield's haematoxylin.

**Hormidium**

(i) See 'Algae' (p. 94).
(ii) Stain in Delafield's haematoxylin.

**Hydra**

**S/C**
(i) Dealers.
(ii) Stems of pond weeds, especially duckweeds and *Elodea canadensis*.
Feed on *Daphnia.*

**P**
Alcohol (70%)

*Preparation techniques*
(i) Stain (living) in Nile blue sulphate.

* *Gerrard's Bulletin*, May 1939, T. Gerrard & Co.

(ii) *To protrude nematocysts.*
(*a*) Irrigate with sodium chloride (5% aq.); dilute iodine; acetic acid (1% aq.).
(*b*) Stain in acetic-methylene blue.

*To kill in an expanded condition for microscopical mounting.*
1 Place first in a little cold water: then add boiling water.
2 Narcotize slowly with menthol.
3 Suddenly apply Bouin's fluid, or formaldehyde (10%), or mercuric chloride (satd. aq.), all at 60°C; Perenyi's fluid (see p. 239).

*To kill unexpanded.*
1 Hot Bouin's fluid.
2 See 'Coelenterates' (p. 119).

*To see cell structure.*
Kill and macerate in acetic acid (1%) with a trace of osmium tetroxide. (5 min)
Disintegrate with small camel-hair brush.
Temporary preparations may be mounted in glycerol or formaldehyde (5%).
For technique see 'Coelenterates iii (*a*)' (p. 120).

*Whole mount.*
See 'Animal Tissue, General histology. Method I (*a*)' (p. 99). Mayer's hydrochloric acid-carmine (p. 196) is also a suitable stain.

*To stain nematocysts in a whole mount.*
1 Kill with mercuric chloride (satd. aq.) at 60°C.
2 Wash thoroughly in alcohol.
3 Stain very strongly with methylene blue.
4 Dehydrate rapidly.
5 Clear cedar-wood oil.
[Nematocysts (→ blue); rest of body (→ unstained).]

*Sections.*
1 Embed by the Peterfi 'Celloidin'-paraffin wax method (p. 67).
2 Section at 5 μm.
3 Remove wax from sections with xylene.
4 Remove xylene with alcohol (100%).
5 Hydrate through alcohol (90%), (70%), to distilled water.
6 *For general histology.* Stains: Delafield's haematoxylin; Mallory's stain; methylene blue-acetic.
7 Wash in distilled water. (20 s)
8 Rinse in acetic acid (0.1% aq.). (10 s)
9 Rinse in distilled water. (20 s)
10 Dehydrate successively in alcohol, (70%), (90%), (100%). (10 s each)
11 Dehydrate in fresh alcohol (100%). (10 s)
12 Clear in xylene.
13 Mount in D.P.X.

**Hydractinia**

*Preparation techniques*
(i) *Whole mount.*
1 Stain in undiluted alum-carmine (Grenacher's). (12 h)
2 Wash in distilled water. (Several changes – 3 h)
3 Dehydrate in alcohol (30%), (50%) and (70%).
4 De-stain in alcohol (70%) containing 2% of hydrochloric acid. (Until the animal appears light red. 5 h).
*Note:* The precise concentration of hydrochloric acid may be a matter for trial and error with any particular tissue. Too low a concentration will not de-stain. Too high a concentration will remove stain from both nuclei and cytoplasm, resulting in a lack of differentiation. Best results are obtained by prolonged de-staining with a moderate concentration of hydrochloric acid.
5 Wash in alcohol (95%).
[6 If desired, counterstain in fast green FCF, or methyl blue.
*Note:* Counterstaining is best done progressively. To make the correct concentration of counter-stain add the stock solution of stain, drop by drop, to alcohol (95%) until a pale solution is obtained. Place the tissue in the stain and watch the progress of staining under the (binocular) microscope. Stop staining when the desired depth of stain has been obtained.]
7 Wash in alcohol (95%).
8 Dehydrate in alcohol (100%).
9 Clear in methyl salicylate (oil of wintergreen).
10 Mount in D.P.X.
(ii) See also 'Coelenterates' (p. 119).

**Hydrodictyon reticulatum**

**S/C**
See 'Culture Media 3' (p. 203).

**Hydroids**

**P**
Formaldehyde (4%).

*Preparation techniques*
(i) See 'Coelenterates' (p. 119); 'Obelia i' (p. 153).
(ii) See 'Echinus' (p. 125).

**Hymenomycetes***

Material for nuclear division is best secured at midnight. Treat as for 'Fungi' Preparation techniques x (p. 133).

**Impressions or Replicas of Opaque Surfaces†**

Opaque (primary, 'reversed') and transparent (secondary, 'true') replicas of opaque surfaces (either living or dead; dry or wet), suitable for individual or class examination, either by hand-lens or by optical microscope, can be obtained in the following way.

**1** Mix some silicone-rubber with its appropriate catalyst and pour the mix over the surface it is desired to replicate (e.g. leaf and stem surfaces, human skin, human palate, insect eye, transverse section of wood, etc.).
**2** Allow the silicone-rubber to harden. (5 min)
**3** Using forceps with care, ease and lift away the opaque impression.
**4** Wash the impression with a camel-hair brush in detergent.
**5** Wash with distilled water.
**6** Blot the impression with a hardish filter-paper.

*Note:* (i) It is essential that the filter-paper used should be free from loose cellulose, otherwise the secondary, transparent impression to be made next will not be true.
(ii) If desired, this primary, 'negative', impression may be used for class inspection.
To make the transparent impression proceed as follows:

**7** Have ready a desiccator containing phosphorus pentoxide (care).
**8** Dry the primary impression *completely* by laying it flat, impressed surface *uppermost,* in the desiccator. (10–15 min)
*Note:* Complete drying at this stage is *essential,* otherwise the secondary impression will *not* be transparent and will be useless for microscopic examination.
**9** *As quickly as possible,* pour clear, uncoloured nail-varnish (a nitro-cellulose preparation) over the impressed surface of the primary impression and *quickly* replace the lid of the desiccator.
**10** Allow the secondary impression to harden. (10–15 min)
**11** Using forceps, *slowly* and *gently* remove the secondary impression from the primary impression and *quickly* place it between two clean slides.
**12** Bind the slides together with plastic tape and seal their edges with the same material.

*Note:* The transparent secondary, 'true', impression is best viewed through the microscope with transmitted light directed somewhat obliquely, rather than normal, to the object.

**Insects**

**P**
(i) *Small.*
(*a*) Ethyl acetate (especially useful if the animals are required for dissection, because the muscles are kept relaxed).
(*b*) Alcohol (70%).
(ii) *Large.*
Dry.

*Preparation techniques*

(i) *Small.*
(*a*) *Kill:* See 'Killing Bottle iii' (p. 230); ammonium carbonate; chloroform.
(*b*) *Permanent whole mount.*
**1** Kill and clear in Berlese's fluid (p. 190).
**2** Mount in Berlese's fluid.
**3** Dry off in oven.
**4** Cover and seal.
(*c*) *Mouth parts:*
**1** Boil the whole head in potassium or sodium hydroxide (10%). CARE. (5 min)
**2** Wash in water. (2 min)
**3** Dehydrate in alcohol (30%), (50%), (70%), (90%), (100%). (2 min each)
**4** Clear in xylene.
**5** Either (α) Mount whole head in D.P.X.
or (β) Remove mouth parts and mount separately.
(*d*) *Parts of small insects.*
**1** Dehydrate up to alcohol (90%).
**2** Proceed as for 'Echinus Preparation techniques for ova' (p. 125) from process **7** onwards.

* After Gwynne-Vaughan and Barnes, 1937, *Structure and Development of the Fungi,* Cambridge, University Press.
† After J. Sampson, *Nature,* **191**, 4791, 932, Aug. 26, 1961.

(ii) *Medium or large.*

(*a*) *Kill:* Ethyl acetate; laurel or cyanide (see 'Killing Bottle', p. 230); chloroform.

(*b*) *Mouth parts and other organs:* See 'Periplaneta' (p. 156).

(*c*) *Whole mounts.*

Embed in resin. See 'Technique of Resin Embedding' (p. 69).

(iii) *Larvae.*

(*a*) *Small.*

($\alpha$) Treat as small whole insects as at i(*b*) above.

($\beta$)

**1** Clear in potassium hydroxide (10%).
**2** Wash in distilled water.
**3** Stain in acid fuchsin.(Take care NOT to overstain)
**4** Wash in distilled water.
**5** Mount in polyvinyl alchol-lacto-phenol (p. 241), on a slide.
**6** Dry off the mountant gently in a warm oven.
**7** Mount in 'Euparal'.
**8** Cover with a cover-slip.

(*b*) *Dipterous.*

**1** Build up a ring of asphalt varnish (ii, p. 246) on a slide.
**2** Fill the cavity with Amann's medium (lacto-phenol).
**3** Place a larva within the cavity.
**4** Cover with a cover-slip. (Leave for 2 d)
*Note:* During this period the preparation may be regarded as semi-permanent and treated accordingly.
**5** Seal the preparation with asphalt varnish.

(*c*) *Large,* e.g. *Caterpillar.*

**1** Boil in dilute potassium or sodium hydroxide (2%). CARE. (3–4 min)
**2** Wash in water. (10 min)
**3** Cut in half lengthwise.
**4** Dehydrate in alcohol (30%), (50%), (70%), (90%), (100%). (10 min each)
**5** Clear in cedar-wood oil. (Till transparent)
**6** Wash in xylene.
**7** Mount in D.P.X.

See also 'Acarine' (p. 94); 'Aphis' (p. 102); 'Apis' (p. 103); 'Mosquito' (p. 148); 'Periplaneta' (p. 156).

**Intestine**

See 'Alimentary Canal' (p. 96).

**Inulin**

**S/C**

*To find:*

Soak dandelion (*Taraxacum officinale*) roots in alcohol (70%) the night before examination. Crystals small and spherical.

Orcein (alc.) is a suitable stain.
Boil in dil. hydrochloric acid.
(Inulin → orange red.)

**Iron**

*Preparation techniques*

*Iron compounds in sections including haemosiderin.*

**1** Bring sections to water.
**2** Wash in distilled water.
**3** Place in acid potassium ferrocyanide [(p. 241)]. (15 min)
**4** Wash in distilled water.
**5** Stain in eosin Y [see (*e*), p. 212]. (3 min)

**Keratin**

Haematoxylin and eosin Y (→ bright pink); Mallory's (→ bright red). Crossmon's (→ red).

**Kerona**

**S/C**

Search tentacles of *Hydra.*

**Kidney**

*Preparation techniques*

(i) *Fix.*Do not fix in Bouin's fluid. Use formol-saline or mercuric-formaldehyde.

(ii) Stain.

Ehrlich's haematoxylin (counterstained with eosin Y alc.).

**Laevulose**

See 'Sugars. Tests For, (*c*) Laevulose' (p. 173).

**Lamium Album**

*Stem.* See Methods **9** (p. 76); **10** (p. 77); **16** (p. 81); **17** (p. 82).

**Leaf**

**S/C**

Any leaves may be used, but those of *Buxus sempervirens* are particularly useful for Method (i) below).

*Preparation techniques*

(i) *General structure.*

*Note:* This method is *not* suitable for very thin leaves.

**1** Treat the material as in 'Techniques of Maceration (i) **(1–5)**' (p. 46).
**2** Arrange a leaf with its lower side (mid-vein more prominent) downwards.
**3** Cut a small square from the leaf blade, avoiding both mid-vein and leaf-margin.
**4** Float the square in water in a watch-glass. It will separate into three layers – upper epidermis, mesophyll, lower epidermis.
**5** Transfer each layer, by means of a camel-hair brush, to glycerol (10%) respectively on three slides.

Care must be taken to mount the upper epidermis with its upper side upwards; and the lower epidermis with its *lower* side *upwards.*

(ii) *Bundle ends – To distinguish lignified tissue and venation.* *

**1** Place a leaf in eau de Javelle (fresh). (24–28 h)
**2** Wash in running water (in a beaker covered with muslin). (24 h)
**3** Stain in ammoniacal fuchsin (p. 216).
**4** Wash in industrial methylated spirit.
**5** Dehydrate.
**6** Clear.
**7** Mount in D.P.X.

[Lignified tissue (→ red); unlignified tissue (→ clear, colourless).]

(iii) *Epidermis.*

(*a*) As above.

(*b*) Use leaves or stem in a fresh or hardly wilted state.

**1** Cut a slit in the epidermis.
**2** Place the tip of a scalpel under the epidermis.
**3** Peel epidermis off.
**4** Mount in glycerol.

(*c*)

**1** Macerate thin leaves in sodium hydroxide (5% or weaker), or boiling water. (1 min)
**2** Strip epidermis from under-side of leaf, and, with a camel-hair brush, remove debris.
**3** Wash twice in distilled water.

Either (α),

**4** Stain in eosin Y aq.
**5** Mount in acetic acid (2%), or glycerol, or glycerol-jelly.
**6** Seal.

Or (β),

**4** Stain in safranin o or Delafield's haematoxylin.
**5** Dehydrate.
**6** Clear.
**7** Mount in D.P.X.

(*d*) See Methods **1** and **2** (p. 73).

(iv) *Hairs.*

As (i) or (iii) (*a*) or (*b*), above.

(v) *Mesophyll.*

(*a*) As (i) above.

(*b*)

**1** Boil leaf in potassium hydroxide (10% aq.). (5 min)
**2** Wash in water.
**3** Tease in drop of glycerol (50%) on slide.
**4** Remove lumps and drain off glycerol.
**5** Mount in glycerol-jelly.

(vi) *Middle Lamella.*

(*a*)*

**1** Warm thin sections of tissue in alcohol (95%). (Until the chlorophyll is removed)
**2** Transfer to sodium hydroxide (5% aq.) and warm *gently,* preferably on a water-bath.
**3** Wash in distilled water.
**4** Stain in dilute ruthenium red or methylene blue.

(Cellulose walls → colourless; middle lamella → stained.)

(*b*) See also 'Pectic Subtances' (p. 155).

(vii) *Primordia.*

*Note:* This method can also be used for flower primordia.

*To demonstrate apical growing point.*

**1** Sow seeds of cauliflower (*Brassica olercea botrytis cauliflora*) thinly in a shallow box containing suitable damp *seed* compost

* After Eric Ashby, *School Science Review,* **XV**, 60, 511, June 1934.

* After Lorna I. Scott, University of Leeds.

['Culture Media 2 (*a*)' (p. 203)]. Sieve a very thin layer of compost over them. Cover the box with a sheet of glass which must be inverted daily to allow moisture, which will have condensed on the underside of the glass, to evaporate. Maintain at a temperature of about 18°C until the seeds germinate.

**2** When germination occurs, remove the glass sheet and maintain the seedlings at a temperature of about 10°C. The compost must not be allowed to dry out and should be wetted occasionally by spraying gently with (preferably rain) water.

**3** When the seedlings have developed two 'rough' leaves transfer them to grow singly in *potting* compost (p. 203) in small flower-pots. This 'pricking out' is conveniently done with the aid of a match-stick, the compost being pressed round the roots of the transplanted seedling.

**4** Allow the seedlings to develop into plants about 7.5 cm high.

**5** To demonstrate the apical growing point, very carefully remove the leaves successively (making a count of them) until the apex is exposed. The leaf and flower primordia are readily seen.

*Note:* The removal of leaves is done without prior removal of the plant from the pot, which later serves as a holder for demonstrating and examining the growing point.

(viii) *Stomata.*
(*a*) Use material preserved in alcohol (70%).
(*b*) Stain in Delafield's haematoxylin.
(*c*) See Method i (p 142), or iii (p. 142) above.
(*d*) See also 'Standard Methods', **1** and **2** (p. 73); and 'Methods for Plant Tissue' (p. 158).
(*e*) *Impression of leaf surface:*
See 'Impressions of Opaque Objects' (p. 140).

(ix) *Transparencies.*
See 'Transparencies of Plant Material' (p. 176).

(x) *Venation.*
See Method (ii) (p. 142).

(xi) *General histology.*
See 'Methods for Plant Tissue' (p. 159).

**Leech**

See 'Hirudo' (p. 138).

**Lens Cells**

See 'Astacus iv' (p. 104).

**Lepus**

**S/C**
(i) Dealers. Purchase alive. First anaesthetize in a mixture of chloroform vapour and air. Then kill by increasing the percentage of chloroform.
(ii) Dead animals may be obtained much more cheaply from farmers, but usually some damage has been done by shot or snare.

**P**
Formaldehyde (3%).

**Lernaeopoda globosa**

**S/C**
In nasal fossae of some dogfish.

**Lernaeopoda scyllicola**

**S/C**
In extra-cloacal region of *male* dogfish only.

**Leucocytes**
(i) See 'Blood' (p. 108).
(ii) *Leucocyte count.* See 'Haemocytometer' (pp. 223 ff).

**Lichens**

(i) *Fix.* Carnoy's fluid.
(ii) Stain in Heidenhain's haematoxylin; counterstain with Congo red.

**Ligament**

*Preparation techniques*
(i) *Fix.* Formol-saline (4%).
(ii) *Embed.* 'Celloidin' method required in order to obtain good sections. See 'Celloidin' Embedding' (p. 66).
(iii) Stains: van Gieson's; Mallory's; Weigert's stain.

**Lignin**

*Specific stains:* Aniline sulphate or aniline chloride [→ golden yellow: more intense if followed by sulphuric acid (50%)]; nascent indophenol blue (mixture of *a*-naphthol and dimethyl-paraphenylenediamine) (→ very pale blue); phloroglucin followed by hydrochloric acid (50%) (→ red-purple).

*Other stain:* Iodine and sulphuric acid (50%) (→ yellow-brown).

*Suitable stains*

Loeffler's methylene blue (counterstain with eosin Y); safranin o (→ red) (counterstain with Delafield's haematoxylin, or anilin blue ws, or fast green FCF in clove oil); iodine green (counterstain with Mayer's carmalum, or acid fuchsin, or eosin Y, or erythrosin bluish); Hanstein's fuchsin violet (→ reddish); ammoniacal basic fuchsin (→ red) (counterstain with fast green FCF); basic fuchsin (→ red); methyl green (→ green); xylene-methylene blue (→ blue); xylene-nile blue sulphate (→ blue).

See also 'Leaf' (ii) (p. 142) and 'Xylem' (p. 180).

**Limpet**

See 'Patella' (p. 155).

**Lipids**

*Suitable stains*

Sudan black (→ blue-black); Oil red o (→ red); Nile blue sulphate (→ neut. lipids – pink).

**Liver**

*Preparation techniques*

(i)* *Fix.* Formol-saline (4%); mercuric-formaldehyde.
(ii)* *Section* at 8 μm–10 μm
(iii) Stains: Ehrlich's haematoxylin and eosin Y alc; Heidenhain's iron haematoxylin.

**Liver Fluke**

See 'Fasciola hepatica' (p. 127).

**Liverworts**

**S/C**
(i) Banks above streams.
(ii) Damp walls in greenhouses.

**Living Organisms**

Suitable stains: Methylene blue aq.; Janus green B; methyl green; neutral red; Bismarck brown Y.

*Fixing, etc., small.* See 'Protozoa' (p. 164).

**Locust**

See 'Schistocerca gregaria' (p. 169).

* After Carleton, 1957, *Histological Technique,* University Press, Oxford.

**Lugworm**

See 'Arenicola' (p. 103).

**Lumbricus**

**S/C**
(i) Dealers.
(ii) In dry weather water the soil well and place over it a thoroughly wet sack. Examine towards nightfall and early morning.
(iii) Compost heaps and manure heaps.

**P**
Alcohol (90%).

*Preparation techniques*

(i) *Before killing:* Keep for a few days on wet filter-paper in a covered dish. During this time material in the gut is excreted. *Regard this pre-treatment as essential if* sections are to be made.
(ii) *Kill.* Chloroform vapour; alcohol (70%) (5–10 min) (inclined to harden unduly); drop into hot (not boiling) water, or hot sodium chloride (20% aq.); chromacetic (12 h if also for fixation).
(iii) *Fix.* Alcohol (95%).
(iv) *Whole specimens (or typical parts of whole specimens).*
Use small worms.
**1** *Kill.* Alcohol (30%).
**2** Stains: borax carmine; or Delafield's haematoxylin followed by tap water.
**3** Clear in cedar-wood oil.
**4** *Preserve.* Cleared specimen in a tube of cedar-wood oil.
(v) *Nephridium.*
(*a*) *To demonstrate in a dissection.*
Flood the dissection either with mercuric chloride (sat. aq.); or with methylene blue [0.125% in sodium chloride (0.6% aq.).] (10 min)
(*b*) *Permanent preparation.*
It is difficult to remove an entire nephridium. The beginner should detach one, *with a septum,* and hold the septum (not the nephridium) in the forceps.
**1** *Fix.* Alcohol (70%). (2 min)
**2** Stain in borax carmine. (2 min)
**3** Dehydrate,
either, in alcohol (70%), (90%), (100%). (2 min each)
or, in 2 ethoxy ethanol. (2 min)

**4** Transfer to fresh alcohol (100%) or 2 ethoxy ethanol in a small specimen tube.
**5** Clear in cedar-wood oil. Hold the tube of dehydrating agent (from **4**) at an angle to the vertical. Very gently, pour cedar-wood oil down the side of the tube to form a lower layer. As the specimen clears it will sink in the cedar-wood oil.
**6** When specimen is clear, pipette off the bulk of the dehydrating agent and allow the remainder to evaporate.
**7** Pass the specimen quickly through xylene.
**8** Mount in D.P.X.

(*c*) *Parasitic nematode in nephridium.* See 'Rhabditis' (p. 167).

(vi) *Ovary.*

(*a*) *From preserved specimens:*

*Note:* The ovaries in preserved specimens stand out very clearly as two white triangles which may be picked up with forceps.

**1** Remove all extraneous tissue from the ovaries.
**2** Stains: borax carmine or haematoxylin.
(**3** After haematoxylin, blue in tap water.)
**4** Dehydrate in 2 ethoxy ethanol.
**5** Clear in xylene.
**6** Mount in D.P.X.

(*b*) *From fresh specimens.* *

**1** Dissect out and examine in water.
It is easier for the beginner to detach the ovary with a piece of septum, and to use the septum for handling with the forceps.
**2** Remove all traces of extraneous tissue.
(**3** If a stained preparation is required, stain in borax carmine or haematoxylin. After haematoxylin, blue the stain in tap water.)
**4** By means of a pipette, transfer to two drops of glycerol (50% aq.). (5 min)
**5** Add glycerol (pure) drop by drop. (15 min)
**6** Prepare a paper frame (see p. 58) and soak it first in water and then in glycerol.
**7** Transfer to pure glycerol enclosed by paper frame on slide.
**8** Cover.
**9** Seal with gold size.

(vii) *Seminal vesicles.*

(*a*)

**1** Smear a cover-slip with glycerol-egg albumen.
**2** Scrape some of the contents of the wall of the vesicula seminalis on to the prepared cover-slip and make a smear.

* After Green, *School Science Review,* **XV**, 408; March 1934.

**3** *Fix.* Schaudinn's fluid.
**4** Stain in Delafield's haematoxylin.
**5** Blue in alkaline alcohol.
**6** Dehydrate, clear and mount by the usual processes.

(*b*) Stain in Hofmann's violet (0.25%).

(*c*) See also Method 14 (p. 79). 'Monocystis' (pp. 147, 148) and 'Spermatozoa' (p. 171).

(viii) *Sections.* Stain in Delafield's haematoxylin.

(ix) *Wax-embedded sections.* See Method **(20B)** (p. 86).

### Lung*

*Preparation techniques*

(i)

**1** If possible obtain the lung from an animal killed by a blow on the head.
**2** Ligature trachea of dead animal and dissect out all contents of thoracic cavity in one piece.
**3** Fix all contents in 'corrosive-formaldehyde'. (12–48 h)
**4** Wash fixative out in usual way, cut lung into pieces ($\frac{1}{2}$ x $\frac{1}{2}$ x 1 cm) and place in alcohol (70%) covered by pad of cotton wool. (*Many days.*) The object is to get rid of air. As an alternative the material might be placed in alcohol and subjected to reduced pressure in a vacuum-embedding bath.

(ii) Stain in Heidenhain's iron haematoxylin and van Gieson's.

### Lycopersicum esculentum

*Squash of fruit.* See Method **3** (p. 74).

### Lymph Nodes

*Fix.* Zenker-formol.

Stains: Mallory's or silver technique for reticulin (p. 120).

### Lymphocytes

(i) See 'Blood' (pp. 108 ff).

(ii) *Lymphocyte count:* See 'Haemocytometer' (p. 223 ff).

* After Carleton, 1957, *Histological Technique,* University Press, Oxford.

**Macromysis**

*Preparation technique for Chromatophores.*

1 Remove the abdomen, leaving the first abdominal segment attached to the thorax.
2 Divide the abdomen into roughly equal dorsal and ventral parts by using a safety-razor blade to roll the abdomen so that either right or left side is uppermost and then pressing vertically downwards.
3 Remove the muscles from the inner surface of the *ventral* portion. Do this with two mounted needles and take care not to damage nerve cord or chromatophores in the body wall. Examine in drop of water on slide to see that result is satisfactory.
4 Dehydrate in alcohol (50%) and (70%). (2 min each)
5 Stain in light green SF yellowish in alcohol (90%). (10 min)
6 Dehydrate in alcohol (90%). (2 min)
7 Dehydrate in alcohol (100%). (2 min)
8 Dehydrate in fresh alcohol (100%). (2 min)
9 Clear in clove oil.
10 *Mount with other ventral surface uppermost,* D.P.X.

**Maltose**

See 'Sugars. Test for, (*d*) Maltose' (p. 174).

**Marine Organisms (Small)**

P
See 'Aquatic and Marine Animals, Small' (p. 103).

**Medusae**

See 'Obelia ii' (p. 153).

**Meiosis**

See 'Chromosomes, 2' (p. 118).

**Mesentery, Cement Substance in Cell Outlines**

See 'Epithelia iv' (p. 126).

**Mesophyll of Leaf**

See 'Leaf v' (p. 142).

**Mite on Anodon Gill**

See 'Atax ypsilophorus' (p. 104).

**Mitochondria**

(*a*) *Animal tissue:*
(i) *Champy-Kull method.*
1 *Fix.* Champy's fluid (p. 198). (Small pieces — 24 h)
2 Wash in distilled water. (Small pieces 30 min)
3 Place in:

Acetic acid (glacial) . . . . . . 25 ml
Chromium trioxide (1% aq.) . . . 50 ml

4 Wash in distilled water. (30 min)
5 Place in potassium dichromate (3% aq.) (72 h)
6 Wash in tap water (running). (24 h)
7 Dehydrate progressively up to alcohol (100%).
8 Clear in xylene.
9 Embed in paraffin-wax.
10 Section at 4–6 $\mu$m.
11 Attach sections to slide.
12 Remove wax with xylene.
13 Remove xylene with alcohol (100%).
14 Flood the slide with Altmann's acid fuchsin-anilin (p. 216).
15 Heat gently until the liquid steams.
16 Allow to cool and repeat the steaming and cooling process 2–3 times during 10 min.
17 Rinse in distilled water.
[18 If desired, counterstain in toluidine blue o (p. 251). (30–90 s)]
19 Wash in distilled water.
20 Differentiate in aurantia (*very poisonous*, see p. 190). (Few s)
21 Transfer to alcohol (90%) to arrest action of aurantia. (Examine under microscope and repeat differentiation if necessary)
22 Wash in alcohol (100%).
23 Clear in xylene.
24 Mount in D.P.X.

(ii) *Cowdry's method.*
**1–17** as (*a*) i **1–17**, above.
18 Stain in methyl green (1% aq.). (20–40 s)
19 Rinse in distilled water.
20 Examine under the microscope. If insufficiently stained, repeat **18** and **19** until the desired depth of stain is reached. If overstained, remove excess stain with alcohol (70%), examine and, if necessary, repeat **18** and **19**.
21 Dehydrate to alcohol (100%).

22 Clear in xylene.
23 Mount in D.P.X.
(iii) *Metzner's method.* *
Fix material in Helly's fluid (p. 227) or in Altmann's fluid (p. 187). Material fixed in Helly should be post-chromed in satd. potassium dichromate solution at 37°C for 48 h.

Dehydrate, embed in paraffin and cut sections as thin as possible (2 $\mu$).

1 Bring sections through xylene to abs. alcohol.
2 Wipe the bottom of the slide dry, place it on a tripod and flood the sections with a 20% solution of acid fuchsin in a satd. solution of anilin in water.
3 Heat the slide gently by passing the flame of a small Bunsen burner underneath it until vapour is seen rising from the stain.
4 Leave slide on the bench to cool for about 4 min.
5 Rinse stain away with a stream of distilled water.
6 Place slide in a mixture of satd. picric acid in abs. alc. 20 ml, 20% alcohol 80 ml. (1 min)
7 Place slide in a mixture of satd. pricric acid in abs. alc. 20 ml, 20% alcohol 140 ml. (1 min)
8 Rinse slide twice in fresh absolute alcohol. (10 sec in each)
9 Xylene.
10 Mount in D.P.X.

Mitochondria should be stained red, cytoplasm, pale yellow. Nucleoli and red blood corpuscles also colour red.

If this result is not achieved vary the times at stages **6** and **7** until it is. If the slide is examined at stage **9** and the differentiation has not proceeded far enough, it is possible to return through absolute alcohol to stage **7** and continue differentiation. If the slide has been over-differentiated then the slide must be thrown away and another stained using shorter periods in stages **6** and **7**.

(*b*) *Plant tissue:*
1 *Fix.* Zirkle's fluid (p. 253).
2 Wash thoroughly.
3 Usual processes to embedding.
4 Usual processes to remove wax, xylene, alcohol, to water.
5 Place in potassium permanganate (1% aq.). (5 min)
6 Transfer to oxalic acid (3% aq.). (2–3 min)
7 Stain in Heidenhain's iron alum-haematoxylin.
8 Usual processes to mounting in D.P.X.

* Modified by Dr. J. R. Baker, F.R.S. from the original technique.

**Mitosis**

See 'Chromosomes, 1' (p. 115).

**Molluscs**

See 'Aquatic and Marine Animals' (p. 103); 'Anodon' (p. 102); 'Helix' (p. 138).

**Monocotyledon Stem**

(i) See 'Plant Tissue' (pp. 158–161).
(ii) Stain in Hanstein's fuchsin-violet.

**Monocystis lumbrici**

*Adult and stages of life-history.*
**S/C**
Seminal vesicles and attached to funnels of vasa efferentia of freshly gathered earthworms.
(i) *Kill* earthworms in alcohol (70%). (5–10 min)
(ii) *To find adults.* Remove a whole seminal vesicle; squash it *gently* on a slide under a cover-slip and then wash away the debris. *Monocystis* will usually be found clinging to the vasa efferentia.
(iii) Remove a portion of seminal vesicle and slit it open on a slide. Gently scrape the inner surface with a scalpel and mix the solid and fluid material.

*Preparation techniques*

1. *Quick method* * – *Useful in examinations.*
1 Make a smear of seminal vesicle on a slide.
2 Dry by waving in warm air.
3 Stain by pouring Delafield's haematoxylin onto the slide. (Several min.)
4 Wash in tap water or alkaline-water (p. 188).
5 Dry by waving in the air.
6 Mount in D.P.X.

2. Carry out all processes on a cover-slip and use covered watch-glasses for the various liquids.
1 Place a drop of the liquid, etc., from the seminal vesicles on a square cover-slip.

* Suggested by G. S. Sellick, Highgate School, London.

2 Make an additional smear on another cover-slip by gently drawing the first, flat across the second.
3 Proceed as in process **4** onwards under 'Peranema' (p. 156), but note processes:
   **10** Differentiate until cytoplasm and nuclei in developing spermatozoa are well contrasted;
   **11** After washing in alkaline alcohol – twice, if necessary – the blue should be clear and without any purple.
4 Before mounting and sealing make sure that any stages of development particularly required are present.

3. See Method 14 (p. 79).

4. *Especially useful for trophozoites.*

*Note:* The cover-slip should be held in a slit in a match-stick, and NOT in the fingers, nor in metal forceps.

1 Smear contents of seminal vesicle of freshly killed earthworm, very thinly, on a clean cover-slip.
2 *Fix.* Mercuric-acetic [solution (*b*) (p. 233)] by *quickly* inverting the cover-slip in the fixative. (2 min)
3 Wash in distilled water. (2 min)
4 Dehydrate in alcohol (30%) and (50%). (2 min each)
5 Remove fixative in alcohol (70%) to which a few drops of iodine solution have been added. If colour disappears add more iodine. (Till colour remains – about 2 min)
6 Dehydrate in alchol (70%). (2 min)
7 Stain in borax carmine. (10 min)
8 Rinse in alcohol (70%). (Quickly)
9 Differentiate in acid alcohol. (Care – till bright pink)
10 Wash in alcohol (70%). (Thoroughly – but quickly)
11 Dehydrate in alcohol (100%). (5 min)
12 Clear in clove oil. (3 min)
13 Pass through xylene. (Quickly)
14 Mount in D.P.X.

[Pseudo-navicellae (→ unstained); larger trophozoites (→ pink with clearly defined nuclei); smaller trophozoites can be found in sperm morulae under high power.] *

* Adapted from *School Science Review,* XVII, 66, 297; December 1935. From Department of Zoology, University of Glasgow.

5. See 'Protozoa' (p. 164).

**Monocystis magna (Trophozoites)**

**S/C**

Remove the roof of the *seminal vesicles* of an earthworm. The four ciliated funnels of the vasa efferentia should now be exposed. Wash with saline delivered from a pipette. The attached trophozoites appear as white threads.

*Preparation technique*

1 Remove a portion of one of the funnels of the vasa efferentia to which the trophozoites are attached.
2 *Fix.* Warm Schaudinn's fluid (60°–70°C).
3 Proceed as from **5** in *Monocystis lumbrici* Method 4 (above).

**Mosquito**

See 'Insects; Preparation Techniques (i) and (ii)' (pp. 140, 141).

*Aedes – 4th instar larva, for imaginal discs.*

1 *Fix.* Larva in formol-acetic-alcohol (ii, Bles's formula)(p. 215).
2 Cut off the head and the end of the abdomen bearing the siphon.
3 Turn the animal on its back and make a median, vertical, longitudinal cut to divide it into two halves.
4 With a needle, remove the gut from the thorax.
5 Stain in alcoholic haematoxylin (p. 221). (2 min)
6 Differentiate in acid alcohol.
7 Wash in alcohol (70%).
8 Blue in alkaline alcohol.
9 Dehydrate in alcohol (90%) and (100%). (2 min each)
10 Dehydrate in fresh alcohol (100%). (2 min)
11 Clear in xylene.
12 Mount one half with external surface uppermost, the other half with the internal surface uppermost, in D.P.X.

**Mosses**

**MP**

Do not fix before sectioning. Stored material may be softened in glycerol.

*Suitable stains.*

Delafield's haematoxylin; Magdala red and aniline blue ws. Whole leaves may be mounted in Faure's gum chloral (p. 220).

**Moulds**

**S/C**
See 'Culture Media 3' (pp. 203–208).

*Preparation technique*
See 'Fungi Preparation technique (vi)' (p. 130).

**Mucin**

(i)
1 Stain in Carazzi's haematoxylin.
2 'Blue' in tap water.
3 Rinse in distilled water.
4 Stain in Mayer's mucicarmine (cold). (20 min)
5 Wash in distilled water.
[6 Counterstain in metanil yellow. (½ min)]
[7 Rinse in distilled water.]
8 Dehydrate. (Quickly)
9 Clear in xylene.
10 Mount in D.P.X.
Omit stages **6** and **7** if desired.

(ii) *PAS method.*
Most mucins are strongly coloured by this technique. See carbohydrates (p. 112).

(iii) *Alcian Blue**
1 Bring paraffin sections through xylene and alcohols to water.
2 Stain 20 min in a fresh solution of 1% Alcian blue 8GX in 3% acetic acid.
3 Rinse 3% acetic acid.
4 Rinse distilled water.
5 Stain nuclei if desired in 1% neutral red (30 s).
6 Dehydrate in alcohols, clear xylene.
7 Mount in D.P.X.

Acid mucins are coloured a strong blue or blue-green.

**Mucor**

**S/C**
See 'Culture Media 3' (pp. 203–208).

*Preparation technique*
(i) *Mt.* Dip a portion rapidly in alcohol (70%) and mount in dilute glycerol.

* After H. F. Steedman, 1950. *Quart J. micr. Sci.*, **91**, 477.

(ii) *Hyphae. Temp. stains.*
(*a*) *Protoplasm.* Iodine and basic fuchsin.
(*b*) *Cell wall.* Schulz's soln. (→ violet).

(iii) As 'Fungi Preparation techniques (vi)' (p. 130).

**Muscle**

*Fix.* Formol-saline (5%).
Do not impregnate with paraffin for longer than 1 h or the tissue will be hardened.

*Suitable stains*
Haematoxylin and eosin Y (→ pink); van Gieson's (with or without iron haematoxylin (→ yellow); Mallory's (→ red); borax carmine; picric acid (may be preceded by haematoxylin); Heidenhain's iron haematoxylin.

*Striated muscle:* See Method **18** (p. 83).
*Unstriated muscle:* See Method **19** (p. 83).

**Mushroom**

See 'Fungi' (p. 130).

**Mussel**

See 'Anodon' (p. 102).

**Myelin Sheaths**

*Luxol Fast Blue technique* (after Kluver and Barrera*)
1 Bring sections of material fixed in formalin through xylene to absolute alcohol.
2 Stain in 0.1% Luxol Fast Blue MBS in 95% alcohol (6–18 h at 60°C).
3 Rinse 70% alcohol.
4 Wash in water.
5 Differentiate in 0.05% aq. lithium carbonate. (½–2 h)
6 Wash in water.
7 Counterstain nuclei if required in 1% aq. neutral red. (1 min)
8 Rinse in water; dehydrate in alcohols, clear in xylene.
9 Mount in D.P.X.

Myelin sheaths are coloured a deep blue.

**Mysis**

See 'Amphioxus (vi) *Whole Specimens*' (p. 97).

* Kluver, H. and Barrera, E. 1953. *J. Neuropath exp. Neurol.*, **12**, 400.

**Mytilus**

See 'Anodon' (p. 102).

**Nail**

See 'Skin' (p. 170).

*Suitable stains*

Haematoxylin and eosin Y (→ bright pink); iron haematoxylin and van Gieson's (→ black); Mallory's (→ bright red).

**Nematodes**

**S/C**

(i) See 'Ascaris' (p. 104) and 'Rhabditis' (p. 167).
(ii) *Proleptus* sp. found in intestine of *Scyllium.*

*Preparation techniques*
*Rapid examination.*

1 Kill in alcohol (90%).
2 Alcohol (100%). (30 min)
3 Clear in beechwood creosote BP.

*Unstained preparations.*

(*a*)

1 Wash in sodium chloride (1% aq.).
2 Fix in boiling alcohol (70%). (On water bath)
3 Store in fresh alcohol (70%).
4 Place in a tube containing the following mixture:
   Alcohol (100%) . . . . . . . . 70 ml
   Glycerol (5%) . . . . . . . . . 30 ml
   (In an oven at 60°C (24–48 h) till alcohol and water have evaporated)
5 Examine in pure glycerol.
6 Mount in glycerol-jelly.

*To roughen cuticle before staining:* Potassium hydroxide (5%). (2–4 h)

*Stained preparations*
*Note:* Nematodes are difficult to stain.

(*a*)

1 Either
   Kill and fix in a hot mixture of:
   Mercuric chloride (satd. aq.) . . . 100 ml
   Alcohol (95%) . . . . . . . . 100 ml
   Acetic acid (glacial) . . . . . . . 1 ml
   or
   Treat for 24 hours or longer with eau de Labarraque (p. 211), commercial soln. diluted with 4–6 vols. water, or used undiluted and hot for a short time.
2 Stains: Borax carmine; Mayer's carmalum (small specimens); picric acid.

(*b*) Use the method suggested for 'Amphioxus (vi), Whole Specimens' (p. 97), but stain in Mayer's alcoholic cochineal (p. 200).

See 'Ascaris' (p. 104) and 'Proleptus' (p. 163).

**Nereis**

**P**

Alcohol (70%).

*Preparation techniques*
*Prostomial palps; peristomial tentacles (for sensory apparatus).*

1 Kill the animal by placing it in sea water and gently raising the temperature to 30–35°C.
2 Allow the tissues to relax by keeping the dead animal in warm sea water overnight.
3 Remove the head.
4 Stain in intra-vitam (reduced) methylene blue in sea water, in a specimen tube. (3–4 min)
   Reduced methylene blue soln. (p. 235) 0.5 ml
   Clean sea water . . . . . . 10 ml
5 Examine in a watch-glass of sea water under the microscope. Tissue should appear speckled blue.
6 With a very sharp scalpel, remove a palp.
7 Mount in a drop of sea water, and cover.

[Nerve tissue (→ deep blue)
*Note:* Colour disappears fairly quickly.]

*Parapodium*

1 With a *sharp* scalpel, or razor blade, remove a whole, undamaged segment from a preserved *Nereis.*
2 Stains: borax carmine; borax carmine-picric acid aq. or alc. (About 15 min)
3 Differentiate in acid alcohol. (Until bright and transparent)
4 Dehydrate in alcohol (90%). (10 min)
5 Dehydrate in alcohol (100%). (10 min)
6 Dehydrate in fresh alcohol (100%). (10 min)
7 Clear in xylene (*fairly long time*); or clove oil (*very long time*).
8 Under a lens, cut the parapodia and any attached tissue away from the segment.
9 Using a raised cover-slip, mount in D.P.X.

**Nerve Collar, Helix**

See 'Helix' (p. 138).

## Nerve Tissue

*Note:* Nerve tissue varies to such a degree with different locations that it is impossible here to give detailed methods. For these refer to a larger work on animal histology. The following must be regarded as very bare suggestions:

(i) *To emphasize nerve tissue during a dissection.* Flood the area with picric acid (satd. aq.) and wash under tap.

(ii) *Fix.* 1% Ammonium dichromate; Formaldehyde (10%); Müller's fluid (*daily changes for several weeks*).

*Preparation techniques*

(i) *Suitable stains.*

(*a*) *General work.* Methylene blue; van Gieson's after picric acid fixation.

(*b*) *Axis cylinders.* * Haematoxylin and eosin Y (→ mauve); iron haematoxylin and van Gieson's (→ grey); Mallory's (→ red).

(*c*) *Neuroglia fibres.* * Haematoxylin and eosin Y (→ pink to mauve); iron haematoxylin and van Gieson's (→ yellow); (Mallory's (→ red).

(*d*) *Spinal cord.* Borax carmine; haematoxylin.

(ii) *Method for nerve axons.* †

**1** Fix the tissue in mercuric-formaldehyde (p. 233).
*Note:* Tissues may remain in this fixative for months without harm; or, if desired, they may be transferred to formol-saline for storage.

**2** Refer to Method **20** and **20A** (p. 85), and carry out all the processes from process **3** up to and including process **7** (removal of wax from sections).
*Note:* Material should be sectioned at about 25 μm.

**3** Hydrate sections on slide down to alcohol (70%).

**4** Transfer to iodine [0.5% in alcohol (70%)]. (10 min)

**5** Transfer to sodium thiosulphate (0.1% aq.). (Until sections are colourless)

**6** Wash in running tap water. (10 min)

**7** Wash in distilled water. (Two changes)

**8** Transfer to silver nitrate (A.R. quality). (20% aq.). (2 h, or overnight)
*Note:* This solution may be used repeatedly.

**9** Wash in distilled water. (3 changes during 10 min)

**10** Impregnate with buffered silver nitrate/pyridine solution (Special formula (*c*) ii, p. 248) using not less than 20 ml of solution for each slide, *in thoroughly clean vessels.* (24 h at 37°C)
*Note:* Silver and gold solutions are very sensitive to light. *If any cloudiness or precipitate appears at any stage in this impregnating process the solution must be regarded as contaminated and must be rejected.*

**11** Remove slide(s) and shake off superfluous solution.

**12** Transfer to hydroquinone/sodium sulphite reducing solution. (Special formula iii, p. 228.) (Not less than 2 min at 25°C)

**13** Wash in running tap water. (3 min)
*Note: The slides must be kept separated, otherwise the reducing solution will be carried over.*

**14** Rinse in distilled water.
If desired, leave in distilled water until convenient to proceed to:

**15** Tone in gold chloride solution (p. 220). (3 min)
*Note:* (i) Refer to cautionary note under process **10**, above.
(ii) If the sections are still brown at the end of 3 min, continue the toning process.

**16** Rinse quickly in distilled water.

**17** Transfer to oxalic acid (2% aq.). (2–10 min)
*Note:* (i) Examine the slides under the microscope at intervals during this process. *Treatment should stop when the axons are blue-black.*
(ii) Over-treatment may result in diminution of contrast.

**18** Rinse in distilled water.

**19** Transfer to sodium thiosulphate (5% aq.). (5 min)

**20** Wash in tap water. (10 min)

**21** Rinse in distilled water.

**22** Dehydrate to alcohol (100%).

**23** Clear in xylene.

**24** Mount in D.P.X.

**25** Seal.

**26** Label.

(iii) *Method for nuclei, axons, dendrites in spinal cord.*

**1** Smear grey matter from fresh spinal cord on cover-slip.

*After Hartridge and Haynes, 1936, *Histology for Medical Students*, Oxford.

† After W. Holmes, Department of Zoology, University Museum, Oxford, from the *Proceedings of the Neuropathological Club*, July 1952.

2 Fix in alcohol (95%).
3 Stain in warm Nissl's methylene blue, or methylene blue (1% alc.).
4 Wash in alcohol (95%).

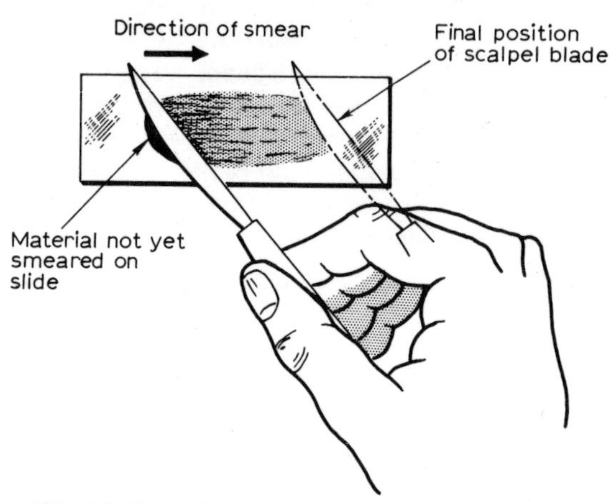


Fig. 6.6 Method of making a smear on a slide with a scalpel blade.

5 Wash in alcohol (100%). (2 min)
6 Clear in benzene-phenol.
7 Mount in D.P.X.

**Nitella**

Stains: Iodine and basic fuchsin.

**Nuclei**

*Fix.* Acetic acid (1%).

*Suitable stains for temporary mounts*

(i) *Animal.*
Iodine (for unfixed tissue). Specially useful for squamous epithelium from cheek.
(ii) *Animal and Plant.*
Iron aceto-carmine.

*Suitable stains for permanent mounts*

(i) *Animal.*
Haematoxylin and eosin Y (→ blue); iron haematoxylin and van Gieson's (→ black); Mallory's (→ red); Mayer's acid haemalum; aceto-carmine aq. (stains and fixes; differentiate in water); Heidenhain's haematoxylin (→ dark blue); Leishman's (→ red); Loeffler's methylene blue.
(ii) *Plant.*
Hofmann's violet (0.002%); methyl green; safranin O; crystal violet and Gram's iodine, counterstained with orange G in clove oil; borax carmine; Hanstein's fuchsin-violet (→ red); Renaut's eosin Y-haematoxylin.
(iii) *Animal and Plant.*
Acetic-iodine green; Delafield's or Heidenhain's haematoxylin; eosin Y; safranin O; methylene blue.

**Nucleic Acids**

(i) *Ribonucleic and Deoxyribonucleic acids.*
See Method **23** (p. 91) for pyronin/malachite green technique.

(ii) *Feulgen Technique for Deoxyribonucleic acid (DNA)*

1 Bring paraffin sections to water, treating with iodine and sodium thiosulphate solutions if a mercury-containing fixative was used.
2 Wash in running water. (2 min)
3 Hydrolyse DNA by placing slides in N hydrochloric acid maintained at 60°C. (Time varies according to fixative used; see notes)
4 Rinse in distilled water.
5 Place in Schiff's reagent (p. 245). (1½ h)
6 Drain and rinse in 3 changes of sulphurous acid solution (p. 250). (2 min each)
7 Wash in running water. (5 min)
8 Counterstain cytoplasm if desired in 0.25% light green in 70% alcohol. (c. 15s)
9 Dehydrate quickly through 70%, 95%, abs. alcohol.
10 Clear in xylene and mount in D.P.X.

DNA is coloured in shades of reddish purple.

*Note:* The following hydrolysis times may be tried initially.

| | | | |
|---|---|---|---|
| Formalin | 8 min | Helly | 8 min |
| Carnoy | 6 min | Chrome acetic | 14 min |
| Zenker | 5 min | Champy | 25 min |
| Susa | 18 min | | |

**Nyctotherus**

**S/C**
Rectum of *Rana.*

*Preparation techniques*

(i) See 'Protozoa' (p. 164).
(ii) See 'Peranema' (p. 156) but before proceeding

make sure by microscopic examination that the fluid *does* contain *Nyctotherus* in addition to *Opalina*. Note process **10**: Make sure that the cytoplasm is almost colourless after differentiation; and in process **11** make sure that the preparation becomes thoroughly blue.

### Obelia

**S/C**

(i) Suppliers.
(ii) Hydroids attached to seaweeds in rock pools.
(iii) Medusoids obtained by tow-net.

*Preparation techniques*

(i) *Hydroids*

(*a*)

**1** Narcotize in menthol (a few crystals sprinkled on the surface of the water in a watch-glass).
**2** Fix in alcohol (70%); or formaldehyde (5%); or mercuric chloride (sat. aq.).
**3** Wash thoroughly. (Washing agent depends on fixative and subsequent stain)
**4** Stains: Nigrosin ws (peculiarly superior to any other stain); borax carmine; Hanstein's fuchsin-violet.
**5** Wash in alcohol (50%).
**6** Differentiate in acid alcohol (e.g., if using borax carmine, until pale bright pink).
**7** Dehydrate in alcohol (90%). (About 5 min)
**8** Dehydrate in alcohol (100%). (About 5 min)
**9** Dehydrate again in alcohol (100%). (About 5 min)
**10** Clear in xylene
**11** Mount in D.P.X.
**12** Cover with a raised cover-slip (pp. 58, 59).

(*b*) See Method suggested for 'Hydractinia (i) Whole Mount' (p. 139).

(ii) *Medusae.*

*Note:*

(*a*) This preparation provides a good test for mastery of staining and differentiation.

(*b*) Avoid crushing and folding. Pick up with a wide-mouthed pipette held vertically.

(*c*) Do *not* attempt to transfer medusae from dish to dish. Instead, use only one watch-glass and add, and remove, successive liquids by means of a pipette.

**1** As for *Hydroid* i (*a*) **2** (above).
**2** As for *Hydroid* i (*a*) **3** (above).
**3** Stain in borax carmine. (About 15 min)
**4–8** As for *Hydroid* i (*a*) **5–9.**
**9** Clear in clove oil by the following method:
**9a** Prepare a 50/50: : alc. (100%)/clove oil mixture in quantity sufficient to half-fill a medium-sized specimen tube.
**9b** Run down the inside of the tilted tube of mixture first, a little clove oil (to form a layer under the mixture), and then a little alc. (100%), (to form a layer above the mixture).
**9c** Using the method suggested above, transfer the dehydrated specimens from the alc. (100%) to the specimen tube.
*Leave the tube corked.* (About 1 h)
**9d** When the specimens have sunk to the bottom of the tube pipette off the liquid.
**10** Mount in D.P.X.; use a raised cover-slip (see pp. 58, 59).

(iii) *To show otocysts.*
Overstain heavily and differentiate.
*Note:* Otoliths destroyed by acid in differentiation.

### Oedogonium

(i) Fix in formol-acetic-alcohol.
(ii) See 'Algae' (p. 94).

### Oils

See 'Fats and Oils' (p. 128).

### Onion

(i) *Epidermis of leaf.*
See Methods **1** and **2** (p. 73).
(ii) *Root tips.*
See 'Chromosomes Method (iii)' (p. 116), and Method **2** (p. 73).

### Opalina

**S/C**

Rectum of *Rana.*

*Preparation techniques*

(i) See 'Protozoa (i)' (p. 164).
(ii) *To see nuclei:* Fix and stain with acetic-methyl-green.
(iii) See 'Peranema' (p. 156).

*Other suitable stains*

Borax carmine; safranin o.

**Orthoptera**

*Testis (for chromosomes).*
See 'Chromosomes (iv); (v); 2 (*a*)' (pp. 117, 118)

**Oscillatoria animalis**

**S/C**
See 'Culture Media 3' (p. 203).

**Ova**

See 'Rana' (p. 165), and 'Echinus' (p. 124).

**Ovary**

*Fix.* * Bouin's fluid; formol-saline (4%); mercuric-formaldehyde.
*Suitable stains.* * Haematoxylin and eosin Y ; Mallory's (after-mercuric-formaldehyde).
Clear in benzene-phenol or cedar-wood oil.
*Of Lumbricus.* See 'Lumbricus (vi)' (p. 145).

**Oxyntic Cells of Stomach Lining**

*Suitable stains.* † Haematoxylin and eosin Y (→ bright pink); iron haematoxylin and van Gieson's (→ yellow); Mallory's (→ orange).

**Pancreas**

See 'Salivary Gland' (p. 168).

**Pandorina morum**

**S/C**
See 'Culture Media 3' (p. 203).

**Paragonimus**

Mayer's paracarmine (p. 197).

**Paramecium**

**S/C**
(i) Dealers. On arrival, allow the tube of culture to stand for 1 hour, undisturbed. Pipette off a small quantity of culture from the *surface* of the liquid, and examine under the microscope (low-power objective; light stopped down). If the culture is alive, it may be propagated. [See 'Protozoa' (p. 164).] Feed by placing three or four boiled wheat grains in the Petri dish. Do *not* overfeed.
For further culture transfer the thickened, Petri dish culture to a glass jar (15 cm x 10 cm x 5 cm) three parts filled with hay infusion [see (iii), below] .*
(ii) Bolting-silk tow-net dragged in ponds and ditches. Examine silt.
(iii) *Hay infusion.* Boil some chopped hay in water. Add to the cooled liquid a little dry, chopped hay. Bacteria appear first, then *Colpidium*, then *Paramecium.* Avoid breaking surface scum, and subculture *twice every three months.*
(iv) See 'Culture Media 3' (p. 203).
(v) *Paramecium bursaria:* See 'Culture Media 3' (p. 203).

*Preparation techniques*
(i) *General Methods.* See 'Protozoa v' (p. 165). Suitable stains are methyl green; acetic-carmine; borax carmine; fast green FCF; iron haematoxylin.
(ii) *To see meganucleus.* Place a drop of culture on a slide and add a drop of acetic-carmine or acetic-methyl-green.
*Note:* The meganucleus tends to obscure the micronucleus.
(iii) *To see food vacuoles.* Irrigate on the slide with Indian ink or with *very* dilute neutral red.
(iv) *To see digestive changes.* Make a suspension of yeast stained with Congo red. Place a drop of the *Paramecium* culture on a slide and add two drops of the yeast suspension. Food vacuoles coloured blue indicate an acid content; those coloured red, an alkaline content.
(v) *To see defaecation.* Feed with Indian ink.
(vi) *To see contractile vacuole movement.* Cover with a *small* piece of cover-slip and allow to become almost dry by sucking out most of the water with a piece of filter-paper.
(vii) *To discharge trichocysts.* Irrigate with tannic acid (1% aq.), or with iodine (*very* dilute).
(viii) *To stain trichocysts, etc.* Use *extremely* dilute methyl green.

* After Carleton, 1936, *Histological Technique,* University Press, Oxford.
† After Hartridge and Haynes, 1936, *Histology for Medical Students,* University Press, Oxford.

* Adapted from *Gerrard's Bulletin,* June 1939. T. Gerrard & Co.

(ix) *To see the pellicular lattice; Bresslau's method.*

**1** Place a drop of culture on a slide and add one drop of anilin blue ws (3% aq.).
**2** Use a second slide to mix the two drops and spread them to make a film having an area approximately, but not greater than, that of a cover-slip.
**3** Dry rapidly. (A hair-dryer is useful for this purpose.)
**4** Place a drop of D.P.X. on the film.
**5** Cover with a cover-slip and allow to dry.

*Note:* The animals will be distorted and the pellicular lattice, which becomes visible by reason of stain held in the hollows between the ridges, will not appear uniform.

(x) *To see the basal granules and connecting fibrils in cilia: Klein's method.*

**1** Place a drop of culture on a slide and spread it out.
**2** Dry rapidly. (A hair dryer is useful.)
**3** Stain in silver nitrate (2% aq.). (6–8 min)
**4** Wash in distilled water. (Thoroughly)
**5** Place in distilled water in a porcelain dish either in sunlight, or under an ultra-violet lamp. (Until the silver nitrate is reduced and the preparation appears brown; about 20 min under ultra-violet lamp.)
**6** Dry in the air.
**7** Place a drop of D.P.X. on the film.
**8** Cover.

### Parapodia, Nereis

See 'Nereis' (p. 50).

### Parasites in Blood

(i) Stains:* Leishman's or Giemsa's (→ blue with ruby red chromatin).
(ii) See 'Blood Methods (v) and (vi and vii)' (pp. 109–110).

### Patella

**MP**

*Kill and fix.* Formaldehyde (10%). This solution will preserve specimens indefinitely.

### Pectic Substances (Mucilage; Gums)

*Suitable stains*

Ruthenium red; neutral violet (0.01% aq.) (→ brown-red).

Mountants: Glycerol; glycerol-jelly; D.P.X.

See also 'Gums' (p. 137).

*Pectin in middle lamella of leaf.*

**S/C**

Sections should be cut from a fleshy root such as that of a carrot or turnip.

*Preparation techniques*

(i)

**1** Place sections in alcoholic hydrochloric acid: (24 h)

| | |
|---|---|
| Alcohol (100%) . . . . | 75 ml |
| Hydrochloric acid (conc.). | 25 ml |

*Note:* The pectin is converted to pectic acid, which is insoluble in alcohol.

**2** Wash in distilled water.
**3** Transfer to ammonium oxalate (0.5%). (24 h)

*Note:* The pectic acid is converted to ammonium pectate, which is soluble; and the calcium to calcium oxalate, which is insoluble.

**4** Mount in ammonium oxalate solution.
**5** On tapping the slide, the cells fall apart.

(ii)

**1** Warm sections in sodium hydroxide (dil.).
**2** Wash in tap water.
**3** Stains: methylene blue or ruthenium red.

[Cellulose (→ unstained); pectin of middle lemella (→ stained).]

### Pellia

*Capsules.* Use the method suggested for *Pinus* pollen (p. 157).

### Penicillium

**S/C**

Dox's agar (p. 204).

*Preparation techniques*

Mounting: Dip a portion rapidly in alcohol (70%) and mount in dilute glycerol.

As Fungi Method (vi) (p. 132).

### Pennaria

*Whole mount.*

See 'Hydractinia, Whole Mount' (p. 139).

### Pennatula

*Kill.* Alcohol (70%).

*Fix and preserve.* Formaldehyde (5%).

*After Hartridge and Haynes, 1936, *Histology for Medical Students,* University Press, Oxford.

**Peranema**

*Nucleus and flagellum*

1 Smear a clean cover-slip, thinly, with glycerol-egg albumen.
2 With a needle spread a small drop of culture, thinly, over the surface of the prepared cover-slip. Use the edge of a piece of clean filter-paper to remove any surplus fluid.
3 Place the cover-slip, *face upwards,* on a clean slide. Taking care not to let the objective touch the fluid, examine under a microscope to make sure *Peranema* are present.
4 Fix in warm (60°–70°C) Schaudinn's fluid in a watch-glass. Place the cover-slip, *face downwards,* on the surface of the fixative. (5 min)
5 Invert and submerge the cover-slip in the fixative. (10 min)
6 Dehydrate in alcohol (50%). Keep the cover-slip *face upwards.* (2 min)
7 Dehydrate in alcohol (70%). Keep the cover-slip *face upwards.* (2 min)
8 Transfer to iodine (alcoholic) (i, p. 229). (2 min)
9 Stain in haematoxylin (alcoholic) (p. 221). (10 min)
10 Differentiate in acid alcohol. (Watch under microscope.) (Quickly)
11 As soon as the cytoplasm is pale, transfer the cover-slip to alkaline alcohol. (2 min)
12 Dehydrate in alcohol (90%). (2 min)
13 Dehydrate in alcohol (100%) (twice). (2 min each)
14 Clear in 50/50 alcohol (100%)/xylene. (2 min)
15 Clear in xylene. (2 min)
16 Mount in D.P.X. Place a drop of D.P.X. on the centre of a slide and very gently lower the inverted cover-slip, one edge first, the other supported by a needle, on to the slide.
17 Leave the preparation in a warm place to harden.
18 Gently clean the surface of the cover-slip.

**Periplaneta**

**S/C**

(i) Dealers.
(ii) Bakehouses by a suitable trap, with hinged top. Supply with water, bread, butter or other fat, bacon rind, and shelter from light.
*To kill.* Place in closed vessel of chloroform or drop into boiling water.

*Preparation techniques*

(i) *Mouth parts.*
(*a*) *To remove flesh.* Boil in dilute sodium hydroxide (2%). CARE. (Not more than 5 min)
(*b*) Stain: As well unstained; but if it is desired to see the muscle tissue, do *not* boil in sodium hydroxide, but stain in picro-carmine.
(*c*) See also 'Insects i (c)' (p. 140).

(ii) *Trachea.*
*Suitable stains* borax carmine followed by picric acid (alc. or aq.) or methylene blue; picro-carmine.
Mountants: Glycerol-jelly or D.P.X.

(iii) *Salivary gland.*
1 Remove on to cover-slip below water to prevent collapse.
2 *Fix.* Alcohol (70%).
3 Stains: borax carmine; Delafield's haematoxylin.
4 Dehydrate thoroughly.
5 Mount in D.P.X.

(iv) *Fat body.*
Stain in borax carmine.

(v) *Leg muscle.*
Stains: van Gieson's; borax carmine.

(vi) *Whole mount.*
Embed in resin. See 'Technique of Resin Embedding' (p. 69).

**Peronosporaceae**

*Fix.* Alcohol (70%) and wash in water; or chrom-acetic, and wash in running water. (6–12 h)

*Free-hand sections.*

(*a*)
1 Wash sections of herbaceous material in distilled water.
2 Stain in phenol-thionin. (5–8 min)
3 Wash in distilled water.
4 Dehydrate in alcohol (95%). (2 min)
5 Differentiate in orange G. (5 min)
[Saturated solution of orange G in alcohol (100%).]
6 Wash thoroughly in alcohol (100%).
7 Clear in xylene.
8 Mount in D.P.X.

[Parasitic fungus (→ violet-purple); cellulose walls (→ yellow or green); lignified tissue (→ blue).]

*Note:* By taking out of orange G, back to water the parasite is shown against unstained walls.

(*b*) See 'Plant Tissue II (*a*)' (p. 159).

*Wax-embedded sections.*

See 'Fungi (x)'. Staining with safranin o and fast green FCF, as method (x) (*a*) (p. 134); and 'Rusts' (p. 168).

**Peziza**

**S/C**
See 'Culture Media 3' (p. 203).

**Phloem**

*Suitable stains*

(i) *General.* Methyl green (→ blue).
(ii) *Bast fibres.* Hanstein's fuchsin-violet (→ deep red).
(iii) *Bast parenchyma.* Hanstein's fuchsin-violet (→ hardly stained).
(iv) *Callose.* Anilin blue ws (dissolves from cell walls in glycerol).
(v) *Sieve Plates.* Anilin blue ws; Delafield's haematoxylin.
(vi) *Sieve Tubes.* Hanstein's fuchsin-violet (→ hardly stained); eosin Y (alc.).

**Phytophthora**

**S/C**
Potato agar (p. 204).

**Pilobus**

**S/C**
See 'Culture Media 3' (p. 203).

**Pinnotheres**

**S/C**
In mantle cavity of *Mytilus,* and in Ascidians.

**Pinus**

*Pollen*

1 Build up of a ring of asphalt varnish on a slide.
2 Fill the cavity with anilin blue ws-lactophenol (p. 189).
3 Place the pollen grains within the cavity.
4 Cover with a cover-slip. (Leave for 2 d)
*Note:* During this period the preparation may be regarded as semi-permanent and treated accordingly.
5 Seal the preparation with asphalt varnish.

**Pituitary***

*Fix.* Formol-saline (5%); mercuric-formaldehyde.
*Suitable stains.* Haematoxylin and eosin Y; eosin Y and Borrel's methylene blue (p. 234); Mallory's (after mercuric-formaldehyde).

* After Carleton, 1936, *Histological Technique,* University Press, Oxford.

**Planaria***

1 Narcotize in:

| | |
|---|---|
| Ethyl alcohol (100%) . . . . | 10 ml |
| Distilled water . . . . . . | 90 ml |

(Few min – 1 h)

*Notes:*
(i) Narcotization must *not* be sudden. The animal must, as it were, be taken unawares Therefore, *add the alcohol to the medium in which the animal is living, in small quantities, at intervals, very gradually.*
(ii) Small specimens may be narcotized on a square cover-slip previously coated with paraffin-wax.
(iii) Large specimens may be narcotized in a dish.

2 *Fix.* Warm (30–60°C) Bouin's fluid. (12 h)

*Notes:*
(i) Warming helps to counteract contraction.
(ii) *Small specimens on cover-slips:*
**(a)** Cover the specimen with *thin* tissue paper folded back over the square cover-slip.
**(b)** Invert the cover-slip in Bouin's fluid.
(iii) *Large specimens:*
**(a)** Lift out of the dish of narcotic on a slide. (The less the specimens are moved about the better).
**(b)** Cover the slide with *thin* tissue paper and hold everything in position by binding round lightly with knitting wool.
**(c)** Immerse in Bouin's fluid.

3 Dehydrate:
**(a)** First remove the tissue paper, *but only if it comes away easily.* Do nothing to warrant unnecessary handling.
**(b)** Transfer small specimens on the cover-slip (with any adherent tissue paper) and large specimens to alcohol (70%). (24 h)
**(c)** Transfer to alcohol (90%). (24 h)
**(d)** Transfer to alcohol (100%). (Two changes over 12 h)

4 Clear:
**(a)** Transfer specimens to a specimen tube about one quarter full of alcohol (100%).

* This method may also be used for other small animals, e.g. *Hydra,* with modifications of the narcotization and fixation processes. See also 'Fasciola' (p. 127).

**(b)** By means of a pipette, place a similar volume of cedar-wood oil in the bottom of the tube, under the alcohol.

**(c)** As the specimens clear, so they will sink to the bottom of the tube.

**(d)** When this stage is reached, pipette off the alcohol and leave for 3–4 h.

**(e)** Transfer to fresh cedar-wood oil and leave till required for mounting.

**5** Mount in D.P.X.

*Notes:*

(i) Small specimens are best first placed in a drop of resin on a cover-slip which is then inverted in a small drop of resin on the slide.

(ii) Large specimens should be mounted in a cavity first formed on the slide by making two 'boundaries' of cardboard or celluloid strips. As the solvent evaporates add more resin at either end of the cavity.

**Planocera**

*Fix.* Bouin's; formaldehyde (5%).

*Suitable stain.* Mayer's hydrochloric acid-carmine. [See 'Amphioxus, Whole Specimens' (p. 97).] [Digestive system (→ purplish-red to orange); reproductive system (→ brilliant crimson).]

**Plankton**

*Kill and fix.* Formaldehyde (10%) at the rate of 10 ml per 100 ml of water containing the plankton. Stir the plankton slowly and gently. Pour formaldehyde down the side of the vessel while the plankton is in motion, and keep stirring for a minimum of 2 min. After a few h transfer to formaldehyde (5%). Preserve in formaldehyde (10%). Processed specimens may be kept in clove oil.

Treat quantities in a tube as recommended in Method **12** (p. 78).

When examining, raise cover-slip on two streaks of 'Vaseline'. For temporary mounts ring cover-slip with 'Vaseline'.

*Suitable stains.* borax carmine; fast green FCF. Clear in clove oil.

See also 'Aquatic and Marine Animals' (p. 103).

**Plant tissue** (other than algae and fungi).

*Preservation techniques*

(i) Cut the tissue into pieces 1 cm x 1 cm x 0.5 cm.

(ii) *Unfixed material.* Mixture of equal parts of alcohol (95%), glycerol and distilled water.

(iii) *Material fixed in chrom-acetic.*

**1** Wash in running water.

**2** Dehydrate (p. 51) up to, and preserve in, alcohol (70%) (to which a little glycerol has been added).

*Note:*

(*a*) The addition of glycerol to the alcohol used in storage prevents undue hardening of the tissues.

(*b*) Material which has turned brown in alcohol may be decolourized by placing it in:

| | |
|---|---|
| Alcohol (70%) | 100 ml |
| Sulphuric acid (conc.) | 1 ml |
| Potassium chlorate | few crystals |

for a *few days.*

Then transfer to, and preserve in:

| | |
|---|---|
| Alcohol (70%) | 50 ml |
| Glycerol | 50 ml |
| Water | 50 ml |

(iv) *To fix and preserve.* *

(a)

| | |
|---|---|
| Alcohol (70%) | 85 ml |
| Formaldehyde (40%) | 10 ml |
| Acetic acid (glacial) | 5 ml |

(b) Formaldehyde (4%).

(v) *Tissues which have been embedded in wax* may be preserved just as they are, in the block of wax.

(vi) *To preserve green colour of museum specimens.*

(*a*) Dissolve cupric acetate to saturation in acetic acid (comml.). Decant. Mix with an equal vol. of distilled water (for delicate plants use 4 vols. of water). Boil in a glazed earthenware or glass vessel. Drop specimen into the hot solution. Boil gently ($\frac{1}{2}$ h for strong plants and 5 min for delicate plants). Remove with wooden forceps. Wash thoroughly in running water for 12 h. Mount in formalin (2%).

(*b*) *Solution A.* *

| | |
|---|---|
| Alcohol (industrial) | 90 ml |
| Formaldehyde (40%) | 5 ml |
| Glycerol | 2.5 ml |

*Solution B.*

| | |
|---|---|
| Acetic acid (glacial) | 2.5 ml |
| Copper chloride | 10 g |
| Uranium nitrate | 1.5 g |

Mix equal volumes of solutions A and B.

*Adapted from *Gerrard's Bulletin,* May 1939. T. Gerrard & Co.

(vii) *To preserve green colour of algae.* See 'Algae (iv)' (p. 94).
(viii) *To preserve fungi.* See 'Fungi' (p. 130).

*Preparation techniques*
*Suitable Fixatives*
(*a*) Chrom-acetic.
(*b*) Alcohol (70%) . . . . . . 85 ml
Formaldehyde (40%) . . . 10 ml
Acetic-acid (glacial) . . . 5 ml
(*c*) Formalin-alcohol (for delicate algae and fungi).

*Cutting fixed tissue without embedding.* First stiffen tissue in alcohol (100%) (15 min), and cut in alcohol (50%).

*Suitable stains*
(*a*) *Bulk.* Borax carmine.
(*b*) *Fresh sections.* Safranin o and haematoxylin (lignified tissue → red; cellulose → purple); safranin o and fast green FCF in clove oil (lignified tissue → red; cellulose → green); Hanstein's fuchsin-violet (esp. monocot. stem); Bismarck brown Y.
(*c*) *Protein cell contents.*
*Temp.* Iodine (→ brown).
(*d*) *Protoplasm.* Eosin Y; erythrosin bluish.
(*e*) *Thick objects and whole mounts.* Haematoxylin (differentiated).

*Mounting*
(*a*) See 'Mountants' (p. 55 *et seq.*).
(*b*) Water-washed, stained sections may be first soaked and then mounted in Farrants' medium. (No dehydrating, clearing, or sealing required.)
(*c*) Canada balsam.

*See also* 'Chromosomes' (p. 114), 'Leaf' (p. 142), 'Lignin' (p. 143), 'Maceration' (p. 45), 'Phloem' (p. 157), 'Root' (p. 167), 'Vascular System of Plants' (p. 178), 'Xylem' (p. 180).

*General histology.* Before starting any method, consult Chapter 7 (p. 183) to find out all you can about the stain, its uses, and how it is made up. To avoid repetition, the final processes of dehydration, clearing, and mounting have not been listed unless special methods are desirable. In any case, details of the processes will vary according to the dehydrating agent (ethyl alcohol, 2 ethoxy ethanol, or butyl alcohol) in use, and reference should be made to the appropriate section on dehydration (p. 51 ff). D.P.X. is a satisfactory permanent mountant.

Full details of routine methods are given in Chapter 5 (p. 71).

I SINGLE STAINING

(*a*) *Delafield's haematoxylin*
A general purpose stain for sections.
**1** Stain in stock solution of Delafield's haematoxylin (p. 222). (1 min)
**2** Wash in tap-water or v. dilute ammonia (p. 188). (2 min)

(*b*) *Borax carmine*
Useful for bulk staining and especially for *Fucus.*
**1** Stain in stock solution of borax carmine (p. 196). (24 h)
**2** Differentiate in acid alcohol. (15 min)
**3** Transfer to alcohol (70%). (1 h)
**4** Transfer to alcohol (100%). (1 h)

II. DOUBLE STAINING

(*a*) *Anilin blue WS – picric acid*
**1** Stain in anilin blue ws – picric acid (formula i, p. 189). (2 min)
**2** Rinse in distilled water. (A few s)
**3** Mount in acid glycerol (see 'Glycerol iii', p. 220).

(*b*) *Safranin O – anilin blue ws in 2 ethoxy ethanol.* *
**1** Stain in safranin o – anilin blue ws in 2 ethoxy ethanol (p. 244) on a slide. (3–5 min)
**2** Blot off excess stain and add 2 ethoxy ethanol. (This removes excess stain and dehydrates.) (2 min)
**3** Blot off and add more 2 ethoxy ethanol. (2 min)
**4** Blot off.
**5** Mount in D.P.X.
[Cellulose (→ blue); lignin (→ red); phloem (→ brighter blue).]

*Notes:*
(i) Sections may be cut in water or in alcohol (50%).
(ii) The blue colour does not develop completely until after the lapse of a few minutes.
(iii) If the parenchyma has a purplish tint, process **2** should be lengthened.

(*c*) *Safranin O and fast green FCF in 2 ethoxy ethanol*
**1** Stain in safranin o – fast green FCF in 2 ethoxy ethanol (p. 244). (5–10 min)
**2** Rinse in 2 ethoxy ethanol.
**3** Mount in D.P.X.

* From information supplied by T. Gerrard & Co.

*Note:* for detailed results of staining with safranin o and fast green FCF see Method **17** **(p. 81)**.

[In general: cellulose (→ green); lignin (→ red).]

III. COUNTERSTAINING

(*a*) *Safranin O counterstained with fast green FCF in clove oil*

(α)

1 Stain in stock solution of safranin o (p. 244). (5 min)
2 Dehydrate from alcohol (50%) to alcohol (100%).
3 Counterstain in fast green FCF (iii (*b*), (p. 213) (in clove oil). (2 min)
4 Wash in alcohol (100%). (½ min in a covered vessel)
5 Clear in clove oil.
6 Pass quickly through xylene.
7 Mount in D.P.X.

(β)

1 Alcohol (50%).
2 Safranin O.
3 Dehydrate alcohol (70%), (90%).
4 Fast green FCF (in alcohol and clove oil).
5 Clear in clove oil/alcohol (96%) : : 60/40. (The addition of 1 drop of dilute acid to the watch-glass of clove oil/alcohol will differentiate.)
6 Pass through a watch-glass of benzene-phenol to which 1 drop of alcohol (100%) has been added.
7 Mount in D.P.X.

(γ)

1 *St.* sections in safranin O [1% in alcohol (50%)]. (30 min)
2 Dehydrate in alcohol-xylene (p. 187).
3 Stain in fast green FCF in clove oil (iii (*b*), p. 213) added to the alcohol-xylene used in **2**. (2–4 min)
4 Wash in alcohol-xylene. (Quickly)
5 Mount in D.P.X.

(*b*) *Safranin O counterstained with fast green FCF in benzyl alcohol**

*Note:* This method avoids the use of absolute ethyl alcohol and is suitable for either temporary or permanent preparations.

1 Stain sections in safranin O (formula ii, p. 244). (3–5 min)
2 Wash in alcohol (70%).
3 Wash in alcohol (90%). (1 min)
4 Stain in fast green FCF in benzyl alcohol (i, p. 213). (1 min or less)
5 Either clear and mount in benzyl alcohol for temporary preparations, or clear in benzyl alcohol and mount in D.P.X.

(*c*) *Safranin O counterstained with fast green FCF in ethyl alcohol*

1 Stain sections in safranin O (1% in alcohol 50%)). (30 min)
2 Dehydrate in alcohol-xylene (p. 187).
3 Stain in fast green FCF (0.5% in ethyl alcohol (100%). (Few s)
4 Wash in alcohol-xylene.
5 Mount in D.P.X.

[Cellulose (→ green); cytoplasm (→ green); lignin (→ red); nuclei (→ red).]

(*d*) *Safranin O counterstained with Delafield's haematoxylin*

1 Stain in stock solution of safranin O (p. 244). (1 min)
2 Transfer to alcohol (50%). (2 min)
3 Wash in distilled water. (1 min)
4 Stain in stock solution of Delafield's haematoxylin (p. 222). (3 min)
5 Transfer to tap water or very dil. ammonia (p. 188). (Sections to look faintly purple.) (1 min)

[Lignin (→ red); cellulose (→ blue).]

(*e*) *Safranin O counterstained with picric-anilin blue WS or anilin blue WS (alc.)*

1 Safranin O. (5 min)
2 Wash in alcohol (85%).
3 Picric-anilin blue ws (i, p. 189) or anilin blue WS (alc.) ((*c*), p. 189). (2 min)
4 Differentiate in acid alcohol. (Few s)
5 Wash in alcohol (95%). (1 min)

[Lignin (→ red); cellulose (→ blue).]

(*f*) *Malachite green or iodine green, counter-stained with Magdala red*

1 Malachite green (aq.), or iodine green (aq.). (1 min)
2 Wash out some green with alcohol (95%).
3 Wash in distilled water.
4 Magdala red (aq.). (10 min)
5 Wash in distilled water.

[Lignin (→ green); cellulose (→ pink).]

(*g*) *Acid fuchsin counterstained with malachite green or iodine green*

1 Acid fuchsin (aq.). (2 min)
2 Wash in distilled water.

* Adapted and modified from Catton, W. T. (1941) *School Science Review,* **XXII**, **87**, 325, March.

3 Malachite green (aq.). (1 min – until fuchsin is displaced from cellulose)
4 Wash in distilled water.
[Lignin (→ green); cellulose (→ red).]

*(h) Crystal violet-anilin counterstained with Gram's iodine and Bismarck brown Y (alc.)*

1 Crystal violet (aq.) with anilin oil (p. 201). (5 min)
2 Drain off excess.
3 Gram's iodine. (3 min)
4 Wash alcohol (95%).
5 Bismarck brown Y (alc.). (5 min)
[Lignin (→ violet); cellulose (→ brown).]

*(i) Crystal violet counterstained with Gram's iodine and eosin Y (in clove oil)*

1 Wash sections in alcohol (70%).
2 Stain in stock solution of crystal violet (alc.). (3–5 min)
3 Wash rapidly in alcohol (75%), or (95%).
4 Transfer to Gram's iodine.
5 Wash thoroughly in alcohol (90%).
6 Dehydrate in alcohol (100%).
7 Stain and clear in eosin Y in clove oil.
8 Pass through fresh oil of cloves.
9 Wash in xylene. (Quickly)
10 Mount in D.P.X.
[Lignin (→ violet); cellulose (→ red).]

## Platyhelminthes

See 'Fasciola hepatica' (p. 127); 'Planaria' (p. 157); and 'Taenia' (p. 174).

*Preparation technique**

1 Place the living worm on a slide in a small quantity of Ringer's solution ['Saline Solutions i (*a*)' (p. 244)].
2 Place two small spots of petroleum jelly ('Vaseline') one on either side of the worm both to act as a temporary adhesive for the cover-slip and to reduce the surface tension effect of the thin film of liquid.
3 Cover with a cover-slip and apply just sufficient pressure to distend the worm without crushing it unduly.
4 Immerse the whole mount in alcohol (70%) (3 h)
5 Transfer to alcohol (50%). (3 h)
6 Transfer to alcohol (30%). (3 h)
7 Immerse the whole mount in Gower's acid carmine (p. 196). (4–24 h)
8 Wash in alcohol (30%). (3 h)
9 Wash in alcohol (50%). (3 h)
10 If necessary differentiate in acid alcohol [0.5% of hydrochloric acid in alcohol (70%)]. Examine under the microscope at intervals. (3–12 h)
11 Wash in alcohol (70%). (3 h)
12 Wash in alcohol (90%). (3 h)
13 Dehydrate in 2 ethoxy ethanol. (1 h)
14 Rinse in fresh 2 ethoxy ethanol. (1 h)
15 Clear in xylene. (1 h)
16 Remove the cover-slip with a sable brush and allow it to drop into the clearing vessel.
17 Mount in D.P.X.
18 Cover with a clean cover-slip.
19 Label.

*Note:* Free-living turbellarians seem to be more difficult to stain than their parasitic relations.

* After Dr. E. Lees, University of Bradford, modified from Johri and Smith, *Parasitology*, 1956.

## Pleodorina

**S/C**

See 'Culture Media 3' (p. 203).

## Pleurobrachia

*Kill.* Formaldehyde (5%) in sea water.*
*Fix.* Formaldehyde (5%). Preserve in 70% alcohol.
Stain in methyl green.

## Pollen Grains

*Suitable stains*

Acetic-carmine (dil.); acetic-methyl-green; iodine in potassium iodide; methylene blue aq.

*Clearing agents*

Chloral hydrate; phenol aq.; sodium hydroxide aq.

Mountants: glycerol; glycerol-jelly.

*Preparation technique*

1 Tease out stamens in water.
2 Drain off water and leave pollen on slide.

* After Bolles-Lee, 1937, *Microtomist's Vade-Mecum*, Churchill.

3 Either (*a*) add 1 drop of glycerol (for temporary preparation) or
(*b*) add 1 drop of glycerol-jelly for a permanent mount, to which, in either instance, a little diluted acetic-carmine has been added.*
4 Mix the pollen into the glycerol or glycerol-jelly.
5 Cover with a cover-slip.
6 Either (*a*) seal with glycerol-jelly (temporary mount) or
(*b*) seal with a permanent sealing medium (p. 246).

*To see germination*

1 Take flowers of *Stellaria medialis* (Chickweed) fully open, after mid-day, or closed flowers that were open the previous day.
2 Remove ovary with stigma attached.
3 Stain in methylene blue aq. (1 min)
4 Wash in distilled water.
5 Mount in distilled water.
6 Cover with a cover-slip.

(Germinating pollen grains, i.e. pollen tubes, in style → violet; stigmatic surfaces → violet (due to pectin); walls of pollen grains → blue.)
See also 'Pinus. *Pollen*' (p. 157).
See also 'Chromosomes 2 (*b*)' (p. 119).

**Pollen Mother Cells**

See 'Chromosomes 2 (*b*)' (p. 119).

**Pollen tubes**

*Culture Media*

These consist of solutions of cane sugar in water, although some species grow best in water alone (see (*a*)) below. Strasburger recommends that 1.5% of gelatine should be added to the medium.

†(*a*) *In water only.*
*Agapanthus; Aquilegia* (Columbine); *Lamium Galeobdolon* (Archangel, Yellow Dead-nettle); *Lilium* (Lily); *Lobelia; Lysimachia nummularia* (Creeping Jenny, Moneywort); *Nicotiana* (Tobacco).

*(*b*) *In cane-sugar solutions.*

| | |
|---|---|
| For *Tulipa* (Tulip) | 1–3% |
| For *Allium* (Onion) | 3% |
| For *Leucojum aestivum* (Snow-flake) | 3–5% |
| For *Narcissus poeticus* (Pheasant Eye) | 3–7% |
| For *Paeonia corallina* (Paeony); *Papaver* (Poppy); *Staphylea; Tradescantia* | 5% |
| For Orchidaceae | 5–10% |
| For *Convallaria majalis* (Lily of the Valley) | 5–20% |
| For *Epilobium* sp. (Willow-herb); *Lychnis Githago* (Corn cockle); *Geranium* sp.; *Malva* sp. (Mallow); *Scilla nutans* (Wild Hyacinth) | |
| For *Montbretia; Tritonia* | 7.5% |
| For *Gloxinia; Torenia Asiatica* | 10% |
| For *Lathyrus* sp. (Sweet-Pea) | 10–15% |
| For *Echeveria retusa* | 15% |
| For *Sedum* sp. (Stonecrop); *Viola tricolor* (Pansy) | 30% |
| For Compositae; *Iris sibirica* | 30–40% |

*Suitable stain*

Acetic-methyl green.

*Methods of Culture*

(i) As the growing pollen tube is negatively aerotropic, it is best to use the 'hanging-drop' method (p. 208).
(ii) Culture in covered watch glasses.
(iii)†
1 Cut out a piece of cellophane rather less than 2 cm square.
2 Place a few *fresh* pollen grains in the centre of the square.
3 Float the cellophane on the culture medium, maintained at an average temperature of 21°C (few min — several h, according to species).
4 Lift cellophane square on to a slide.
5 Cover very gently with a cover-slip.

* Suggested by Professor J. G. Hawkes, Sc.D., University of Birmingham.

† The author is indebted to Messrs. George Allen and Unwin Ltd., publishers of Strasburger's *Handbook of Practical Botany*, 1930, English Edition, for permission to reproduce the examples given in (*a*) and many of those in (*b*).

* The author is indebted to Messrs. George Allen and Unwin, Ltd., publishers of Strasburger's *Handbook of Practical Botany*, 1930, English Edition, for permission to reproduce the examples given in (*a*) and many of those in (*b*).

† Method due to Cecil Prime, Whitgift School.

**Polystomella**

**S/C**
Marine Biological Station, Citadel Hill, Plymouth.

*Preparation technique*

1 Dehydrate in alcohol (30%), (50%), (70%). (5 min each)
2 Decalcify by placing in acid alcohol. (Till shell removed)
3 Wash in alcohol (70%). (Till all acid alcohol removed)
4 Stain in borax carmine. (Overstain deeply)
5 Differentiate in acid alcohol.
6 Dehydrate in alcohol (70%), (90%), (100%). (2 min each)
7 Clear in benzene-phenol.
8 Mount in D.P.X.

**Polystomum**

**S/C**
In bladder of *Rana.*

**Polytoma**

*To see flagella:*
Irrigate under cover-slip with dilute iodine.

**Polyzoa**

(i) *To kill.* Hot mixture of mercuric chloride (sat. aq.) and iodine (alc. soln.).
(ii) *Fix and preserve.* (Alcohol (70%).) See 'Aquatic and Marine Animals' (p. 103).

*Preparation technique*

See 'Amphioxus, Whole Specimens' (p. 97).

**Porifera**

*To kill and fix.*
(*a*) Alcohol (70%). Preserve in alcohol (90%).
(*b*) See 'Aquatic and Marine Animals' (p. 103).

*Preparation techniques*

*Spicules*

1 Boil small portion of sponge in conc. sodium hydroxide (aq.). CARE. (Till matrix dissolves.)
2 Allow spicules to settle.
3 Decant sodium hydroxide.
4 Add water; shake; allow to settle; decant washings.
5 Add alcohol (95%); shake; allow to settle; decant the alcohol.
6 Add alcohol (100%); shake; allow to settle; decant alcohol.
7 Mount in D.P.X. or Euparal.

**Proleptus**

**S/C**
In intestine of *Scyllium* and *Acanthias.*

*Preparation techniques*

(i) See 'Nematodes' (p. 150).
(ii)*
1 Place specimen in

| | |
|---|---|
| Alcohol (100%) . . . . . . . | 22 ml |
| Chloroform . . . . . . . . | 15 ml |
| Acetic acid (glacial) . . . . . | 5 ml |
| Phenol. Add crystals to increase volume by . . . . . . . . . | 10 ml |

2 Add methyl salicylate (oil of wintergreen) drop by drop.
3 Add Canada balsam slowly.
4 Mount in Canada balsam.

**Prothalli of Fern**

See 'Fern, Prothalli' (p. 129).

**Protococcus**

**S/C**
(i) Dealers.
(ii) Palings, bark of trees April-June approx.

*Preparation techniques*

(i) *General Method.* See 'Protozoa' (below).
(ii) Stain in iodine and basic fuchsin.

**Protophyta**

**S/C**
Culture media as *Daphnia* (p. 122).

* After Green, *School Science Review,* XV, December, 1933.

**Protoplasm** (especially plant protoplasm).

*To demonstrate streaming of plant protoplasm:* Examine staminal hairs of *Tradescantia reflexa* or *T. virginica;* cells near mid-rib of leaf of *Elodea Canadensis*; tips of root-hairs of mustard (*Sinapis alba*) or cress (*Lepidium sativum*) grown on pieces of flower-pot kept in a moist chamber. (*Note:* the root-hairs must be undamaged and are best lifted off the surface on which they have been grown, by means of a camel-hair brush under water and transferred to a slide by the brush.)

*Suitable stains*

Alkanet (→ pale rose-red) (½ h); acetic-anilin blue WS; eosin Y; erythrosin bluish; Hanstein's fuchsin-violet (→ bluish violet).

**Protozoa**

**S/C**

(i) Culture Collection of Algae and Protozoa. The Botany School, University of Cambridge.
(ii) See 'Culture Media 3' (pp. 203–208), and under the names of the various genera.

*Note:* All vessels must be chemically and biologically clean.

The pH value of the culture solution should be in the range pH 6.0–7.6 and should be tested with bromothymol-blue test paper or with a pH meter. (At pH 5.9 bromothymol-blue is yellowish-green; at pH 7.7 it is dark blue.)

To maintain the culture solution at the required pH value place about 25 ml of buffer solution of suitable pH value (see pp. 194–195) in a Petri dish and add a portion of the protozoa culture. Keep under cover at room temperature (and not lower than 20°C). The culture should remain active for several days.*

Culture in sterilized Petri dishes filled to a depth of 12 mm with culture (make up loss with distilled water daily), and keep almost covered with the upper half of the dish.

Examine from time to time; cut down food supply if unwanted forms appear; sub-culture when necessary by stirring the culture, transferring half to distilled water in a Petri dish to a depth of 12 mm.†

* Adapted from *Protonotes.* T. Gerrard & Co., London.
† Adapted from *Gerrard's Bulletin*, June 1939. T. Gerrard & Co., London.

*Preparation techniques*

(i) *Alive.*

Place a drop of the fluid containing the protozoa on a slide, cover, and treat throughout by irrigation.

(*a*) *To retard or prevent movement on the slide.*

(α) Add a drop of carragheen solution (p. 198).
(β) Place a few strands of cotton wool on the slide.
(γ) Add a few drops of benzanine hexachloride soln. (p. 190); or chlorobutol soln. (p. 199); or sodium alginate soln. (p. 249).

(*b*) *To show cilia.*

Add a drop of glycerol or Indian ink or carmine suspension.

(*c*) *To slow up vacuole movement.*

Add sodium chloride (0.25% aq.).

(*d*) *Suitable stains.*

Very dil. methylene blue aq.; Nile blue sulphate; very dilute neutral red.

(*e*) See Method **1** (p. 73).

(ii) *Dead.*

(*a*) *Fix.* Osmium tetroxide (0.25%) in drop on slide under cover-slip; osmium tetroxide vapour; glacial acetic acid vapour.

(*b*) *Suitable stains.* Acetic-methylene blue (kills and stains); acetic-carmine; alum carmine (Grenacher's); borax carmine; haematoxylin; Hofmann's violet; methyl green; safranin O (2–3 min).

(*c*) See Method **2** (p. 73).

(iii) *Permanent preparations.*

*Suitable fixatives.* Mercuric-acetic (poison-care). (Wash 3–4 times with water, or, if an alcoholic stain is to be used, with alcohol. Add a few drops of iodine solution to the washing liquid. If colour disappears add more iodine); osmium tetroxide (0.25%); Schaudinn's fluid (at 60°–70°C). (Wash as mercuric-acetic.)

*Suitable stains.* As temp. preparations.

(iv) *Large specimens.*

(*a*) Treat as ordinary material, carrying out the operations with a quantity of animals in a piece of glass tubing as recommended in Method **12** (p. 78).

(v) *Small specimens.*

1 Smear slide thinly with egg albumen.
2 Place drop of culture on slide.
3 Air dry as long as possible but *not* to *kill animals.*
4 Add mercuric-acetic with pipette. (2 min)
5 Wash distilled water, to which a few drops of iodine have been added. Add more iodine as colour disappears. (20 min–$\frac{1}{2}$ h)
6 Stain in Delafield's haematoxylin.
7 Differentiate in acid alcohol.
8 Wash alcohol (70%). (1 min)
9 Wash alcohol (90%). (1 min)
10 'Blue' in alkaline alcohol.
11 Dehydrate.
12 Clear in benzene-phenol.
13 Mount in D.P.X.

(vi) *Shelled protozoa.* See 'Polystomella' (p. 163).

(vii) See also 'Trematodes, Larval stages' (p. 176).

**Pyronema**

*Oogonia.* See 'Fungi Method (xiv)' (p. 136).

**Pythium**

**S/C**

(i) Sow cress (*Lepidium sativum*) seeds very closely and keep in a very damp atmosphere.
(ii) See 'Culture Media 3' (pp. 203–208).

**Raia**

See 'Scyllium' (p. 169).

**Rana**

**S/C**

(i) Dealers.
(ii) Collection. Brickfields, marshy places. In winter look in long grass, under stones, and in mud at pond bottom. Feed on small worms and slugs.

*Preservative solutions*

(i) Formaldehyde (3%).
(ii) See 'Animal Tissue' (p. 98).
(iii) *Spawn.*
 (*a*) Perényi's fluid (p. 239).*
 (*b*) Formaldehyde (4%).
 (*c*) See also 'Gatenby's Fluid' (p. 218).
(iv) See 'Embalming fluid' (p. 211).

*To pith:*

1 Either (*a*) Place the frog in urethane (1%);
 or (*b*) Hold the frog in a duster and chloroform it by holding a pad soaked in chloroform over its nostrils;
 or (*c*) If neither urethane nor chloroform is available, the frog may be rendered unconscious by giving it a sharp jab with a blunt scalpel in the depression between atlas and skull.
2 Extend its hind limbs and feel with the nail for the depression beneath the skin at the back of the head (articulation of skull and vertebral column) – it lies in a line joining posterior borders of the two tympanic membranes. Divide the skin and muscles here to expose the neutral canal. Pass a stout wire (a blunt curved mounted needle is useful) into the cranium, only partially withdraw the probe (to lessen risk of missing the neural canal), turn it round and pass it down the neural canal in the vertebral column.

*To kill.*

Allow at least 20 min in a closed vessel containing a pad of cotton wool soaked in chloroform.

*Preparation techniques*

(i) *Spawn.*

*Gatenby's method.*†

1 Place eggs in Gatenby's fluid (p. 218). (Use at least 40 ml for 20–30 eggs.) (24 h)
2 Remove albuminous envelope.
3 Wash in running water. (1 h)
4 Dehydrate in alcohol (30%), (50%), (70%). (30 min each)
5 Dehydrate in alcohol (90%). (1 h)

* After Stork and Renouf, *Fundamentals of Biology,* London, Murray.
† Adapted from Bolles-Lee, *Microtomist's Vade-Mecum,* 1937, London, Churchill.

6 Dehydrate in alcohol (100%) (two changes). (1 h each)
7 Clear in benzene. (15 min)
8 Add shreds of paraffin wax. (In oven: do not overheat.) (30 min)
9 Transfer to pure wax. (15–20 min)
10 Transfer to fresh wax. (15–20 min)
11 Embed.
12 Cut at 6 μm with a very sharp razor.
13 Usual processes leading to staining (any method) and finishing.

(ii) *Tadpole.*
*Fix.* Bouin's fluid. (Small, 12 h; large, 18 h.)
Wash in several changes of alcohol (70%).

(iii) *Unstriated muscle fibres in bladder.* See Method **19** (p. 83).

**Ranunculus — Root**

See Methods **9** (p. 76); **10** (p. 77); **15** (p. 80); **17** (p. 81).

**Respiration of Plant Cells***

(i) The methods outlined at (ii) below, can be used for an investigation of the effect of environmental conditions on the respiration of micro-organisms, and of the distribution of respiratory activity in the tissues of higher plants.

The methods depend on the fact that triphenyl tetrazolium chloride, which is the chloride of a complex organic base, can be reduced to an insoluble red compound by living cells in the presence of a suitable hydrogen donor and enzyme system.

*The rate of development of the red colour is directly proportional to the rate of respiration of the cells.*

Temperature has two effects upon respiration. Within the biological range, a rise in temperature of 10°C doubles the reaction rate, i.e. $Q_{10} = 2$. However, at temperatures over 40° there is a progressive diminution of the respiratory rate, and this diminution is also progressive with the time involved in the reaction. The diminution is the result of the denaturation of the cell enzymes (proteins) by heat.

* After Dr. J. M. Merrett, University of Bradford.

In these experiments the temperature of incubation, and the lapse of time between the time at which the chosen incubation temperature is reached and that at which the reaction is started (by the addition of triphenyl tetrazolium chloride to the yeast suspension) are both important.

Thus for example, if a yeast suspension is incubated at (say) 50°C for 15 min before the triphenyl tetrazolium chloride is added, it will be found that the time taken for the standard colour (chosen by experiment beforehand) to develop is longer than if the triphenyl tetrazolium chloride had been added immediately the incubation temperature was reached.

Provided they remain indentical for any one series of experiments, the quantities of the reactants taking part are not critical. The quantities suggested below have been found convenient in practice.

(ii) *Suggested experiments for the demonstration of comparative respiratory rates.*

(*a*) *In seedlings of Fabia vulgaris* (*Broad Bean*).
1 Halve a broad bean seedling longitudinally.
2 Boil one of the halves in water.
3 Immerse both halves in triphenyl tetrazolium chloride (0.5% aq.), (p. 251).
(Areas of respiratory activity → red.)

(*b*) *In radicles of Fabia vulgaris.*
1 Prepare a number of slides each bearing a drop of triphenyl tetrazolium chloride (0.5% aq.), (p. 251).
2 Cut sections of a bean radicle at varying distances from the apex and mount them in a successive series on the prepared slides.
3 Examine successive slides under the microscope and note the areas in which the red colour is distributed.
(Areas of respiratory activity → red.)

(*c*) *In yeast — effect of temperature upon respiratory rates.*
1 Make a colour standard for comparison by incubating the following mixture in a small test-tube.
Glucose solution (p. 219) . . . 0.25 ml
Yeast suspension (p. 253) . . . 2 ml
At 35°C for 20 min.
2 Add triphenyl tetrazolium chloride (p. 251) 1 ml.
3 As soon as the desired colour standard (a pale pink is suggested) has developed, stop the reaction by adding mercuric sulphate (p. 233) (2 drops).

*Note:* This colour standard will be used for comparison in experiments 1, 2 and 3 below.

EXPERIMENT 1.

1. Prepare a series of small test-tubes each containing glucose solution and yeast suspension in quantities as (*c*) **1** opposite, p. 166.
2. Incubate the tubes at different temperatures in the range 15°C to 40°C.
3. Add triphenyl tetrazolium chloride [as at (*c*) **2** opposite, p. 166] *as soon as the desired temperature of incubation is reached.*
4. Note (*a*) the temperature of incubation; (*b*) the time at which the triphenyl tetrazolium chloride was added; (*c*) the lapse of time after its addition until the chosen standard colour develops.

EXPERIMENT 2.

Repeat experiment 1 at temperatures above 40°C.

EXPERIMENT 3.

1. Prepare a series of small test-tubes each containing glucose solution and yeast suspension in quantities as at (*c*) **1** above.
2. Incubate the tubes at different temperatures above 40°C, *but continue incubation for a given time, say* 15 min.
3. Add triphenyl tetrazolium chloride [as at (*c*) **2** above].
4. Note (*a*) the temperature of incubation; (*b*) the period of incubation until the triphenyl tetrazolium chloride is added; (*c*) the time at which it is added; (*d*) the lapse of time after its addition until the chosen standard colour develops.

### Retina

See 'Eye' (p. 127).

### Rhabditis

**S/C**

Nematode parasitic in nephridium of earthworm.*

1. Kill 3 or 4 earthworms with hot (not boiling) water.
2. Remove immediately, and place in a tin box lined with blotting paper and half full of damp earth.
3. Keep at summer temperature (15°–16°C).
4. The first batch of worms is sexually mature at the end of 4–5 d, but, to see cell division after fertilization, females should not be collected till after 6 d at least. Collect with a camel-hair brush.

* See Johnson, G. E., *Quart. J. Microscop. Sci.*, **58**, 605.

*Preparation technique*

*To show cell division after fertilization.*

1. Obtain female specimens as explained under notes on culture.
2. Transfer the specimen to a slide with a camel-hair brush, and burst it by gentle pressure with a cover-slip.
3. Examine with a 4 mm objective.

*Note:* This preparation is a good test of the efficiency of a micro-projector for screen demonstration to a class.

### Rhizobium trifolium

**S/C**

See 'Culture Media 3' (p. 203).

### Rhizopus

**S/C**

See 'Culture Media 3' (p. 203).

### Rhyncocystis pilosa

**S/C**

Seminal vesicles of earthworm (*Lumbricus terrestris* and *Allolobophora terrestris*).

*Preparation technique*

See 'Monocystis' (p. 147); and 'Peranema' (p. 156).

### Root

(i) See Methods **9** (p. 76); **10** (p. 77); **11** (p. 77); **13** (p. 79); **16** (p. 81); **17** (p. 81).
(ii) See 'Plant Tissue' (p. 158).
(iii) See 'Chromosomes' (p. 114).
(iv) See 'Endodermis of root' (p. 126).

## Rotifers

**S/C**

Collect in a bolting-silk tow-net from ponds. Rather local in habit.

*Preparation techniques*

(Rousselet's method.)

**1** Narcotize. (About 15 min till cilia cease moving) Purpose is to keep cilia extended. Run the narcotic gently down the side of the containing vessel.
*Suitable narcotics:*
(*a*) Cocaine hydrochloride (1%)
(*b*) Cocaine hydrochloride (2%) . . . 30 ml
Alcohol (96%) . . . . . . . . 10 ml
Distilled water . . . . . . . . 60 ml

**2** Kill and fix.
*Suitable agents:*
(*a*) Weak Flemming's fluid: (3–4 min)
Acetic acid (glacial) . . . . . . 5 ml
Chromium trioxide (1%) . . . . 75 ml
Osmium tetroxide (2%) . . . . 20 ml
(*b*) Osmium tetroxide (0.25%). (1 min)
If blackened, bleach in hydrogen peroxide.

**3** Wash in distilled water. (Several times)

**4** Stain in *very weak* Fleming's fluid, viz.:
Weak Flemming's [as **2**(*a*), above ] . 1.5 ml
Distilled water . . . . . . . . 98.5 ml
(*Watch under the microscope – the nervous system should become slightly tinged with yellow*.)

**5** Mount in formalin (3%) in a cavity slide. (Transfer the animals with a dipping pipette.)

**6** Blot off any moisture round the edges of the cavity.

**7** Cover gently.

**8** Seal with gold size.

## Rusts

**S/C**

*Puccinia graminis* hyphae within the young leaves of *Berberis vulgaris* in spring. Uredospores of *Puccinia graminis* on the stems of some varieties of wheat. Uredospores of other rust fungi may be found on *Senecio vulgaris* (groundsel) in summer. Aecidia of *P. poeae* are frequently to be found on *Tussilago farfara* (Coltsfoot).

Note that *P. anemones* (rust of *Anemone nemorosa*, the Wood Anemone) has no uredospores; and that *P. malvacearum* (rust of *Althaea sp.*, the Hollyhock) has only teleutospores. *Phragmidium bulbosum* (rust of *Rubus fruticosus* the Blackberry) causes purple spots on the leaves of the host.

**P**

Infected material may be stored in Calberla's fluid (p. 193).

(i)

**1** Mount sections of young leaves of *Berberis vulgaris* in chloral hydrate aq. to which a little acid fuchsin [see 'Fuchsin, Acid (*b*)' (p. 215)] has been added.

(ii)

**1** *Fix.* Acetic-alcohol. (15–30 min)

**2** Wash in alcohol (90%) or (95%). (2–3 h)

**3** If desired, store in Calberla's fluid (p. 193).

**4** Either (*a*) *for hand sections,* refer to 'Fungi, method xi (*a*)' (Excluding process **2**) (p. 135) and Durand's method (p. 135).
or (*b*) *for wax-embedded sections,* dehydrate in alcohol (100%) and then proceed from process **12** of 'Fungi method (x)' (p. 133), and stain either by method (x) (*a*), (p. 134), or by method **PMP** (xi) (*a*) (p. 135), process **2** onwards; or with Delafield's haematoxylin counterstained with Congo red. Preparations stained with Congo red must be well washed before mounting in D.P.X.*

(iii) See also 'Peronosporaceae' (p. 156).

## Saccharomyces cerevisiae

See 'Yeast' (p. 180).

## Salivary Gland

(i) *Fix.* Mercuric-formaldehyde; formol-saline.
(ii) *Suitable stains.* Haematoxylin and eosin Y; Mallory's stain (after fixation in mercuric formaldehyde).
(iii) *For Mucin.* See 'Mucin' (p. 149).
(iv) *Of Periplaneta.* See 'Periplaneta (iii)' (p. 156).

* Recommended by Gwynne-Vaughan and Barnes, 1937, *Structure and Development of the Fungi,* Cambridge, University Press.

**Saprolegnia**

**S/C**
See 'Culture Media 3' (p. 203).

**Schistocerca gregaria (Locust)**

**S/C**
Anti-locust Centre, 1 Princes Gate, London, S.W.7.

*Preparation techniques*

(i) *Chromosomes* – See 'Chromosomes 1 methods (iv) and (v)' for mitosis (p. 117); and 'Chromosomes 2(*a*)' for meiosis (p. 118).

(ii) *Campaniform sensillum.*

**1** Remove one of the 2nd pair of legs of *Schistocerca* at its very base.
**2** Hold the tibia vertical, with the coxa, trochanter and femur lying horizontally on the bench.
**3** Cut the trochanter and femur (together) away from the remainder.
**6** Slit the trochanter and femur longitudinally, vertically and medianly.
**7** Cut the femur transversely, about half way along its length, so that the two basal halves, each with half a trochanter attached, are freed.
**8** Boil the piece of leg in potassium hydroxide aq. (CARE. Gently. $\frac{1}{2}$ min)
**9** Add water. Drain off after a few moments.
**10** Repeat the washing with water.
**11** Dehydrate in alcohol (70%) and (90%). (2 min each)
**12** Dehydrate in alcohol (100%). Two changes. (2 min each)
**13** Clear in clove oil.
**14** *Mount with the outside of the cuticle uppermost,* Canada balsam or D.P.X.

[Sensillum (→ as dark elliptical ring with sense cell at centre).]

**Schistosoma Mansoni**

*Fix.* Formaldehyde (5%).
Stain in Mayer's paracarmine (p. 197).

**Scyllium (Dogfish)**

**S/C**
(i) Dealers.
(ii) Occasionally from fishmongers, but usually arrive eviscerated.

**P**
(i)
**1** Formaldehyde (10%). (24 h)
**2** Formaldehyde (5%). (7 d)
**3** Formaldehyde (3%). (Stock)
(ii) See 'Animal Tissue ii' (p. 98).

*Note:* First open abdominal cavity and pericardial cavity and remove a 6 mm square from the roof of the cranium.

*Placoid scales.*
See 'Teeth ii(*c*)' (p. 176).

**Scyphozoa**

*Larvae:* Stain in Mayer's hydrochloric acid-carmine.

**Sea Anemone**

See 'Anemone' (p. 97).

**Sea Fir**

See 'Sertularia' (p. 170).

**Sea Mat**

See 'Polyzoa' (p. 163).

**Sea Pen**

See 'Pennatula' (p. 155).

**Sea Slug**

See 'Doris' (p. 124).

**Sea Squirt**

See 'Tunicates' (p. 177).

**Sea Urchin**

See 'Echinus' (p. 124).

**Seaweeds (Small)**

See 'Algae' (p. 94).
After fixation proceed as for 'Echinus *ova*, (p. 125) from process **2** onwards.

**Sections, Frozen**

See page 68.

**Seeds**

**S/C**

See 'Culture Media 2' (p. 203).

1 Cut pieces of 4-ply wood 7.5 cm x 3.5 cm.
2 Bore a hole 2.25 cm diameter in the centre of each piece. (Two holes, suitably spaced, may be bored if desired, but difficulty may be found in retaining the 'slide' on the microscope stage.)
3 Glue a clean slide on to one side of the wood. Avoid getting glue on the glass over the hole(s).
4 Place the seeds in the cavity thus made. (Loose, or fixed with a touch of Canada balsam.)
5 Glue another slide on the wood to cover the cavity, observing the same precautions as before.
6 Label, either in the usual position or, if two holes are used, by means of a piece of paper placed, after suitable inscription, on the strip of wood between the two holes which are then covered as in **5**. If the latter method is adopted, avoid gluing the label.*

**Seminal Vesicles (of Lumbricus)**

See Method **14** (p. 79); 'Lumbricus vii' (p. 145); 'Monocystis' (pp. 147–148); and 'Spermatozoa' (p. 171).

**Sertularia**

(i) *Kill.* In a hot mixture of mercuric chloride (sat. aq.) and iodine (alc. soln.).
(ii) *Fix and preserve.* Alcohol (70%).

**Sieve Tubes**

*Suitable stains*

Safranin O and fast green FCF (p. 244).
Basic fuchsin-violet (p. 217).

**Skeleton**

To stain the whole skeleton of small vertebrates without staining the flesh, see 'Bone (iii)' (p. 111); and 'Cartilage (iv)' (p. 112).

**Skin**

**P**

(i)

1 If necessary to skin the animal, make as few incisions as possible.

(*a*) *Large mammals.* Make a full-length incision along the mid-ventral line and incisions on the insides of the limbs which are severed at the knees (the lower parts being retained). Withdraw the hind limbs first. Keep the skull in turpentine.

(*b*) *Small mammals.* Make one incision only, from the middle of the mid-ventral line to the pectoral region.

(*c*) *Birds.* Make an incision under the skin of a wing. Plug the mouth with cotton wool and leave the skull in.

(*d*) *Small reptiles.* Make an incision at the point where skull is attached to cervical vertebrae. Evert the decapitated trunk through the mouth.

(*e*) *Large reptiles.* As mammals.

(*f*) *Fish.* Make an incision along the more damaged side from tail to gills. *Keep the skin damp while removing myotomes.* Rub in preservative and fill cavity with sawdust.

2 Remove all traces of fat, keep free from damp, and rub in a preservative frequently. Arsenical soap (Bécoeur's, p. 248) is the best preservative, but great care must be exercised in its use, or poisoning of the operator may occur. Browne's soap (p. 249) is a non-poisonous substitute. Burnt alum and saltpetre (see 'Taxidermy', p. 250) are of value, but tend to make the skin hard.

(ii) See also 'Preservation of Museum Specimens', Dollman, *School Science Review,* **XVIII**, 69, 91; Oct. 1936.

*Preparation techniques*

(i) *Method for sections.* *

| | |
|---|---|
| 1 *Fix.* Formol-saline (5%). | (24 h) |
| 2 Dehydrate to alcohol (100%). | (24 h) |
| 3 Clear in acetone. | (1 h) |

* After A. Powell Jones, 1936, *Science Masters' Book,* Part II, London, Murray.

* After Carleton, *Histological Technique,* 1926, University Press, Oxford.

4 Impregnate paraffin wax (m.p. 50°C). (6 h)
5 Section at 2–4 μm.
6 Stain in Heidenhain's iron haematoxylin and van Gieson's.

(ii) *Stratum lucidum.* *
*Suitable stains.* Haematoxylin and eosin Y (→ bright pink); iron haematoxylin and van Gieson's (→ yellow); Mallory's (→ orange).

(iii) *Of inside of cheek.* See 'Epithelia (iii)' (p. 126); and Methods **5** (p. 75); **6** (p. 75); and **15** (p. 80).

(iv) *Keratin in.* See 'Keratin' (p. 141).

(v) See also 'Epithelia' (p. 126).

**Slugs**

(i) *Kill.* Drown in water.
(ii) *Fix and preserve.* (Alcohol (60%)).

**Snowberry**

See 'Symphoricarpus racemosus' **(p. 174)**.

**Spermatozoa**

(i) *General method.* †
1 Smear a cover-slip with glycerol-egg albumen.
2 Smear cut testis on the cover-slip.
3 *Fix.* Bouin's fluid. (3 min)
4 Wash alcohol (50%). (2 min)
5 Dehydrate alcohol (70%). (2 min)
6 Dehydrate alcohol (90%). (Overnight)
7 Hydrate to distilled water.
8 Stain in crystal violet. (3 min)
9 Dehydrate.
10 Clear.
11 Mount in D.P.X.

(ii) *Other suitable stains.* Hofmann's violet (0.25%) (2–3 min); safranin O.

(iii) See 'Protozoa' (p. 164).

* After Hartridge and Haynes, 1930, *Histology for Medical Students,* University Press, Oxford.

† After Lee, 1950, *Microtomist's Vade-Mecum,* Churchill, London.

**Spermatozoids**

*To restrict movement.*
Gum arabic (10% aq. filtered).

*Suitable stain*

Crystal violet (nuclear).

**Spinal Cord**

See 'Nerve Tissue' (p. 151).

**Spindle Fibres**

See 'Chromosomes' (p. 114).

**Spirogyra**

**S/C**
(i) Dealers.

(ii) Collect from ponds.

(iii) *To induce conjugation.* *
Between mid-February and May, place in a 2–4% cane-sugar solution in a sunny position and allow to become almost dry.

(iv) See 'Culture Media 3 and 5' (pp. 203, 209). *Spirogyra* species tend not to grow very abundantly but may be helped along by the addition of 0.1% of Yeast Extract (Oxoid). Sub-culturing is necessary fairly frequently.

*Preparation techniques*

(i)
1 *Fix* in chrom-acetic Formula iii (p. 199). (24 h)
2 *Wash* in tap water. (24 h)
3 *Wash* in distilled water. (24 h)
4 Stain in *either,* anilin blue WS. (2 h)
*or,* phloxine B. (1 h)
5 *Wash* in distilled water (*until excess stain is removed*).
6 Clear and mount in lactophenol, in a cavity slide or within a ring of shellac.
7 Seal with shellac.

* Strasburger, 1930, *Handbook of Practical Botany,* Allen and Unwin, London.

(ii)
1 Place algae in glycerol (10%) in watch-glass.
2 Allow water to evaporate by heating in oven to 30°C.
3 When soln. has thickened almost to strength of pure glycerol, transfer to drop of pure glycerol on slide.
4 Cover.
5 Seal with D.P.X. or gold size.

(iii) See also 'Algae' (p. 94).

**Spirostomum**

**S/C**
See 'Culture Media 3' (p. 203)

**Spleen**

*Preparation techniques*

(i) *Smears.*
1 Press slide on freshly cut spleen. Pull slide off so that some spleen is sucked on to the slide.
2 Wave in the air to dry.
3 Treat as for remaining stages of 'Blood (v)', (p. 109).

(ii) *Impregnation with paraffin.* Not for longer than 1 h, or tissue will harden.

(iii) See 'Lymph Nodes' (p. 145).

**Sponge**

See 'Porifera' (p. 163).

**Squamous Epithelium**

See 'Epithelia' (p. 126); and Method **5** (p. 75); Method **6** (p. 75); Method **15** (p. 80).

**Starch**

(i) *Granules.* To see these, cut potato at *right*-angles to the skin, and mount sections in water.

(ii) *Suitable stains and reagents.*
Chloral hydrate (→ starch grains swell); iodine (→ blue); Schulze's soln. (→ blue).

(iii) *Unstained mounts.*
1 Add alcohol (90%) to a little dry starch in a small test-tube and shake up.
2 Decant alcohol.
3 Add 'Euparal Essence' and shake up.
4 Transfer a little of the suspension to a slide.
5 Drain off 'Euparal Essence'.
6 Mount in 'Euparal' which, having a lower refractive index than other resins, enhances visibility.

*Suitable stain*

Safranin O (→ pink).

**Starfish**

See 'Asterias' (p. 104).

**Stem**

(i) *Suitable stain.* Hanstein's fuchsin-violet.
(ii) See 'Plant Tissue' (p. 158); and Methods **9** (p. 76); **10** (p. 77); **16** (p. 81); **17** (p. 81).

**Stentor**

**S/C**
(i) Dealers.
(ii) Collect and culture as *Euglena* (p. 127).

*Preparation techniques*

See 'Protozoa' (p. 164 ff), and 'Volvox' (p. 178).

**Stereum purpureum**

See 'Fungi (xi)' (p. 135), but stain with Delafield's haematoxylin.

**Sting of Wasp or Bee**

Kill the insect, compress its abdomen to extrude the poison sac and sting, and cut these away with a sharp scalpel.
Glycerol (10%) makes a suitable mountant for temporary preparations.

**Stomach**

See 'Alimentary Canal' (p. 96).

### Stomata

*In leaf:* See 'Leaf iii and viii' (pp. 142, 143).

### Suberin

*Suitable stains and reagents.*

Iodine + sulphuric acid (50%) (→ yellow-brown) (similarly for cutin); nascent indophenol blue (a mixture of α-naphthol and dimethyl-paraphenylenediamine) (→ deep violet) (similarly for cutin); neutral violet slightly acidified with hydrochloric acid (→ violet); phloroglucin + hydrochloric acid (→ deep pink) (similarly for cutin); Schulze's soln. (→ yellow-brown).

Alkanet (→ red) (slow); Sudan black B; Sudan III.

### Sucrose

See 'Sugars, Tests for, (*e*) Sucrose' (p. 174).

### Suctoria (*Dendrocometes; Spirochona*)

**S/C**

Attached to the gills of the fresh-water *Gammarus*.

Prepare as 'Peranema' (p. 156).

### Sugars, Tests for

(*a*) *General.*

1 Solution under test . . . . . . . 5 drops
α-naphthol (20% alc. soln.) . . . 5 drops
Distilled water. . . . . . . . . 2 ml

2 Shake together. Pour very gently, down the side of the tube:
Sulphuric acid (conc.) . . . . . . 2–5 ml
*Hold the tube on the slant.*

(Sugar: → faint to deep violet colouration at the junction of the liquids.)

(*b*) *Dextrose (glucose).*

(i) (α) *For sections.*

1 Mix together on a slide:
Phenylhydrazine hydrochloride . 1 drop
Sodium acetate in glycerol (p. 249) 1 drop

2 Place the section in the mixture and cover with a cover-slip.

3 Proceed to (β) **3** and **4**.

5 If desired, seal the cover-slip with gum mastic/paraffin wax.

(β) *For quantities.*

1 Sugar . . . . . . . . . . . 1 g
Phenylhydrazine hydrochloride . . 2 g
Sodium acetate (solid). . . . . . 4 g
Distilled water . . . . . . . . 20 ml

2 Filter.

3 Heat on a water-bath or in a water-jacketed oven. (30 min)

4 Allow to cool.

Dextrose → glucosazone in yellow, *needle-like crystals in* sheaves. [Cf. maltose, (*d*) (i) (p. 174).]

*Note:* This test is somewhat slow, but very delicate.

(ii)

1 Add Fehling's solutions A and B (p. 214).

2 Boil.

Dextrose → brick red ppt. of cuprous oxide. [Like laevulose, but unlike sucrose.]

(iii) As (e) (i) (p. 174).
(Dextrose → turquoise blue colour soon changing to light green.)

(iv) As (*c*) (ii) (below).
Dextrose → no colouration.

(v) As (*c*) (iii) below.
(Dextrose → no crystalline osazone unlike laevulose.)

(vi) As (*e*) (ii) below.
(Dextrose → no charring, unlike sucrose.)

(*c*) *Laevulose* (*Fructose*).

(i) Sugar solution . . . . . . . . 5 ml
Acetic acid (glacial) . . . . . 0.2 ml
Ammonium molybdate (4% alc. soln.) 10 ml

Laevulose gives a deep blue coloration. This test is almost, but not quite, specific for laevulose. Other sugars do give the reaction but less fully and less rapidly.

(ii)

1 Sugar solution . . . . . . . . 5 ml
Hydrochloric acid (conc.) . . . . 5 ml
Seliwanoff's reagent (p. 248) . . a few drops

2 Warm gently. Laevulose gives a fire-red colour. This test also indicates the presence of a ketone group in the sugar.

(iii) Laevulose gives a crystalline osazone with methyl phenylhydrazine (unlike dextrose which does not react).

(iv)

1 Add Fehling's solutions A and B.
2 Boil.

Laevulose, like dextrose, gives a precipitate of cuprous oxide.

(v) Add conc. sulphuric acid to the solid. There is *no* charring.

(*d*) *Maltose.*

(i) As (*b*) (i) (*β*) above. Maltose gives an osazone with yellow broad crystals in star like clusters.

(ii)

1 Sugar solution . . . . . . . . 5 ml
  Solid sodium carbonate . . . c. 1 gm
  Cole's solution (p. 200) . . . . 2 drops
2 Boil for at least ½ minute.

Maltose gives a yellow colouration.

(*e*) *Sucrose.*

(i) Sugar solution . . . . . . . . . 15 ml
  Cobaltous nitrate (5% aq.) . . . . 5 ml
  Mix thoroughly. Add:
  Sodium hydroxide (50% aq.) . . . 2 ml
  {Sucrose (pure) → permanent amethyst violet colour.}

(ii) Add sulphuric acid (conc.) to the solid.
  {Sucrose → chars, unlike dextrose and laevulose.}

(iii) As (*b*) (i) (p. 173).
  {Sucrose → no reaction, unlike dextrose and maltose.}

(iv) As (*b*) (ii) (p. 173).
  Sucrose: → no ppt. [Unlike dextrose and laevulose.]

**Sunflower**

See 'Helianthus' (p. 138).

**Suprarenal Body***

(i) *Fix.* Immediately after death with either formaldehyde (5%) or mercuric-formaldehyde. *Suitable stains.* Delafield's haematoxylin and eosin Y; Heidenhain's iron haematoxylin and van Gieson's.

*To show adrenalin.*

1 Fix potassium dichromate (2% aq.). (30 min)
2 Add 10% of formaldehyde (40%) and continue fixation. (3 d)
3 Wash in running water.
4 Embed in paraffin wax and section.
5 Counterstain sections in Delafield's haematoxylin (adrenalin → yellow-brown).

* After Carleton, 1926, *Histological Technique,* University Press, Oxford.

**Symphoricarpus racemosus**

See Methods **3** (p. 74); **4** (p. 74).

**Tadpole**

See 'Rana (ii)' (p. 165).

**Taenia**

**S/C**

(i) Suppliers.
(ii) Faeces of infected dog.
(iii) Intestine of infected rabbit.
(iv) Cysticerci from viscera, especially liver and mesentery, of infected rabbit

(i) *Suitable fixatives.*

Alcohol (70%); Bouin's fluid; formaldehyde (5–10%); formol-saline (5%); mercuric-acetic; mercuric chloride (sat. aq.).

(ii) *Suitable stains.*

(*a*) *Whole mounts.* Borax carmine (prolonged overstaining followed by differentation); Mayer's hydrochloric acid-carmine (anatomy → a bold crimson against a pink background); Mayer's haemalum.

(*b*) *Sections.* Delafield's haematoxylin; Mallory's stain.

*Preparation techniques*

(i) *Whole mounts.*

(*a*)

1 Wash 4–6 segments in sodium chloride (1% aq.).
2 Fix in hot mercuric-acetic (50°C). Allow to stand. (Till cool.)
3 Wash in running water. (12 h)
4 Stain in borax carmine.
5 Wash in alcohol (50%).
6 Dehydrate in 2 ethoxy ethanol.

7 Wash in fresh 2 ethoxy ethanol.
8 Clear in xylene.
9 Mount in D.P.X.

(*b*)*
1 Fix in formol-saline (5%). (48 h)
2 Wash in distilled water. (Several changes)
3 Cut into pieces of not less than 4 segments in length.
(*Note:* The outer segments act as a protective barrier against any possible over-treatment of the inner two segments.)
4 Stain in Mayer's haemalum (p. 220). (72 h)
5 Wash in distilled water. (Until surplus stain removed)
6 Blue in tap water or in alkaline-water (p. 188).
7 Bleach in 'Parazone' (dil.) (p. 239).
(Until the edges of the segments are colourless and the internal structure is clearly seen.)
*Note:* This process may be a matter of trial and error in order to find the best concentration of 'Parazone' for the particular tissue. If the 'Parazone' solution is too strong the tissue may disintegrate.
8 Wash in acid-alcohol (70%).
9 Blue in tap water or in tap water substitute. (20 min)
10 Dehydrate successively from alcohol (30%) to alcohol (100%).
11 Clear in beechwood creosote B.P.
12 Cut off the over-bleached outer segments.
13 Mount (singly) the suitably stained inner segments in D.P.X.

(ii) *Cysticercus.*
(*a*) *Everted scolex.*
1 Place the cysticercus in warm saline.
2 Transfer to the centre of a slide.
3 Cover with a piece of filter-paper.
4 Place a piece of glass rod (diameter 5mm approx.) transversely on the filter-paper on the slide and, with the flat palm of the hand, roll the rod with gentle pressure over the filter-paper. The scolex will be everted and the cysticercus will adhere to the slide, while the filter-paper absorbs the moisture.
5 Stain in borax carmine; or Mayer's hydrochloric acid-carmine (p. 196).
6 Wash in alcohol (50%).
7 Dehydrate in 2 ethoxy ethanol.
8 Wash in fresh 2 ethoxy ethanol.
9 Clear in xylene.
10 Mount in D.P.X.
(*b*) See 'Amphioxus, Whole Specimens' (p. 97).

(iii) See also 'Fasciola' (p. 127); and 'Planaria' (p. 157).

* After R. L. Williams, *Science Master's Book, Part III, Series III.* 1952 (Murray).

**Tannin**

*Microchemical test on fresh sections.*

Treat the section on the slide with iodine (Gram's or Lugol's) mixed with a drop of ammonium hydroxide (p. 188).
(→ brilliant red.)

*Preparation technique*

1 Fix small pieces of tissue in copper acetate (7% alc.). (8–10 d)
2 Cut sections and place in ferrous sulphate (0.5% aq.). (3 min)
3 Wash in water.
4 Wash in alcohol (70%).
5 Mount in glycerol-jelly.

*Note:* Tissue fixed in copper acetate may be preserved in alcohol (70%) and cut for treatment with ferrous sulphate later.
[Tannin regions (→ dark iron-blue).]

**Tape Worm**

See 'Taenia' (p. 174).

**Taxidermy**

See 'Skin' (p. 170).

**Teeth**

(i) Treat as bone (p. 110).
(ii) *Suitable stains.**
(*a*) *Dentine.* Haematoxylin and eosin Y (→ pink); iron haematoxylin and van Gieson's (→ black); Mallory's (→ bright red).
(*b*) *Enamel.* Haematoxylin and eosin Y (→ pink); iron haematoxylin and van Gieson's (→ grey to black); Mallory's (→ orange).

* After Hartridge and Haynes, 1930, *Histology for Medical Students*, University Press, Oxford.

(c) *Placoid scales of Scyllium* (*Dogfish*).
*To demonstrate the pulp cavity.*

After treatment by potassium hydroxide (5% aq.); add a little borax carmine to the alcohol (70%) and leave overnight.

**Tendon**

See 'Ligament' (p. 143).

**Testis**

(i) See 'Spermatozoa' (p. 171).
(ii) *See 'Ovary' (p. 154), but do *not* fix mammalian testis in formol-saline.
(iii) *Harden.* Alcohol (70%).
(iv) *Suitable stains.*
(*a*) See 'Animal Tissue – General histology' (p. 99).
(*b*) Ehrlich's haematoxylin and eosin Y (alc.).

**Textile Fibres**

See 'Fibres' (p. 129).

**Thread Worms**

**S/C**

In nephridia of *Lumbricus.* See 'Rhabditis' (p. 167).

**Thymus***

*Fix* in Formol-saline (5%) or mercuric-formaldehyde.

*Suitable stains.* Heidenhain's iron haematoxylin and van Gieson's; Mallory's (after mercuric-formaldehyde).

**Thyroid***

*Fix* in Mercuric-formaldehyde or formol-saline (5%).

*Suitable stains.*
Mallory's (after mercuric-formaldehyde); haematoxylin and eosin Y.

**Tomato**

See Method **3** (p. 74).

**Trachea of Insect**

See 'Periplaneta' (p. 156) and 'Acarine' (p. 94).

* After Carleton, 1926, *Histological Technique,* University Press, Oxford.

**Transparent Preparations of Plant Material**

(i) *Leaves and small herbaceous stems.*

**1** Remove chlorophyll with alcohol (70%).
**2** Wash with distilled water.
**3** Place in a watch-glass and cover with crystals of chloral hydrate.
**4** Add just sufficient distilled water to dissolve the chloral hydrate.
**5** Leave until the tissue has cleared.
*Note:* If a temporary preparation is required the tissue may be mounted in glycerol or chloral hydrate at this stage.

For Permanent Preparations proceed to:

**6** Wash thoroughly in warm distilled water.
**7** Stain in mrthyl violet 2B (1% aq.). (24–72 h)
**8** Dehydrate successively to alcohol (100%).
**9** Clear in xylene.
**10** Mount in D.P.X.

(ii) *Thicker herbaceous stems – to demonstrate vascular bundles.*

(*a*) *Stems not dense.*

**1** Place in lactic acid (75%). (1 week)
**2** Place in glycerol (70%). (3–4 d)
**3** Mount in glycerol.

(*b*) *Stems dense.*

*Temporary mount*

**1** Place in lactic acid (70%). (1 week)
**2** Stain in basic fuchsin previously decolourized by adding to it just sufficient ammonium hydroxide (sp. gr. 0.880) for the purpose.
**3** Warm in eau de Javelle until clear.
**4** Mount in glycerol.

*Permanent mount*

**1** Fix tissue in alcohol (75%).
**2** Clear in eau de Javelle (cold). (24 h)
**3** Wash in alcohol (30%). (Several times)
**4** Dehydrate successively to alcohol (100%).
**5** Clear in clove oil.
**6** Mount in D.P.X.

(iii) See also: 'Leaf' (p. 142); 'Maceration' (p. 45); 'Xylem' (p. 180).

**Trematodes**

*Preparation of Larval stages.*

**1** Stain in undiluted alum-carmine (Grenacher's). (6 h)
**2** Wash in distilled water. (1 h)
**3** Dehydrate in alcohol (30%), (50%), and (70%).

4 De-stain in alcohol (70%) containing 0.3% of hydrochloric acid. (Not more than 5 min – until all but nuclear stain is removed).
5 Wash in alcohol (95%).
6 Counterstain in fast green FCF, or methyl blue. *Note:* Prepare the counterstain by adding stock counterstain to alcohol (95%), drop by drop, until a pale solution is obtained.
Counterstain progressively under the (binocular) microscope.
7 Wash in alcohol (95%).
8 Dehydrate in alcohol (100%).
9 Clear in methyl salicylate (oil of wintergreen).
10 Mount in D.P.X.

**Tribonema**

(i) See 'Algae' (p. 94).
(ii) *Fix.* Formol-acetic-alcohol.
(iii) Stain in Haematoxylin (Heidenhain's) (mordant with *liquor ferri*).

**Trichodina**

**S/C**
Search tentacles of *Hydra.*

**Trocophore Larva**

Preserve in Alcohol (100%).
(i) *Whole mounts.* Where appropriate, the following processes should be carried out in flat-bottomed capsules.
1 Smear a clean slide very thinly with egg albumen.
2 By means of a pipette, place one drop of the alcohol containing a few larvae on to the middle of the slide.
3 Allow the albumen to coagulate (effect of the alcohol). *Handle carefully.*
4 Hydrate in alcohol (90%). (2 min)
5 Hydrate in alcohol (70%). (2 min)
6 Hydrate in alcohol (50%). (2 min)
7 Hydrate in alcohol (30%). (2 min)
8 Place a glass plate on the microscope stage to protect it. Examine the slide (face upwards) to check presence of larvae.
9 Stain in acid haemalum. (5 min)
10 Wash in distilled water.
11 Blue in alkaline water (p. 188). (2 min)
12 Examine under microscope. (Nuclei → deep blue; cytoplasm → clear.)
13 Dehydrate in alcohol (30%). (2 min)
14 Dehydrate in alcohol (50%). (2 min)
15 Dehydrate in alcohol (70%). (2 min)
16 Stain in eosin Y —Alcoholic soln. (p. 212). (1 min)
17 Wipe excess stain from the *back* of the slide. (Quickly)
18 Dehydrate in alcohol (90%). (Quickly)
19 Dehydrate in alcohol (100%), *twice.* (Quickly)
20 Clear in xylene.
21 Place a *dry* glass plate on the microscope stage. Quickly examine the slide (*face upwards*), before the xylene evaporates.
22 Replace the slide in xylene.
23 Place a drop of synthetic resin in the centre of a clean cover-slip.
24 Remove the slide from xylene. Wipe the *back* of the slide quickly and place it *back* downwards on the bench.
25 Hold the edge of the cover-slip, *face downwards,* by means of forceps, so that one edge rests on the slide and gently lower it on to the slide and allow it to settle itself.
26 Allow the preparation to dry in a warm place before handling further.

**Trypanosome**

See 'Blood method (vii) (p. 110).

**Tubularia**

See 'Coelenterates' (p. 119).

**Tunicates**

*Kill, fix and preserve.* Alcohol (70%).

**Ulothrix**

(i) See 'Algae' (p. 94).

*Preparation technique*

(ii)
1 Fix and stain in nigrosin WS dissolved in Bouin's fluid. (3 months)
2 Wash in distilled water.
3 Place in glycerol (10%) and allow soln. to concentrate at room temperature.

**Vascular System of Plants**

(i) *In leaves — to demonstrate.*

(*a*)

1 Place the cut stems of wallflower (*Cheiranthus Cheiri*) (with leaves attached) in erythrosin bluish (p. 212). (Several h)

*Note:* The stain Magdala red (C.I. No. 50375) is sometimes recommended for this purpose but it is very expensive. Indeed if the stain purchased as 'Magdala red' was reasonable in price it may have been wrongly labelled and was probably erythrosin bluish (C.I. No. 45430) or possibly phloxine B (C.I. No. 45410).

2 Remove a stem from the stain and cut across the petiole at the base of the leaf, under water. Petioles may be left in water.

(*b*) See also 'Leaf (ii)' (p. 142); 'Transparent Preparations of Plant Material (ii)' (p. 176).

(ii) *To stain the whole vascular system* (*Talboys' method*).*

*Suitable for sections or for whole mounts of segments.*

1 Sever the stem of a growing plant [e.g. *Humulus Lupulus* (hop) or *Lycospersicum esculentum* (tomato)] at soil level.

2 Insert the cut end of the stem in a vessel containing the *colourless derivative* of either basic fuchsin (see Schiff's reagent, p. 245), or crystal violet (p. 201).

*Note:* The rate of movement of the colourless dye derivative will depend partly on the rate of transpiration by the plant, but vascular elements in the immediate vicinity of the cut end of the stem will be deeply stained in from 1 to 3 min. When movement of the colourless derivative has gone far enough to meet requirements,

either (*a*)

3 Cut sections.

4 Counterstain sections in light green SF yellowish (1%) in alcohol (95%).

5 Dehydrate.

6 Clear.

7 Mount.

or (*b*)

3 Cut the stem into short segments.

4 Treat with hot nitric acid (15% aq.) to remove epidermal and cortical tissues. (5–15 s)

5 Wash in distilled water, thoroughly.

6 Dehydrate up to alcohol (100%).

7 Clear in clove oil, for preservation as permanent whole mounts.

(iii) See also 'Phloem' (p. 157); 'Transparent Preparations of Plant Material (ii)' (p. 176); 'Xylem' (p. 180).

* From information supplied by Dr. P. W. Talboys, East Malling Research Station.

**Vaucheria**

**S/C**

(i) Suppliers.

(ii) Collect from ponds.

(iii) See 'Culture Media 3' (p. 203).

(iv) *Zoospores:*

1 Place the parent plants in a jar filled with hard tap water. Zoospores are produced in two to three d at the junction of the water surface with the jar.

2 Remove the zoospores to a dish of water. The zoospores germinate quickly and in one or two weeks the sexual stage is produced.

3 Sub-culture either by cutting up the 'parent' mass or from zoospores.

*Preparation techniques*

See 'Algae' (p. 94).

**Vegetable Fibres**

See 'Fibres' (p. 129).

**Veliger Larva**

See 'Trocophore Larva' (p. 177).

**Volvocales**

**S/C**

See 'Culture Media 3' (p. 203).

**Volvox**

**S/C**

(i) Dealers.

(ii) Collect and culture as *Euglena* (p. 127), and in clear ponds. Rather local in habit.

(iii) Said to occur in temporary flood-ponds on grassland.
(iv) See 'Culture Media 3' (p. 203).

*To preserve green colour.*
See 'Algae (iv)' (p. 94).

*Preparation techniques*

*Suitable stain.* Methyl green.
Mountants: formaldehyde (5%); formaldehyde (5%). 1 vol./glycerol 1 vol.
See 'Protozoa' (p. 164).

(i) *Examination of living specimens:*
Examine under LP either in a watch-glass, or in a cavity-slide. Examine under HP on a plane slide, under a cover-slip supported on a few fibres of glass.

(ii) *To demonstrate cell boundaries and protoplasmic connections between members of a colony:*

1 Place some of the colony in dilute methylene blue soln. (15 min)

| | |
|---|---|
| Methylene blue . . . . . | 0.1 g |
| Distilled water . . . . . | 1 000 ml |

(*Note:* The solution should have not more than a very light tint of blue. If too dark, dilute further.)

2 Place a drop of the stained colony on a watch-glass and examine under HP as in (i) above.

(iii)

1 Place a small drop of culture in a watch-glass.
2 *Fix* by adding Ripart's and Petit's fluid (p. 243).
3 By means of a pipette, withdraw sufficient liquid with included specimens just to fill the cavity of a cavity-slide. (A little practice with water beforehand will be a help in judging the right amount of liquid to withdraw.)
4 Cover the cavity with a round cover-slip of medium thickness (No. 2).
5 Use either a very fine pipette made by drawing out a piece of glass tubing and bending the point to an angle of 45°, or (less efficient) the edge of a piece of clean filter-paper, to withdraw any surplus fluid from the edge of the cover-slip. Care must be taken *not* to withdraw fluid from under the cover-slip, and not to disturb the cover-slip nor to withdraw fluid from under it. Use the filter-paper to remove any surplus fluid from the surface of the slide.
6 Allow the surfaces of slide and cover-slip to dry off.
7 Ring with successive layers of a suitable cement (pp. 246 and 247).
8 Seal with asphaltum black.

**Vorticella**

**S/C**

(i) Dealers.
(ii) Examine water weeds and debris.
(iii) Culture as *Euglena* (p. 127).
(iv) Sometimes found attached to *Cyclops.*
(v) See 'Culture Media 3' (p. 203).

*Preparation techniques*

(i) *General Method.* See 'Protozoa (iv)' (p. 164). but difficult to avoid contraction.
(ii) *Narcotize.* Menthol.
(iii) *Fix.* Suddenly by heat or osmium tetroxide (0.25%).
(iv) *Suitable stains.* Methyl green; light green SF yellowish; iodine and basic fuchsin; iron haematoxylin and orange G.

**Whelk**

See 'Aquatic and Marine Organisms' (p. 103).

**White Deadnettle**

See 'Lamium album' (p. 142).

**Wood**

(*a*) *To soften before sectioning.*

1 Place in polyvinyl alcohol-lacto-phenol (p. 241) and warm. (30 min)
2 Drain off the liquid and allow to cool.

(*b*) See 'Xylem' (below).

**Worm**

See 'Lumbricus' (p. 144).

**Xylem**

(i) *Suitable stains.* Safranin O (→ red); counterstain with anilin blue WS, or methyl green, or Delafield's haematoxylin, or basic fuchsin mixed with methylene blue, or fast green FCF in clove oil.

(ii) *Maceration.*
See 'Technique of Maceration (iv)' (p. 46).

(iii) *Debenham's method for xylem of whole plants, or of organs.* *

Processes must be carried out in covered Petri dishes (at least 10 cm diameter) which must not contain more than 2 large or 5 small pieces of tissue. To avoid damage to tissue, liquids must be pipetted in and out of the dishes.

Use either, (*a*) fresh material,
or, (*b*) material fixed in alcohol (70%),
or, (*c*) dried material. First soak in water at 60°C. (Not less than 3 w)

**1** Clear in lactic acid (70%) or (75%), in oven (58°C–60°C). Replace with fresh lactic acid if clearing is prolonged. (1–3 w)
**2** Replace lactic acid with cold glycerol (70%). (2 d)
**3** Replace with fresh cold glycerol (70%). (1 d)
**4** Replace with glycerol (50%). (1 d)
**5** Replace with 2–3 changes of alcohol (50%). (2–3 d)
**6** If desired to store at this stage,
either, (*a*) store in alcohol (70%),
or, (*b*) wash in alcohol (70%) and store in Calberla's fluid. Before proceeding to **7**, wash in alcohol (70%). (Several changes. 6–24 h)
If not desired to store, proceed to **7**.
**7** Hydrate with alcohol (40%), (30%), (20%), (10%), distilled water. (6 h each)
**8** Bleach with strong eau de Javelle, in oven at 40°C. Watch progress of decolourization under microscope. (20 min – several h)
**9** Wash in cold distilled water. (Several changes – not less than 12 h)
If light material tends to float, do *not* attempt to sink it in the liquid.
**10** Wash in alcohol (10%).
**11** If desired to store at this stage,
**a** Dehydrate to alcohol (60%).
**b** Store in Calberla's fluid.
(This tends to counteract shrinkage suffered in the bleaching process.)
**c** After storage, wash in alcohol (70%). (Several changes. 6–12 h)
**d** Hydrate to alcohol (10%).
If not desired to store, proceed to **12**.
**12** Stain in fresh ammoniacal fuchsin (special formula (ii), p. 216).
(1–3 d, depending on thickness of material)
Keep dishes in a cool place to avoid loss of ammonia.
**13** Wash in alcohol (100%).
(2–3 changes, until red colour is washed out of thin-walled tissue and sclerenchyma)
[Xylem (→ brilliant red, if lignification is sufficiently advanced)]
**14** Dehydrate in fresh alcohol (100%).
**15** Mount.

Then either (*a*) *Thin specimens*

**16** Place a clean slide into the Petri dish of alcohol and float the specimen on to the slide.
**17** Remove slide and wash with alcohol (100%).
**18** Draw off alcohol quickly.
**19** Mount in 'Euparal'.
**20** Cover with a cover-slip. If necessary, remove any bubbles by transferring slide to a hot-plate.

or (*b*) *Thick specimens.*

**16** Prepare a cell on a slide by one of the methods suggested under 'Mounting' (pp. 57–59).
**17** Replace the alcohol in the Petri dish with cedar-wood oil. (Until specimen is transparent)
**18** Place prepared slide in the dish and float the specimen into the cell.
**19** Remove slide from dish and drain oil from cell. (Until specimen is almost dry)
**20** Fill cell with Canada balsam so that a film spreads on to rim of cell. (Balsam should not be too thin, because solvent may loosen the cell.)
**21** Cover. If necessary, remove any bubbles by transferring slide to hot-plate.

(iv) See also 'Transparent Preparations of Plant Material' (p. 176).

**Yeast** (*Saccharomyces cerevisiae*)

**S/C**

(i) National Collection of Yeast Cultures, Brewing Industry Research Foundation.

* E. M. Debenham, *Annals of Botany*, **III**, 10, 369. April 1939. Adapted by kind permission of the Author.

(ii) Brewery or bakery.

(iii) *Stir 1 g brewer's yeast into 200 ml freshly boiled Pasteur's solution that has been cooled by blowing fresh, cold, air through it. Maintain at 20°C for 12 h. Sub-culture after 12 h.

(iv) Mix 10 g brewer's yeast with 200 ml sucrose (5% aq.). Maintain at 30°C.

(v) *To culture on a solid medium:*

**1** For general technique refer to 'Culture Media 1' (pp. 202–203).

**2** Prepare the culture medium as follows:

| | |
|---|---|
| Gelatine | 25 g |
| Beer wort† | 250 ml |

Warm very gently until the gelatine melts. Do NOT boil or even over-heat.

**3** Pour the medium into sterilized tubes, plug and sterilize. Store until required.

**4** When required for inoculation warm (say) four tubes on a water bath at 25°C maximum.

**5** Add a minute quantity of yeast to one tube, taking all the usual precautions against contamination, and shake well.

**6** Pour out all but a few drops of the liquid from this tube into a sterilized Petri dish, again taking all the usual precautions. Cover.

**7** Transfer the few drops of liquid remaining in the tube from **6** into another tube of culture medium. Shake well and transfer all but a few drops of the contents of this tube to another Petri dish.

**8** Repeat the process with the remaining two tubes, thus giving four plates with successively diluted inoculations.

**9** When the inoculated medium has set, invert the covered plates and incubate at room temperature for several days.

**10** Examine at intervals.

(vi) *Hanging drop cultures*

See 'Culture Media 4 (*a*)' (p. 208), and use glucose solution as the culture medium.

(vii) *To produce spores* (*asci*).

Place some yeast or yeast culture on slices of potato or carrot, or on a sterilized plaster-of-Paris plate. Leave for 7 d.

* After Stork and Renouf, 1932, *Fundamentals of Biology*, Murray.

† Beer wort is obtainable from breweries.

*Preparation techniques*

(i) Stain *intra vitam* with Nile blue sulphate.

(ii) *To see glycogen, nucleus, protoplasm, vacuole.*

(*a*) Irrigate with iodine. [Glycogen (→ strong reddish-brown).]

(*b*)

**1** Place a drop of culture on a slide.

**2** Allow to become almost dry.

**3** Stain in potassium permanganate (conc. aq.).

**4** Gently blot off excess liquid.

(iii) *Spores and vegetative cells.*

(*a*)

**1** Smear a small portion of culture, thinly, on a slide or cover-slip.

**2** Allow to become almost dry by waving in the air.

**3** Stain by flooding with Ziehl's phenol-fuchsin (p. 217).

**4** Warm gently over a low flame and allow the liquid to steam. (10 min)

**5** Drain off excess liquid.

**6** Wash in ethanol or in sulphuric acid (1%–2%).

**7** Wash in distilled water.

**8** Stain in methylene blue (sat. aq.). (½–1 min)

**9** Wash in distilled water.

**10** Press gently with filter-paper to remove excess water.

**11** Wave in the air to dry.

**12** Mount in D.P.X.

[Spores (→ red); vegetative cells (→ blue).]

(*b*) ***1–5**, as Method (iii) (*a*) **1–5** (above), but stain in the following:

| | |
|---|---|
| Basic fuchsin | 0.05 g |
| Malachite green | 0.5 g |
| Distilled water | 100 ml |

**6–9** as Method (iii) (*a*) **9–12** (above).

[Spores (→ greenish-blue); vegetative cells (→ pink or violet).]

(iv) *Nuclei.*

**1** Smear a small portion of culture, thinly, on a slide or cover-slip.

**2** *Fix* by warming *gently* over a very low flame.

**3** Stain in 50/50 acid fuchsin (1% aq.)/methyl green (1% aq.). (1 min)

**4** Transfer to tannic acid (5% aq.). (20 s)

**5** Wash in acid-water (p. 252).

**6** Rinse in distilled water.

* After P. Gray, *Nature*, **CLXVII**, 329, 1941.

7 Remove excess water by pressing gently with filter-paper.
8 Wave in the air to dry.
9 Mount in D.P.X.

**Zooeae**

See 'Aquatic and Marine Animals' (p. 103).

**Zoophytes**

Stain in Hanstein's fuchsin-violet (p. 217).

**Zygnema sp.**

**S/C**
See 'Culture Media 3' (p. 203).

# 7 Formulae and hints

### Note on the System of Indexing in this Chapter

Short of giving a multitude of cross-references, reference to which may be time-wasting, the difficulty with any system of indexing is that not only may the author and the reader be accustomed to different designations for the same substance, but also their respective minds may run in different channels at different times and in different circumstances.

For example, the author may think in terms of 'Clarke's Fluid', one reader in terms of 'acetic-alcohol', while yet another, perhaps a little pedantically, may question the historical accuracy of an attribution of origin to any particular person. Although there would seem to be something reasonably specific about the name 'Clarke's Fluid' the fact remains that the name of the originator *is* disputed and there is more than one modification of the 'acetic-alcohol' formula.

The very term 'acetic-alcohol', whether hyphenated or not, itself raises two problems, namely, (i) should the index use the full name 'acetic-', or should it use the abbreviated prefix 'aceto-'? and (ii) should the index list the substance under its supposedly commonly-used name, or under the name of its major, or of its key, constituent?

There remains, also, the problem of substances that have both a generic and a specific, or an originator's name. Such, for example, as 'acid fuchsin' and 'basic fuchsin'; and 'Delafield's haematoxylin' and 'Ehrlich's haematoxylin'. Are these best indexed as such, or should they be indexed, respectively, under 'fuchsin' and 'haematoxylin'?

With such considerations in mind, as far as this chapter is concerned, it has seemed best to list substances, primarily, under their generic names, or, where mixtures are concerned, under the name of their major, or of their key, constituent. Thus, 'Alcohol, acid'; 'Alcohol, alkaline'. Exceptions to this rule have, however, been made where, although the initial name of the mixture is not the name of the major constituent, a certain order of names appears to have become fixed by long usage. Thus, for example, 'formol-acetic-alcohol' (sometimes abbreviated to 'F.A.A.') has been listed as such, and neither under 'alcohol', nor under 'acetic'.

The nomenclature of stains is even more confusing, because different manufacturers, merchants and laboratory suppliers sometimes use different names for the same dye. Fortunately, in this instance, some clarification is possible by reference to the *Colour Index*, the second edition of which was published jointly by the Society of Dyers and Colourists and the American Association of Textile Chemists and Colorists, in 1956.

This Colour Index is in two parts. In Part I, each dye is given a 'preferred designation' and a 'usage number' *according to its application in the textile industry*. In Part II, each dye is given a five-figure C.I. No., or 'constitution number', *according to its chemical constitution*, in so far as this has been elucidated. The Part II C.I. No. should be used when stains are being ordered.

Unfortunately, many synonyms remain. For example, the dye listed in Part I as 'C.I. Basic Violet I' and in Part II as 'C.I. No. 42535' is also known as 'anilin(e) violet', 'dahlia violet B', 'methyl violet B' and 'methyl violet 2B', the latter name being the 'preferred designation' of the United States Commission on Biological Stains.

As a minor contribution to the establishment of further order, and since this book is concerned with the uses of dyes as biological stains rather than as chemicals in the textile industry, *the preferred designations of the U.S. Commission on Biological Stains* have been used throughout. For the same reason the final 'e' in such words as 'anilin' and 'fuchsin' has been omitted, according to the American custom. (On the other hand, contrary to American usage, 'ae' diphthong has been retained in such words as 'haemocytometer', 'haematoxylin' and 'laevulose'.) The Part II C.I. Number is given with each (U.S. Commission) 'preferred designation' and the Part I designation and usage number, together with any other synonyms are also given, but in italics.

Confusion is still liable to arise when indexing the names of mixtures of dyes, or of other substances, perhaps with the (alleged) originator's name attached. An example is the mixture of dyes sometimes called 'Hanstein's rosanilin violet'. This consists of equal parts of the dye known as 'basic fuchsin' [itself a mixture of pararosanilin (magenta O) (C.I. No. 42500), rosanilin (C.I. No. 42510) and magenta II] with methyl violet 2B (C.I. No. 42535). As basic fuchsin is the key substance it has been indexed under 'Fuchsin, Basic-violet (rosanilin-violet) (Hanstein's)'. This system has been adopted where similar problems have presented themselves.

In accordance with the custom enjoined in *An Introduction to Chemical Nomenclature*, by R. S. Cahn (1959), Butterworth, London, organic compounds with names bearing prefixes (e.g. the old-fashioned '$\alpha$-', '$\beta$-', etc., or the more modern, corresponding, '1-', '2-', etc.) have been listed under their basic names. Thus, '$\alpha$-bromonaphthalene' will be found listed under the 'b's'; and '$\beta$-hydroxyquinoline' will be found listed under the 'h's'.

As far as possible, cross-references have been avoided in this chapter, but exceptions have been made where substances appear to be equally well known, or might reasonably be known, by alternative names.

While the arrangement outlined is unlikely to satisfy every reader, it is hoped that it may annoy few, please some, and simply help the remainder. What is really needed, of course, is a sort of 'biological working party' to sort out and standardize the whole system of biological nomenclature and spelling. At present chaos reigns almost supreme.

*Note:* i A list of abbreviations used is given on p. ix.

ii Culture media are listed collectively under 'Culture Media' (pp. 202–209).

**Acetate Buffer Solution – pH 4.7**

*Solution A – Acetic acid* N/5.

| | |
|---|---|
| Acetic acid N . . . . . . . | 200 ml |
| Distilled water to make up to . . | 1000 ml |

*Solution B – Sodium acetate* N/5.

| | |
|---|---|
| Acetic acid N . . . . . . . | 200 ml |
| Sodium hydroxide N. . . . . | 200 ml |
| Distilled water to make up to . . | 1000 ml |

*Solution C – Acetate Buffer pH* 4.7.

| | |
|---|---|
| Solution A . . . . . . . . | 46 ml |
| Solution B . . . . . . . . | 45 ml |
| Distilled water to make up to . . | 250 ml |

Check the final pH with a meter and adjust if necessary.

**Acetic Acid**

(i) *Solution for treatment of tissues:*
Connective tissue (white fibres disappear, yellow fibres defined);

| | |
|---|---|
| Acetic acid (glacial) . . . . . | 1 ml |
| Distilled water . . . . . . . | 99 ml |

(ii) *Solution for dilution of blood sample when taking a white blood cell count:*

| | |
|---|---|
| Acetic acid (glacial) . . . . . | 1 ml |
| Distilled water . . . . . . . | 99 ml |

Methyl violet 2B (1% aq.). Sufficient to tinge the solution.

**Acetic-Alcohol**

See 'Clarke's Fluid' (p. 119).

**Acetic-Alcohol-Formaldehyde**

See 'Formol-Acetic-Alcohol (F.A.A.)' (p. 215).

**Acetic-Carmine**

See 'Carmine, Acetic-' (p. 193).

**Acetic-Orcein**

See 'Orcein, Acetic-' (p. 238).

**Adhesives**

*Apathy's adhesive, for attaching 'Celloidin' blocks to microtome chuck*

| | |
|---|---|
| Alcohol-ether (1/1 mixture) | 100 ml |
| Clove oil | 33 ml |
| 'Celloidin' | 16 gm |

*for Cellophane:*

Add 15% of glycerol to gum arabic; or to gelatine; or to any good gum or glue; or to sodium silicate aq. (waterglass).

*Egg albumen* (*Mayer's glycerol-egg albumen*):

*For attaching sections to slides.* (See also Haupt's adhesive, below).

| | |
|---|---|
| White of egg | 50 ml |
| Glycerol | 50 ml |
| Sodium salicylate | 1 g |

First shake the white of egg with *a few drops* of acetic acid (dil.). Add the other ingredients and shake well together. Filter (*long time*) (if necessary on a filter pump) into a clean bottle.

*for General Purposes:*

'Araldite' (epoxy resin) (water-proof): for glass, metals, porcelain, rubber, wood.
'Bostik' *Adhesives:* Nos. 1 (Clear); 2 (Power, black); 3 (Permanent contact); 4 (Tile, white); 7 (PVA epoxy resin). *Seals:* Nos. 5 (Strip, white); 6 (Permanent, black).

*for Glass:*

(i) 'Araldite'; 'Bostik No. 1'.

| | |
|---|---|
| (ii) Gum arabic | 1000 g |
| Distilled water | 250 ml |
| *Add* Aluminium sulphate (cryst.) | 2 g |
| Distilled water | 20 ml |

*Glycerol Dextrin:* *

*For mounting diatoms.*
Dissolve dextrin in water till it is almost a jelly. Add glycerol and shake thoroughly until as much dextrin as possible has been dissolved in the glycerol. Add a few crystals of phenol. Filter through fine-mesh nylon.

*Haupt's adhesive:*

*For attaching microtome sections to slides: a more reliable adhesive than egg albumen.*

*Note:* Sections should be floated on to the slide in formalin (4%).

| | |
|---|---|
| Gelatine (best grade) | 1 g |
| Glycerol | 15 ml |
| Phenol (crystals) | 2 g |
| Distilled water | 100 ml |

Heat the water to *not more than* 30°C and dissolve the gelatine in it, *at this temperature*. (Gelatine requiring a higher temperature for aqueous solution is not satisfactory. If solution is too slow the gelatine will start to decompose.) When, *and not until*, solution of the gelatine is complete add the phenol and the glycerol and stir well. Filter.

*for Labels:* †

*Solution* (*a*):

| | |
|---|---|
| Gum tragacanth | 30 g |
| Water | 250 ml |

Stand for some hours. Shake *until the liquid froths*, and mix with:

*Solution* (*b*):

| | |
|---|---|
| Gum arabic | 120 g |
| Water | 250 ml |

Strain the mixture through linen and add:

*Mixture* (*c*):

| | |
|---|---|
| Glycerine | 150 g |
| Oil of thyme | 2.5 g |

*for Metals:* 'Araldite'; Bostik No. 1'.

*for 'Perspex':*

(*a*) If the surfaces to be joined are machined and well-fitting, paint the surfaces with chloroform and apply pressure.

* Reproduced by courtesy of Messrs. W. Watson & Sons Ltd.

† After Lee, 1937, *Microtomist's Vade-Mecum*, Churchill, London.

(*b*) If the surfaces to be joined are *not* well-fitting, paint them with a solution made by dissolving 'Perspex' shavings in chloroform until the solution has the consistency of a moderately viscous syrup.

*for Polythene:*

The author does not know of an effective adhesive, other than fusing the two polythene surfaces together with, for example, a warm household iron or the end of an electric soldering iron. Single-ended sleeves of polythene provide reasonably effective air-tight and water-tight containers if the free end is knotted round itself or folded several times and secured with a rubber band.

*for Porcelain:*

'Araldite': 'Bostik No. 1'.

*for Rubber:*

'Araldite'; 'Bostik No. 2'.

*for Wood:*

'Aerolite C'; 'Araldite'; 'Bostik No. 1'; 'Bostik No. 3' (for plywood). See also 'Sealing Media' (p. 246).

### Alcohol, Absolute

See 'Alcohol, Ethyl' (below).

### Alcohol, Acetic

See 'Clarke's Fluid' (p. 199) and 'Farmer's Fluid' (p. 213).

### Alcohol, Acetic-Formaldehyde

See 'Formol-Acetic-Alcohol' (p. 215).

### Alcohol, Acid

(i) Alcohol (70%) . . . . . . . . 100 ml
Hydrochloric acid (conc.) . . . . 0.5 ml

(ii) Specially weak, for Chamberlain's method for fungi:
Wash out a clean bottle with hydrochloric acid (conc.), drain thoroughly, and fill up the bottle with alcohol (70%).

### Alcohol, Alkaline

Alcohol (90%) . . . . . . . . . 99.5 ml
Ammonium hydroxide (sp. gr. 0.880) 0.5 ml

### Alcohol, Benzyl

Benzyl alcohol is much cheaper than ethyl alcohol and dehydrates from ethyl alcohol (70%) or (90%) and also clears. It therefore saves the cost of absolute ethyl alcohol and clove oil.

Benzyl alcohol will *not* dissolve wax. Therefore, when used as a clearing agent prior to wax impregnation, the benzyl alcohol must be removed from tissues by means of a wax solvent, such as xylene, before wax impregnation.

### Alcohol, Ethyl (Ethanol)

(i) *For dehydration.*

(*a*) Alcohol (100%), i.e. 'absolute alcohol', has a tremendous capacity for taking up water. *It will not remain absolute if the stopper is left off the container; or if a person breathes or sneezes into the container; or if, for example, a watch-glass into which it has been poured for the purpose of dehydrating a tissue is left uncovered.* The appropriate precautions are obvious. Alcohol (100%) is extremely expensive.

(*b*) *For all ordinary microtechnical processes, industrial methylated spirit may be substituted for ethyl alcohol provided steps have been taken to remove such traces of water as it may contain.*
The *approximate* analysis of industrial methylated spirit (74° O.P.) is: ethyl alcohol 95%, methyl alcohol 5%, together with small amounts of water. Unlike 'methylated spirit', as sold for domestic purposes, it does not contain paraffin, pyridine or methyl violet. *Industrial methylated spirit for laboratory purposes may be purchased only on licence issued by the Customs and Excise Department.* The address of the nearest local office will be found in the Telephone Directory.
*To remove water from industrial methylated spirit* place about 1 litre of spirit in a 2-litre flat-bottomed flask and add anhydrous copper sulphate. Replace the stopper and agitate the flask from time to time over several days. Filter through a 25 cm diameter coarse filter-paper supported in a fluted funnel having its stem placed well inside the neck of a dry receiving flask. Plug any space between funnel stem and neck of receiving flask with cotton-wool to prevent ingress of moist air. Stopper

the receiving flask as soon as possible. After use, the copper sulphate may be dried on the filter-paper and then calcined and used again.

(*c*) Lower grades of alcohol may be prepared from industrial methylated spirit after first drying it as suggested in paragraph (*b*), above. The Table for the Dilution of Liquids (p. 211) may be used for finding the volumes of water to add to make up various grades.

(*d*) It is a useful saving of time to have Winchester-quart bottles, graduated to hold 2000 ml each, of different strengths of alcohol. This leaves room for thorough shaking. See that the bottles are clean, pour in the required proportion of alcohol, fix a label on the bottle, and mark the label with a horizontal line at the level the alcohol reaches; adding the words '*Industrial methylated spirit to this line →*'. Now, without yet shaking, add the required proportion of distilled water, fix another label, mark the label with a horizontal line at the level the mixture reaches and the words '*Add distilled water to this line →*'. Finally label the bottle with the strength of alcohol it contains. Thorough shaking is now essential.

(ii) *For maceration prior to teasing* . 30%

(iii) *For fixation.*

(*a*) Rapid fixation of animal tissue . . 100%

(*b*) Slow fixation of animal tissue

Alcohol (90%) . . . . . . 1 part by vol.
Water . . . . . . . . 2 parts by vol.

Do not allow the tissue to remain in the fixative for longer than 24 h.

(*c*) Fixation of plant tissue . . . . 90%
After fixation, wash in alcohol.

(iv) *For hardening* . . . . . . . 90%

(v) *For preserving.*

(*a*) general tissue . . . . . . . . . 70%
(*b*) sponges . . . . . . . . . . . 75%
(*c*) worms . . . . . . . . . . . 90%

**Alcohol-Formalin**

Alcohol (70%) . . . . . . . 100 ml
Formaldehyde (40%) . . . . 6 ml

Fixation should be for 15 min for small and delicate pieces of plant tissue, and 12 h for large pieces of coarser tissue.

**Alcohol-Hydrochloric Acid**

*For preliminary treatment of plant tissue for maceration:*

Alcohol (industrial) (95%) . . . 75 ml
Hydrochloric acid (bench) . . . 25 ml

**Alcohol-Xylene**

*To prevent shrinkage on clearing.*

Alcohol (100%) . . . . . . . 50 ml
Xylene . . . . . . . . . . . 50 ml

**Alizarin Red S.** C.I. No. 58005

*Syn: C.I. Mordant Red 3; Alizarin Carmine; Alizarin Red, Water Soluble.* An acid dye.

For bone (Dawson's method, p. 111):

Alizarin red S . . . . . . . 0.1 g
Potassium hydroxide (1%) . . . 1000 ml

**Alkanet** C.I. 75530

*Syn: Alkannin.* A natural dye chemically related to Alizarin.

[Cork (→ red); cuticle (→ red); fats (→ deep red); protoplasm (→ pale rose red) (½ h); resin (→ deep red) (1 h); rubber (→ red).]

Satd. solution of the roots of *Anchusa* (*Alcanna*) *tinctoria* in alcohol (50%).

**Altmann's Fixative (for mitochondria)**

Potassium dichromate, 5% aq. . 1 vol.
Osmium tetroxide, 2% aq. . . . 1 vol.

Use pieces of tissue 2 mm or less in thickness and fix for 24 h. Wash out overnight in running water.

**Alum, Ammonia-**

(i) *For alum-haematoxylin:* 5% aq.
(ii) *For Delafield's haematoxylin:* sat. aq. soln.

**Alum, Iron**

(i) 0.5% aq.
(ii) *Mordant and differentiator for Heidenhain's haematoxylin and Anderson's iron-alum-haematoxylin,* 2% aq.

**Alum, Potassium-**

(i) *For alum-haematoxylin:* 5% aq.
(ii) *For dilution of old Ehrlich's haematoxylin:* Satd. aq. soln.
(iii) *For Renaut's eosin-haematoxylin:* Satd. alc. soln.
(iv) See also 'Haematoxylin, Carazzi's' (p. 221); and 'Haematoxylin, Ehrlich's' (p. 222).

**Amann's Medium (Lacto-phenol)**

A useful clearing agent for sections and small whole mounts (e.g. small, whole flowers can be cleared in two days), and a mountant of high refractive index for *temporary* preparations. Permanent preparations may be mounted in glycerol-jelly and sealed. Particularly useful for the study of cutinized and suberized tissues. Tends to shrink cells. Penetration is aided by warming the fluid.

Amann's Medium may also be used as a vehicle for carrying certain stains. See (iv) (below).

*Note:* The fluid should be kept in a brown glass bottle and, as it dissolves varnish, etc., it should be kept away from microscopes and lenses.

(i) *For acarids, nematodes etc., and other small whole mounts.*

| | |
|---|---|
| Phenol . . . . . . . | 20 g |
| Distilled water . . . | 20 ml |

Dissolve the phenol completely.

*Add:*

| | |
|---|---|
| Lactic acid . . . . | 20 g (= 16.8 ml) |

When solution is complete,

*Add:*

| | |
|---|---|
| Glycerol . . . . . | 40 g (= 33.3 ml) |

Add the medium, drop by drop, to the water containing the organism(s).

(ii) *For fungal hyphae in host tissue (Godwin's method)* xi (*a*) (p. 135).
As, (i) (above), but reduce the amount of glycerol to 20 g.

(iii) *For general mycological purposes.*
As, (i) (above), but reduce the amount of glycerol to 10 g.

(iv) *As a vehicle for stains.*
As, (i) (above), but add, either acid fuchsin 0.5%; or aniline blue WS 0.5%; or, fast green FCF 0.5%.

**Amidol**

*To reduce silver nitrate* (p. 248). 1% aq. soln.

**Ammonium Carbonate**

*For killing small insects.*

Crystals placed in a wide-mouthed, glass-stoppered bottle (depending on the size of insects for which it is intended). Less dangerous than the 'killing bottle' usually supplied by 'lepidopterists' suppliers'.

**Ammonia Solution, for 'Blueing' Haematoxylin-Stained Sections**

| | |
|---|---|
| Ammonia solution (sp. gr. 0.880) | 3 ml |
| Distilled water . . . . . . | 100 ml |

**Ammonium Dichromate**

*For fixing and hardening nervous tissue.*

| | |
|---|---|
| Ammonium dichromate . . . | 10 g |
| Distilled water . . . . . . | 1000 ml |

**Ammonium Hydroxide**

*For use in microchemical test for tannin* (p. 175).

| | |
|---|---|
| Ammonium hydroxide . . . . | 10 ml |
| Distilled water . . . . . . | 90 ml |

**Ammonium Molybdate**

*For test for laevulose. See 'Sugars, Tests for* (*c*) *Laevulose* i' (p. 173).

| | |
|---|---|
| Alcohol (100%) . . . . . . | 96 ml |
| Ammonium molybdate . . . . | 4 g |

**Anilin Blue WS (i.e. Water Soluble)**

*Syn.: C.I. China blue* 22; *China blue; Cotton blue; Marine blue* V; *Soluble blue* M3; *Soluble blue* 2R.

*Note:* According to Conn (*Biological Stains*) the name aniline blue is obsolete and the dye Water blue I (C.I. No. 42755) may be used in its place.

Counterstain to safranin O. Algae (with Magdala red or phloxine B); callose of sieve plates; cellulose; cell contents (→ blue); fungi (with Magdala red); *Spirogyra;* unlignified tissue. Double stain with acid fuchsin.

May be used in alcoholic or in aqueous solution.

(*a*) Anilin blue WS . . . . . . . . 1 g
Distilled water [or alcohol (70%)] . 99 ml

(*b*) *As a general stain for temporary botanical mounts:*
Amann's medium (lacto-phenol) . 99.5 ml
Anilin blue WS . . . . . . . 0.5 g

(*c*) *For algae — Chamberlain's method:*
Anilin blue WS . . . . . . . 1 g
Alcohol (90%) . . . . . . . 99 ml

(*d*) *For algae and fungi.*
(i) Anilin blue WS . . . . . . . . 0.4 g
Distilled water . . . . . . . . 100 ml
(ii) Anilin blue WS . . . . . . . . 0.4 g
Amann's medium (lacto-phenol) . 96.6 ml

(*e*) *For Spirogyra.*
Anilin blue WS . . . . . . . 0.2 g
Distilled water . . . . . . . 100 ml

(*f*) *For fungal hyphae in host tissue* (*Godwin's method*).
[See 'Fungi xi (*a*) (p. 135).]
Anilin blue WS . . . . . . . 0.25 g
Amann's medium (lacto-phenol)
(formula ii for Godwin's method — see p. 188) . . . . . . . . 99.75 g

(*g*) See also 'Anilin blue WS — acetic'; 'Anilin blue WS — lacto-phenol'; 'Anilin blue WS — picric'; 'Mallory's Triple Stain' (p. 232).

**Anilin Blue WS — Acetic**

*Syn.: Hofmann's Blue.*

Callose of sieve plates; protoplasmic cell contents (washes out of cell walls with water or glycerol).

Acetic acid (glacial) . . . . . 1 ml
Alcohol (50%) . . . . . . . 98 ml
Anilin blue WS. . . . . . . . . 1 g

Before staining, wash alcohol-preserved material in water. After staining, wash in water and mount in glycerol.

**Anilin Blue WS — Lacto-phenol. (Anilin Blue WS — Amann's Medium)**

*A stain-fixative.*

Anilin blue WS . . . . . . . 1 g
Glycerol . . . . . . . . . 25 ml
Lactic acid . . . . . . . . . 25 ml
Phenol . . . . . . . . . . . 25 g
Distilled water . . . . . . . 25 ml

*Note:* This stain-fixative is sometimes referred to as 'cotton blue-lacto-phenol', but the name 'cotton blue' is best avoided as it is a synonym both for anilin blue WS and for methyl blue (C.I. No. 42780).

**Anilin Blue WS — Picric Acid**

(i) *For double-staining for general botanical purposes* (p. 159).
Alcohol (70%) (ethyl or isopropyl) 100 ml
Anilin blue WS . . . . . . 0.1 g
Anilin sulphate . . . . . . 0.12 g
Picric acid (sat. aq.) (p. 240) . . 1.2 ml

Dissolve as much of the anilin sulphate as possible. Filter.

[Cellulose (→ blue); cutin (→ yellow); cytoplasm (→ blue); lignin (→ yellow).]

(ii) *For Cartwright's method for fungal mycelium in wood* (Method xii, p. 135).
Anilin blue WS (sat. aq.) . . . 25 ml
Picric acid (sat. aq.) (p. 240) . . 100 ml

(iii) *As a counterstain for safranin* O*; for fresh animal tissue and for chromatin in fresh material.*
Alcohol (80%) . . . . . . . 100 ml
Anilin blue WS . . . . . . . 0.2 g
Picric acid (p. 240) . . . . . . 0.1 g

**Anilin Chloride**

*This is a specific reagent for lignin.*

Lignin (→ yellow).
Alcohol (70%) . . . . . . . 89 ml
Anilin chloride . . . . . . . 1 g
Hydrochloric acid (N/10) . . . 10 ml

**Anilin, Picric-**

*For use in Jensen's method for bacteria.*
('*Bacteria* Method iv (*a*)', p. 106.)

Anilin oil . . . . . . . . . 100 ml
Picric acid (dry) . . . . . . . 1 g

**Anilin Sulphate**

*This is a specific reagent for lignin.*

Lignin (→ yellow).
Anilin sulphate . . . . . . . 1 g
Alcohol (70%) . . . . . . . 89 ml
Sulphuric acid (N/10) . . . . 10 ml

**Anilin Water**

See 'Water, anilin' (p. 252).

**Anilin-Xylene**

*For use in Weigert's method for bacteria and fibrin* (Method iv (*b*), p. 106).

| | |
|---|---|
| Anilin oil | 40 ml |
| Xylene | 60 ml |

**Apáthy's Adhesive**

See 'Adhesives' (p. 185).

**Apáthy's Gum Syrup**

*A useful mounting medium for specimens taken from water and especially if they have been stained with methylene blue. It should not be used for specimens taken from alcohol, nor for specimens stained with haematoxylin.*

| | |
|---|---|
| Gum arabic | 50 g |
| Sucrose | 50 g |
| Distilled water | 50 ml |

Dissolve on a water-bath
*Add:*

| | |
|---|---|
| Thymol | 0.05 g |

**Aurantia** C.I. No. 10360

*Syn.: Imperial yellow.*
An acid dye.
*Note: This dye is extremely poisonous and may cause dermatitis. For use in the Champy-Kull method for mitochondria* (p. 146).

| | |
|---|---|
| Alcohol (70%) | 100 ml |
| Aurantia | 0.5 g |

**Azure A** (C.I. No. not allocated)

A basic dye.

Azure A is one of the components of the mixture of dyes known as methylene azure (C.I. No. 52010) which is itself one of the components of polychrome methylene blue. This latter dye results from the oxidation of methylene blue (p. 234). In the form of azure A-eosinate the dye is used in Giemsa's stain (p. 218).

**Azure B** C.I. No. 52010

A basic dye.

Azure B is one of the components of the mixture of dyes known as methylene azure (C.I. No. 52010) which is itself one of the components of polychrome methylene blue. This latter dye results from the oxidation of methylene blue (p. 234). In the form of azure B-eosinate the dye is used in Giemsa's stain (p. 218).

**Azure I. (Giemsa)**

A trade name applied to a product containing a large proportion of Azure B (above). It is used in Field's stain – solution A (p. 214).

**Azure II. (Giemsa)**

A mixture of equal parts of Azure I and methylene blue.

**Benzanine Hexachloride**

*To retard movement of protozoa.*

| | |
|---|---|
| Benzanine hexachloride | 0.5–1.0 g |
| Distilled water | 100 ml |

**Benzene-Phenol**

Partly overcomes the trouble of benzene, used for clearing, becoming 'milky' due to incomplete dehydration of the tissue.

| | |
|---|---|
| Benzene | 100 ml |
| Phenol | 5 g |

**Benzidine**

This substance was formerly used in testing for blood stains. [See 'Blood ii' (p. 108).] It has, however, been found to possess carcinogenic properties and has been superseded by *ortho*-toluidine (p. 238), for purposes of the test. On no account should benzidine be used.

**Benzol**

*For clearing.* Use 'Benzene-Phenol' (above).

**Berlese's Fluid**

*For mounting delicate insects.*

| | |
|---|---|
| Acetic acid (glacial) | 5 ml |
| Chloral hydrate | 40 g–160 g |
| Glucose syrup | 10 ml |
| Gum arabic | 15 g |
| Distilled water | 20 ml |

1 Prepare the glucose syrup by dissolving

| | |
|---|---|
| Glucose . . . . . . . . . . | 5 g |
| in | |
| Distilled water . . . . . . . | 5 ml |

2 Dissolve the gum arabic in the distilled water.
3 Add the glucose syrup.
4 Add chloral hydrate to saturation.
5 Heat slowly and stir gently.
6 Filter through a small quantity of glass wool.

*Note:* Preparations mounted in Berlese's fluid should be sealed with gold size and, when this is dry, with D.P.X.

(ii) See also 'Gum Chloral' (p. 220).

**Best's Differentiator**

*For use with Best's carmine* (p. 196).

| | |
|---|---|
| Ethyl alcohol (100%) . . . . | 80 ml |
| Methyl alcohol (100%) . . . . | 40 ml |
| Distilled water . . . . . . . | 100 ml |

**Biebrich Scarlet WS*** C.I. No. 26905

*Syn.: C.I. Acid red* 66; *Croceine scarlet; Double scarlet BSF; Ponceau B; Scarlet B; Scarlet EC.*

An acid dye. Counterstain for haematal 8.

| | |
|---|---|
| Biebrich scarlet WS . . . . . | 0.1 g |
| Distilled water . . . . . . . | 100 ml |

**Bismarck Brown Y** C.I. No. 21000

*Syn.: C.I. Basic brown; Basic brown G; Basic brown GX; Basic brown GXP; Excelsior brown; Leather brown; Manchester brown; Phenylene brown; Vesuvin.* A basic dye.

Bacteria; cellulose; living organisms; plant tissue. May be used in solution in isotonic saline (for living organisms), in water, or in alcohol.

| | |
|---|---|
| Bismarck brown Y . . . . . | 0.3 g |
| Isotonic saline [or water, or alcohol (95%)] . . . . . . . . . | 100 ml |

**Bles's Fluid**

See 'Formol-acetic-alcohol, ii' (p. 215).

**Blood Coagulant**

Ferric chloride aq., at 'bench strength', can be used in an emergency when, for example, a blood vessel is accidentally cut during the dissection of a freshly killed animal.

**Boric Acid**

*Formula for buffer solution for use in the silver method for nerve axons* (p. 151). [See also (*c*) ii (p. 248).]

| | |
|---|---|
| Boric acid (A.R. quality) . . . | 12.4 g |
| Distilled water . . . . . . . | 1000 ml |

**Bouin's Fluid (Picro-formol-acetic)**

Penetration good. Fix for up to 18 h but material may remain in fixative for longer periods, if necessary, without harm; wash in alcohol (50%) and (70%). Finally wash sections in lithium carbonate [satd. alcohol (70%)] to remove all traces of picric acid. A good fixative for use before Heidenhain's iron haematoxylin. Much used formerly for cytological work but now replaced for this purpose by improved fixatives such as La Cour's.

| | |
|---|---|
| Acetic acid (glacial) . . . . . | 5 ml |
| Formaldehyde (40%) . . . . | 25 ml |
| Picric acid (satd. aq.) . . . . | 75 ml |

**α-Bromonaphthalene**

*For pre-treatment of root tips, before fixation, to inhibit clumping of chromosomes.*

Saturated solution in distilled water.

*Note:* α-bromonaphthalene is relatively *very* insoluble.

**Buffer Solutions**

1. *Explanation of mode of action.*

In the course of the instructions for the use of certain staining solutions and in the compounding of certain culture solutions, reference is made to the necessity for maintaining the solutions at certain given pH values by the use of *buffer solutions*. The following simple, non-mathematical, explanation of buffer solutions and their action may be of help.

Buffer solutions are solutions of known pH value. Because of their reserve acidity or alkalinity their pH values remain reasonably constant and permanent even though they be diluted with water or contaminated by the addition of *small*

* This dye must not be confused with the dye having the brand name 'Biebrich scarlet R, Med.', which is Sudan IV; synonym, scarlet red.

quantities of acid or alkali, although there is sometimes a slight difference if a *strongly* acidic or alkaline solution is added.

Buffer solutions may be regarded as mixtures in definite, but varying, proportions of a weak acid with one of its salts having a strong base.

For example, the acetic acid – acetate group of buffers consists of

(*a*) acetic acid, $CH_3COOH$, which, in solution, ionizes only slightly into hydrogen ($H^+$) and acetate ($CH_3COO^-$)ions; and

(*b*) sodium acetate, $CH_3COO$ . Na, which, in solution, ionizes completely into sodium ($Na^+$) and acetate ($CH_3COO^-$) ions.

A solution of a mixture of these substances, will, therefore, contain a preponderance of acetate$^-$ ions; a smaller quantity of sodium$^+$ ions; and a still smaller quantity of hydrogen$^+$ ions.

If, by the addition of an acid, hydrogen ($H^+$) ions are added to the buffer solution they will combine with the reserve acetate ($CH_3COO^-$) ions to give acetic acid ($CH_3COOH$), which will dissociate only slightly.

On the other hand, if, by the addition of an alkali, hydroxyl ($OH^-$) ions are added to the buffer solution, they will combine with the hydrogen ($H^+$) ions, and more of the reserve acetic acid will dissociate to replace the hydrogen ions thus removed.

Furthermore, the pH value of the buffer solution remains the same, even though it be diluted. Suppose, for example, the buffer solution be diluted 50%, the concentration both of acetic acid itself and of acetate ions will be reduced by 50%, and hence the pH value will remain the same.

If, therefore, it is desired to maintain, say, a culture solution or a solution of stains at known pH value, all that is required is to add to the solution a buffer solution of the required pH value. *It is not necessary to add any specific proportion by volume of the buffer solution, provided there is sufficient excess to take up any free hydrogen or hydroxyl ions.* The quantity to be added must suit the convenience of the occasion: an excess will not matter.

Provided the 'dissociation constants' of the substances used in the buffer mixture are known, the actual quantities of those substances required to make solutions of known pH values can be calculated. Some of the substances so used are given in the following list, while the amounts of each required to make buffer solutions of the values stated are given in the intervening table.

2. *Substances (indicated by key letters) that may be used to prepare buffer solutions.*

[For quantities to use, see the table shown at 'Buffer Solutions, 3' (pp. 194–195).]

*Group* 1.

A. Acetic acid ($CH_3COOH$) . . . . . 0.1 N
B. Hydrochloric acid (HCl) . . . . . 0.1 N
C. Sodium acetate ($CH_3COONa . 3H_2O$) crystals.
D. Disodium hydrogen phosphate ($Na_2HPO_4 . 12H_2O$) per litre of soln. 30.5 g
E. Sodium hydroxide (NaOH) . . . . 0.1 N

*Group* 2.

F. Acetic acid ($CH_3COOH$) . . . . . 0.1 N
G. Hydrochloric acid (HCl) . . . . . 0.1 N
H. Sodium acetate ($CH_3COONa . 3H_2O$) . . . 13.6 g per litre of solution.
I. Disodium hydrogen phosphate ($Na_2HPO_4 . 12H_2O$) . . . 35.8 g per litre of solution.
J. Sodium hydroxide (NaOH) . . . . 0.1 N

*Group* 3. (After A. J. Mee)

K. Acetic acid ($CH_3COOH$) . . . Gramme-molecules per litre of solution as indicated in table (p. 194).
L. Sodium acetate ($CH_3COONa . 3H_2O$) . . . Gramme-molecules per litre of solution as indicated in table (p. 194).

*Group* 4. (After Sorensen)

M. (Acid salt) – Potassium dihydrogen phosphate ($KH_2PO_4$) . . . M/15 containing 9.078 g per litre of solution.
N. (Basic salt) – Disodium hydrogen phosphate ($Na_2HPO_4 . 12H_2O$) . . . M/15 containing 11.876 g (= 9.47 g of the anhydrous salt) per litre of solution.

*Group* 5. (After W. M. Clark)

O. Hydrochloric acid (HCl) . . . . . 0.1%
P. Potassium hydrogen phthalate [$KH(COO)_2C_6H_4$].
Q. Acetic acid ($CH_3COOH$) and sodium acetate ($CH_3COONa . 3H_2O$) . . . . . . . . . in equal amounts by weight.

R. Disodium hydrogen citrate ($Na_2HC_6H_5O_7$).
S. Potassium dihydrogen phosphate ($KH_2PO_4$) and disodium hydrogen phosphate ($Na_2HPO_4 . 12H_2O$) . . . in equal amounts by weight.
T. Sodium hydrogen carbonate ($NaHCO_3$).
U. Sodium borate ($Na_2B_4O_7 . 10H_2O$).
V. Sodium hydrogen carbonate ($NaHCO_3$) and sodium carbonate ($Na_2CO_3$) . . . . . . . . . . in equal amounts by weight.
W. Sodium carbonate ($Na_2CO_3$).

**Cajal's Fixative (de Fano's modification)**

*For fixation in Cajal's method for Golgi bodies* (p. 137).

| | |
|---|---|
| Cobalt nitrate . . . . . . . . | 1 g |
| Formaldehyde (40%) . . . . | 15 ml |
| Distilled water . . . . . . . | 100 ml |

**Calberla's Fluid**

*For storage of fixed and partially dehydrated fungi and other plant tissue.*

| | |
|---|---|
| Alcohol (100%) . . . . . . . | 30 ml |
| Glycerol (pure) . . . . . . . | 30 ml |
| Distilled water . . . . . . . | 30 ml |

**Calcium Chloride**

*As substitute for glycerol for mounting.* *

| | |
|---|---|
| Calcium chloride (commercial) . | Excess |
| Tap water . . . . . . . . . | 100 ml |

*Add:*
Hydrochloric acid (bench strength), sufficient to dissolve any free calcium carbonate.
Stir well. Allow to settle. Filter.

(i) *Note:* Viscosity and refractive index approximate to those of glycerol (50%).
(ii) Sections should be washed in distilled water or alcohol (50%).
(iii) Sections may be stained in iodine; or phloroglucin (alc. soln.); or Sudan III.
(iv) Sections must *not* be stained in liquids containing alkalis or sulphates.

**Canada Balsam in Xylene**

Heat the resin supplied *until, on cooling, it becomes brittle.*

Dissolve in xylene till a thin solution is obtained. Should preferably be prevented from becoming acid. This is difficult – but the following may be tried:
(i) Stir with calcium carbonate powder or anhydrous sodium carbonate and filter. Place filtrate near a source of heat (*care*) to evaporate to right consistency.
(ii) Keep a piece of calcium carbonate or a small marble in the bottle.
(iii) Paint containers black outside, to exclude light.

Canada balsam has now largely been superseded as a mounting agent by the synthetic resins e.g. D.P.X. (p. 209).

**Carbol-Fuchsin**

See 'Fuchsin, Basic, Phenol-' (p. 216).

**Carbol-Thionin**

See 'Thionin. Phenol-' (p. 250).

**Carmalum, Mayer's**

Cellulose (counterstain with iodine green); cell contents; nematodes (small); nuclei; small entire animals (not marine); unlignified tissue.

| | |
|---|---|
| Alum . . . . . . . . . . | 10 g |
| Carminic acid . . . . . . . . | 1 g |
| Distilled water . . . . . . . | 200 ml |

Dissolve (heat if necessary). Decant or filter, add a preservative (e.g. thymol or 0.10% salicylic acid).

*Note:* Carminic acid is the dye substance of carmine (below) and cochineal and is obtained by treatment of the dried bodies of female cochineal insects.

**Carmine**

A product of cochineal (q.v., p. 200). The cochineal group is C.I. No. 75470. *Syn.: C.I. Natural Red* 4.

**Carmine, Acetic- (Schneider's acetic acid-carmine)**

An acid dye.

*Nuclei.* Stains and fixes. Differentiate in water.

*Amoeba;* nuclei; *Paramecium;* Protozoa; squashes of anthers, ovaries and root tips.

* After T. M. Harris, *Nature*, **149**, 3785, May 16, 1942.

**Buffer Solutions 3**

**Amounts of the substances (indicated by key letters in the Groups shown on pp. 192 and 193) required to produce buffer solutions of known pH value**

| To give pH value of | Group 1 | Group 2 | Group 3 (After Mee) | Group 4 (After Sorensen) | Group 5 (After Clark) | Hydrogen ion concentration |
|---|---|---|---|---|---|---|
| 2.0* | – | – | – | – | O | $10^{-2}$ |
| 3.0 | A. 142.4 ml<br>+250 ml $H_2O$ | F. 1 l<br>+H. 18 ml | – | – | – | $10^{-3}$ |
| 3.6 | – | – | K. 0.185<br>+L. 0.015 | – | – | $10^{-3 \cdot 6}$ |
| 3.9* | – | – | – | – | P | $10^{-3 \cdot 9}$* |
| 4.0 | A. 1 l<br>+C. 2.7 g per l | F. 1 l<br>+H. 18 ml | K. 0.164<br>+L. 0.036 | – | – | $10^{-4}$ |
| 4.4 | – | – | K. 0.126<br>+L. 0.074 | – | – | $10^{4 \cdot 4}$ |
| 4.4–5.0 | – | – | – | – | Q | $10^{-4 \cdot 4}$ – $10^{-5}$* |
| 4.7 | – | – | – | – | Q† | $10^{-4 \cdot 7}$ |
| 4.8 | – | – | K. 0.080<br>+L. 0.120 | – | – | $10^{-4 \cdot 8}$ |
| 5.0 | A. 500 ml<br>+C. 15 g per 500 ml | F. 555 ml<br>+H. 1 l | – | – | R† | $10^{-5}$ |
| 5.2 | – | – | K. 0.042<br>+L. 0.158 | – | – | $10^{-5 \cdot 2}$ |
| 5.5 | – | – | K. 0.019<br>+N. 0.181 | – | – | $10^{-5 \cdot 5}$ |
| 6.0 | B. 250 ml<br>+D. 300 ml | F. 55 ml<br>+H. 1 l | – | M. 8.6 ml<br>+N. 1.4 ml | – | $10^{-6}$ |
| 6.2 | – | – | – | M. 8.0 ml<br>+N. 2.0 ml | – | $10^{-6 \cdot 2}$ |
| 6.4 | – | – | – | M. 7.0 ml<br>+N. 3.0 ml | – | $10^{-6 \cdot 4}$ |
| 6.5 | – | – | – | M. 6.8 ml<br>+N. 3.2 ml | – | $10^{-6 \cdot 5}$ |

| | | | | | | |
|---|---|---|---|---|---|---|
| 6.6 | — | — | — | M. 6.0 ml<br>+N. 4.0 ml | — | $10^{-6 \cdot 6}$ |
| 6.7 | — | — | — | M. 5.6 ml<br>+N. 4.4 ml | — | $10^{-6 \cdot 7}$ |
| 6.8 | — | — | — | M. 5.0 ml<br>+N. 5.0 ml | — | $10^{-6 \cdot 8}$ |
| 6.6–7.0* | — | — | — | — | S | $10^{-6 \cdot 6} - 10^{-7}$* |
| 7.0 | B. 184 ml<br>+D. 234 ml | G. 322 ml<br>+I. 1 l | — | M. 3.9 ml<br>+N. 6.1 ml | — | $10^{-7}$ |
| 7.2 | — | — | — | M. 3.0 ml<br>+N. 7.0 ml | — | $10^{-7 \cdot 2}$ |
| 7.4 | — | — | — | M. 2.2 ml<br>+N. 7.8 ml | — | $10^{-7 \cdot 4}$ |
| 7.6 | — | — | — | M. 1.5 ml<br>+N. 8.5 ml | — | $10^{-7 \cdot 6}$ |
| 7.8 | — | — | — | M. 0.9 ml<br>+N. 9.1 ml | — | $10^{-7 \cdot 8}$ |
| 8.0 | B. 9.4 ml<br>+D. 200 ml | G. 47 ml<br>+I. 1 l | — | — | — | $10^{-8}$ |
| 8.2–8.6* | — | — | — | — | T | $10^{-8 \cdot 2} - 10^{-8 \cdot 6}$* |
| 9.0 | B. 1.0 ml<br>+D. 200 ml | G. 5 ml<br>+I. 1 l | — | — | — | $10^{-9}$ |
| 9.3* | — | — | — | — | U | $10^{-9 \cdot 3}$* |
| 10.0 | D. 200 ml<br>+E. 0.72 ml | I. 1 l<br>+J. 3.6 ml | — | — | — | $10^{-10}$ |
| 10.0–10.4* | — | — | — | — | V | $10^{-10} - 10^{-10 \cdot 4}$* |
| 11.0 | D. 200 ml<br>+E. 7.2 ml | I. 1 l<br>+J. 36 ml | — | — | — | $10^{-11}$ |
| 11.0–12.0* | — | — | — | — | W | $10^{-11} - 10^{-12}$* |

* Approximate values in absence of strong buffers. For boric acid buffer see p. 191; for phosphate buffer see also p. 239; for sodium borate buffer see also p. 249.

† For acetate buffer pH 4.7 see p. 184.

| | |
|---|---|
| Acetic acid (glacial) . . . . . | 45 ml |
| Carmine (powdered) . . | Excess (say 1 g) |
| Distilled water . . . . . . . | 55 ml |

Dissolve the carmine in the acetic acid. Bring just to the boil. Cool. Filter.

*Note:* This stain may be used with or without a mordant. If it is desired to use a mordant, sufficient iron will usually be dissolved from the *steel* needles used for teasing material on the slide. Otherwise, add ferric acetate aq. until the acetic-carmine is bluish-red. If too much ferric acetate is added, a precipitate forms. See also 'Carmine, Iron-acetic-' (p. 197).

**Carmine, Acid- (Gower's)**

*A nuclear stain. For use in preparations of Platyhelminthes* (p. 161).

| | |
|---|---|
| Acetic acid (45%) . . . . . | 100 ml |
| Carmine . . . . . . . . . . | 10 g |

Heat until the carmine dissolves. Bring to boil. Cool. Filter. Dry on the filter paper. *This residue is acidified carmine.*

| | |
|---|---|
| Acidified carmine . . . . . | 1 g |
| Potassium alum . . . . . . | 10 g |
| Distilled water . . . . . . | 200 ml |

Heat together until dissolved. Filter.
*Add:*
Thymol (to prevent fungoid growths) 1 crystal.

**Carmine, Alum- (Grenacher's)**

*Small whole mounts,* e.g. *Hydractinia, Obelia* and *Pennaria* (see '*Hydractinia*, Whole Mount' (p. 139)); Protozoa, larval Trematodes (see 'Trematodes, Larval Forms, (p. 176)).

| | |
|---|---|
| Ammonia alum (sat. aq.) . . . | 100 ml |
| Carmine . . . . . . . . . . | 0.5 g |

Bring to boiling point. Cool. Filter. For suitable counterstains refer to '*Hydractinia*' (p. 139).

**Carmine, Alum- (Mayer's)**

An acid dye.
*Nuclei.* Small entire animals (not marine). (May be followed by picric acid); *Cladophora* sp.

| | |
|---|---|
| Carmine . . . . . . . . . . | 2 g |
| Alum . . . . . . . . . . | 5 g |
| Distilled water . . . . . . . | 100 ml |

Boil for an hour.

**Carmine (Best's)**

*For glycogen* (*in wax-embedded sections*) (p. 136).

| | |
|---|---|
| Carmine . . . . . . . . . . | 2 g |
| Potassium carbonate . . . . | 1 g |
| Potassium chloride . . . . . | 5 g |
| Distilled water . . . . . . | 60 ml |

Warm gently (5 min). Cool. *Add:*

| | |
|---|---|
| Ammonium hydroxide . . . . | 20 ml |

**Carmine, Borax (Grenacher's Alcoholic)**

A neutral dye.
*Nuclei.* A good general stain for sectioned and bulk animal tissue, and bulk plant tissue; animal tissue; small entire objects; chick embryo; *Fasciola; Fucus;* glochidium; *Helix* (nerve collar); *Lumbricus* (ovary); muscle; *Nereis* (parapodia) (with picric acid); nuclei (→ pink); *Obelia; Opalina; Paramecium; Periplaneta* (fat body; leg muscle; salivary duct) (followed by picric acid alc.); plant tissue in bulk; spinal cord; *Taenia.*

| | |
|---|---|
| Borax . . . . . . . . . . | 4 g |
| Carmine . . . . . . . . . . | 3 g |
| Distilled water . . . . . . | 100 ml |
| Heat the above, then add | |
| Alcohol (70%) . . . . . . . | 100 ml |

Stand for two *days*. Filter.

**Carmine, Hydrochloric Acid (Mayer's)**

Ammocoetes; *Amphioxus; Bdelloura;* Bryozoa; *Cyclops;* Crustacea (small); *Dendrocoelum; Fasciola; Gonionemus; Hydra; Mysis; Planocera;* Scyphozoa (larvae); *Taenia.*

*Note:* Tissue may be fixed in formaldehyde (5–10% according to size); or Bouin's fluid (*essential* to wash out all picric acid before staining); or in mercuric chloride (preparations tend to deteriorate after 1–2 years).

| | |
|---|---|
| Carmine . . . . . . . . . . | 4 g |
| Hydrochloric acid | 15–30 drops |
| Distilled water . . . . . . . | 15 ml |

Boil the above together until solution is complete. Cool.
*Add:*

| | |
|---|---|
| Alcohol (85%) . . . . . . . | 95 ml |

*Add:*
Ammonium hydroxide in small quantities until the carmine is on the point of precipitation. Filter.

*Note:* For dilution and for washing use alcohol (90%).

**Carmine, Iron-acetic (Belling's)**

*Chromosomes in fresh tissue,* e.g. fresh smears of anther tips; Orthopteran testes; chromosomes of tumours; salivary glands of *Chironomus* larva; *Drosophila* larva etc.

(i) *For small quantities of tissue.*
Stain with acetic-carmine (p. 193) and tease the material with steel needles.

(ii) *For larger quantities of tissue.*

| | |
|---|---|
| Acetic acid (glacial) | 50 ml |
| Ferric hydroxide | Satis. |
| Distilled water | 50 ml |

Filter.
Add the above solution, *drop by drop,* to:

| | |
|---|---|
| Acetic carmine | 50 ml |

Until the liquid is bluish-red. Do NOT allow any precipitate to form. Then add:

| | |
|---|---|
| Acetic carmine | 50 ml |

**Carmine, Lithium- (Orth's)**

*For use in Weigert's method for bacteria and fibrin.* ['*Bacteria* iv (*b*)' (p. 106).]

| | |
|---|---|
| Carmine | 5 g |
| Lithium carbonate (sat. aq.) | 100 ml |

Boil for 15 min. Cool. Filter.

**Carmine, Muci- (Mayer's)***

*For mucin.*

(i) *Stock solution.*

| | |
|---|---|
| Carmine | 1 g |
| Aluminium hydroxide (powdered) | 1 g |
| Aluminium chloride (anhydrous – freshly powdered in mortar) | 0.5 g |
| Alcohol (50%) | 100 ml |

Boil on a water-bath. Shake frequently ($2\frac{1}{2}$ min). Cool quickly. Filter cold.

*For use,* take

| | |
|---|---|
| Stock solution | 1 ml |
| Distilled water | 9 ml |

Diluted solution will keep for 2 days.
Counterstain with metanil yellow (p. 233).

* Southgate, *Journal of Pathology and Bacteriology*, 30, 729; 1927.

**Carmine, Para- (Mayer's)**

*Small whole mounts* (e.g. *Paragonimus; Schistosoma Mansoni*) *and sections.*

| | |
|---|---|
| Aluminium chloride | 0.5 g |
| Calcium chloride (anhydrous) | 4 g |
| Carminic acid | 1 g |
| Alcohol (70%) | 100 ml |

Warm. Stand 24 h. Filter.

*Note:*
(i) Should *not* be used with tissues having an alkaline reaction or containing a high percentage of calcium carbonate.
(ii) Is best used progressively.
(iii) Moderate over-stain can be removed by soaking the tissue in alcohol (70%) or (83%); severe over-stain by alcohol (83%) containing $2\frac{1}{2}$% of hydrochloric acid.

**Carmine, Picro-**

A neutral stain.
*Nuclei.* A good double stain for general animal histology, especially for sections of nervous tissue. Differentiate in acid water. Mount in Farrants' medium. Stains best with tissue preserved in alcohol (70%). Nuclei (→ red); cytoplasm (→ yellow).

| | |
|---|---|
| Carmine | 10 g |
| Ammonium hydroxide (sp gr. 0.880) | 40 ml |
| Distilled water | 2000 ml |

Dissolve, and *add:*

| | |
|---|---|
| Picric acid | 50 g |

Shake well *for a few minutes,* allow to stand; decant. Allow to stand *a few days,* stirring occasionally. Evaporate to dryness over a water-bath.

To make up the stain:

| | |
|---|---|
| Above residue | 2 g |
| Distilled water | 100 ml |

**Carmine, Picro- (Jensen's)**

*For bacteria* [*Method* iv (*a*) (p. 106)].

*Solution A.*

| | |
|---|---|
| Carmine | 1 g |
| Magnesium oxide | 0.1 g |
| Distilled water | 50 ml |

Boil for 5 min. Cool. Filter.
*Add:*

| | |
|---|---|
| Phenol | 0.03 g |

*Solution B.*

| | |
|---|---|
| Magnesium oxide . . . . . . | 0.25 g |
| Picric acid (0.5% aq.) . . . . | 50 ml |

Boil. Cool. Filter.

*Solution C.*

Picric acid (1% aq.)

*To make up the stain.*

| | |
|---|---|
| Solution A . . Volume as prepared above. | |
| Solution B . . Volume as prepared above. | |
| Solution C . . . . . . . . | 10 ml |

Mix with constant shaking.

**Carnoy's Fluid**

*An especially good fixative for anthers, meristems and root tips.*

*Note:* Clarke's fluid (p. 199) is sometimes erroneously attributed to Carnoy.

| | |
|---|---|
| Acetic acid (glacial) . . . . . | 10 ml |
| Chloroform . . . . . . . . | 30 ml |
| Ethyl alcohol (100%) . . . . | 60 ml |

**Carrageen (Chondrus crispus) and/or Gigartina stellata ('Irish Moss')**

(i) *To retard movement of aquatic organisms.* *

*Note:* All glassware used must be chemically clean.

1. By means of using a range of test-papers find the pH value of the culture solution or liquid in which the organism is living.
2. Place about 200 ml of distilled water in a beaker. Find its pH value and, by adding a buffer solution of the same pH value as that of the culture solution (see 'Buffer Solutions', pp. 194 ff), bring the pH value of the water to that of the culture solution.
3. Bring the buffered water to boiling point. Add a small piece of carrageen. Stir constantly. Boil for 3 min.
4. Allow to cool. When cool, it is desirable that the liquid should have a viscosity approximating to that of pure glycerol at 20°C – but this will vary according to the amount of carrageen added and is a matter for experiment.
5. Decant a small portion of the carrageen solution and add the organisms. They should remain active, but with their movement retarded, for some considerable time.

(ii) *Dry and bleach some seaweed (*Chondrus crispus* and/or *Gigartina stellata*). Place a teaspoonful in half a test-tube of boiling water. Boil gently for a time. When cooled the viscous fluid becomes a yellow jelly.

**'Celloidin'**

See 'Collodion', p. 200.

**Champy's Fluid**

*For fixation of animal tissue for mitochondria*
Methods (i) and (ii) (p. 146).

| | |
|---|---|
| Chromium trioxide (1% aq.) . . | 35 ml |
| Osmium tetroxide (2%). . . . | 20 ml |
| Potassium dichromate (3% aq.) . | 35 ml |

Fix small pieces of tissue for 6–24 h.
Wash in running tap water for a like period.

**Chloral Hydrate**

(i) *For clearing temporary preparations of plant material.*

| | |
|---|---|
| Chloral hydrate . . . . . . | 64 g |
| Water . . . . . . . . . . | 40 ml |

(ii) *For narcotization of small marine animals.*
0.1% aq.

**Chlorazol Black E** C.I. No. 30235

*Syn.: C.I. Direct black* 38; *Direct black* MS (etc.); *Direct deep black* EW *extra* (etc.); *Erie black* GXOO (etc.); *Pontamine black* E (etc.); *Renol black* G; ('etc.' indicates numerous other letters of designation).

Bulk and section staining. Gives black and grey tones.

| | |
|---|---|
| Chlorazol black E (Biological quality) . . . . . . . . . | 1 g |
| Alcohol (70%) . . . . . . . . | 100 ml |

Differentiate with dilute 'Milton' (p. 236).

**Chlorhexidine**

*To delay decay of cut flowers standing in water.*

| | |
|---|---|
| Chlorhexidine . . . . . . . | 5 g |
| Distilled water . . . . . . . | 95 ml |

* After *Protonotes*, T. Gerrard and Co.

* After Stork and Renouf, 1932, *Fundamentals of Biology*, London, Murray.

To every 500 ml of water in which the flowers are standing add 1 ml of chlorhexidine (5%) soln.

### Chlorobutol

*To retard movement of micro-organisms.* *

| | |
|---|---|
| Chlorobutol . . . . . . . . | 1 g |
| Distilled water . . . . . . . . | 125 ml |

Add *not more* than *one drop* at a time, at 3–4 min intervals, to the liquid containing the organism(s) under examination. Overdosing will immobilize the organisms.

### Chlorophyll, to extract from leaves

*Fresh leaves*
Plunge into boiling water until flaccid and then chop up.

*Dry leaves*
Chop up.

Extract the chlorophyll by soaking the chopped leaves in any of the following solvents:

Acetone
Acetone (80%)
Alcohol
Benzene
Chloroform
Ether
Petroleum ether

Stiles says that pure organic solvents will not extract chlorophyll from dry leaf powder unless the solvents contain a certain amount of water.

* After *Protonotes*, T. Gerrard & Co.

### Chromic Acid (Chromium trioxide)

(i) *For hardening eyes.* 0.25% aq.
(ii) *For fixing animal tissue for cytological purposes.* 0.5%.
(iii) *For macerating small animals and plant tissue for histological purposes.* 1% aq.
(iv) *For removing grease from glassware* (see p. 218). Add excess potassium dichromate to conc. sulphuric acid.

### Chrom-osmium-acetic

See 'Flemming's fluid' (p. 214).

### Clarke's Fluid (Acetic-Alcohol)

*A penetrative, fairly rapid fixative, but slower than Carnoy's fluid* (p. 198). *Especially useful prior to nuclear stains.*

*Note:* Sometimes erroneously attributed to Carnoy.

| | |
|---|---|
| Acetic acid (glacial) . . . . . | 25 ml |
| Ethyl alcohol (100%), *or* ethanol | 75 ml |

See also the modification of Clarke's fluid known as Farmer's fluid (p. 213).

### Cobaltous Nitrate

*For test for sucrose. See 'Sugars, Tests for* (*e*) *Sucrose* i' (p. 174).

| | |
|---|---|
| Cobaltous nitrate . . . . . . | 5 g |
| Distilled water . . . . . . . . | 95 ml |

### Cocaine Hydrochloride

*For narcotizing Rotifers.*

(*a*) 1% aq. soln.

### Chrom-Acetic

*A very useful fixative for plant tissue.*

| Formula for | Chromium trioxide (g) | Acetic acid (glacial) (ml) | Distilled water (ml) |
|---|---|---|---|
| (i) *Marine algae* | 1 | 0.4 | 400 |
| (ii) *Algae* | 2 | 1 | 300 |
| (iii) *Filamentous algae* | 1 | 1 | 150 |
| (iv) *Plant tissues* (*General formula*) | 1 | 1 | 98 |
| (v) *Fungi and prothalli* | 2.5 | 5 | 72.5 |
| (vi) *Plant ovaries and root tips* | 7 | 10 | 83 |
| (vii) *Leaves and woody tissue* | 10 | 10 | 80 |

(*b*) 2% aq. soln. . . . . . . . . . 30 ml
Alcohol (96%) . . . . . . . . 10 ml
Distilled water . . . . . . . . 60 ml

**Cochineal** C.I. No. 75470

*Syn.: Natural Red* 4.

This dye is obtained from the dried bodies of female *Coccus cacti*. After treatment with alum, cochineal yields the dye carmine (q.v. p. 193).

**Cochineal, Alcoholic- (Mayer's)**

*Chick embryos (whole mounts); nematodes; pluteus larvae,*

Aluminium chloride . . . . . . 0.5 g
Calcium chloride (anhydrous) . 5 g
Cochineal . . . . . . . . . 5 g

Grind the above together.
*Add:*

Alcohol (50%) . . . . . . . .100 ml
Nitric acid (sp. gr. 1.20) . . 8 drops

Boil. Cool. Allow to stand for 7 days.
Shake up from time to time. Filter.
For method of use see 'Amphioxus, Whole Specimens' (p. 97), but use the stain *undiluted.*

**Colchicine**

*For pre-treatment of root tips, prior to fixation, to inhibit clumping of chromosomes.*

Colchicine . . . . . . . . . 0.2 g
Distilled water . . . . . . . . 100 ml

**Cole's Solution**

*Test for maltose. See 'Sugars, Tests for,* (*d*) *Maltose* ii' (p. 174).

Copper sulphate (10% aq.) . . . 10 ml
Glycerol . . . . . . . . . . 10 ml

**Collodion ('Celloidin')**

*For embedding* (see p. 66).

**1** Remove the 'Celloidin', which may be in the form of 'wool', shreds or chips, from the water in which it is stored. Spread it out on paper and allow to dry overnight, in warm place.

**2** Prepare the solvent mixture:
Ethyl alcohol (100%) . . . . 219 ml
Ether (pure) . . . . . . . . 261 ml

**3** Prepare the stock solution of 'Celloidin' by adding to the above solvent mixture:
'Celloidin' . . . . . . . . . 120 g
*This solution is of strength* 20%.

**4** Prepare an 8% *solution* as follows:
Stock (20%) soln. of 'Celloidin' . 40 ml
Solvent mixture (as **2**, above) . . 60 ml

**5** Prepare a 4% *solution* as follows:
Stock (20%) soln. of 'Celloidin' . 20 ml
Solvent mixture (as **2**, above) . . 80 ml

*Note:*

(i) *Ether vapour is highly inflammable. There must be no naked lights in the laboratory when it is being handled.*

(ii) The solutions of 'Celloidin' must be kept in tightly-stoppered bottles, away from sunlight, and preferably under a bell-jar with its greased rim standing on a glass plate.

(iii) After pouring out 'Celloidin' solution be careful to wipe the stopper and the inside of the neck of the bottle with a clean cloth with a little ether or absolute alcohol on it.

**'Celloidin'-Clove Oil**

*An adhesive for attaching paraffin-wax sections and minute larvae* (e.g. *Echinoderm pluteus, q.v.*, p. 125) *to slides.*

Clove oil . . . . . . . . . . 50 ml
'Celloidin' (20% stock soln. prepared as above) . . . . . . . . . . 50 ml

**Congo Red** C.I. No. 22120

*Syn.: C.I. Direct red* 28; *Congo; Cotton red* B; *Cotton red* C; *Direct red* C; etc.

An acid dye.

Amyloid; axis cylinders; protozoa; rusts (especially after acetic-alcohol fixation) (colours walls of parasite but not of host).

Congo red . . . . . . . . . 1 g
Distilled water . . . . . . . . 100 ml

*Note:*

(i) This stain is blue in acid solution and red in alkaline solution.

(ii) Preparations stained in Congo red must be well washed before being mounted.

(iii) This dye may be used for staining yeast suspension prior to feeding it to *Paramecium* to note changes in colour of food vacuole as digestion proceeds. For this purpose, add to the above solution:

| | |
|---|---|
| Ammonium hydroxide aq. | A few drops. |

**Creosote (Beechwood Creosote BP) ('White' Creosote)**

For clearing whole mounts of *Taenia solium* proglottides, *Distomum hepaticum*, and fresh-water micro-fauna.

Useful if dehydration has not been complete.

*Note:* The liquid is not 'white', but a very pale yellow colour.

**Crystal Violet** C.I. No. 42555

*Syn.: C.I. Basic violet* 3; *Gentian violet; Hexamethyl violet; Methyl violet* 10B; *Violet* C (etc.).

A basic dye.

Gives a deep blue violet (cf. methyl violet 2B, p. 234).

*Nuclear stain.* Bacteria; chromosomes; epithelia; fungus (nuclei); mitotic figures; nuclei (plant) (counterstain with Gram's iodine and orange G in clove oil); spermatozoids.

Can be differentiated with clove oil.

(*a*) *For general use, and for mitotic figures.* [See 'Chromosomes 1 (*c*)' Method vii (p. 118).]

| | |
|---|---|
| Crystal violet | 1 g |
| Distilled water | 99 ml |

(*b*) *For other cytological methods.*

| | |
|---|---|
| Crystal violet | 1 g |
| Alcohol (20%) | 100 ml |

(*c*) A 1% solution in clove oil is often useful.

**Crystal Violet, Anilin-**

Bacteria; plant tissue; mitosis.

*Solution A.*

| | |
|---|---|
| Crystal violet | 2.5 g |
| Ethyl alcohol (95%) | 12.0 ml |

*Solution B.*

| | |
|---|---|
| Anilin | 2 ml |
| Distilled water | 98 ml |

Shake and allow to stand for a few minutes; then filter.

Mix solutions A and B.

**Crystal Violet, Leuco-.** (The colourless dye-derivative.)†

*For use in Talboy's method for staining the vascular system of plants* (ii p. 178).

† From information supplied by Dr. P. W. Talboys, East Malling Research Station.

**La Cour's Fixatives***

*For work with chromosomes.*

| | 2 BD for general work | 2 BE for plant tissue | 2 BX for bulk fixation |
|---|---|---|---|
| | ml | ml | ml |
| Acetic acid aq. (10%) | 30 | 12 | 60 |
| Chromium trioxide aq. (2%) | 100 | 100 | 100 |
| Osmium tetroxide aq. (2%) | 60 | 32 | 120 |
| Potassium dichromate aq. (2%) | 100 | 100 | 100 |
| Saponin aq. (1%) | 20 | 10 | 10 |
| Distilled water | 210 | 90 | 50 |
| | 520 | 344 | 440 |

*Note:* The purpose of the saponin is to lower the surface tension of the fixative. This is an aid to rapid penetration, which, in turn, is conductive to uniform action.

* Reproduced in modified form, by kind permission, from Darlington and La Cour, 1960, *The Handling of Chromosomes*, 3rd Edn., Allen & Unwin, London.

See 'Schiff's solution (iii)' (p. 245), but substitute crystal violet for basic fuchsin and use about 10 ml of the sodium metabisulphite solution (10%) to decolourize the dye.

### Crystal Violet, Newton's

See formula under 'Crystal Violet (*a*)' above.

### Culture Media*

1. GENERAL NOTES

(*a*) *Cleanliness.* It is essential that glassware is clean and grease-free. (See 'Glassware – to clean', p. 218.) *Very* thorough washing, first with tap water and then with distilled water is *essential* after the use of any form of antiseptic or detergent.

(*b*) *Sterilization.* Sterilization of glassware is essential when preparing bacterial and certain other culture media and solutions. If an autoclave is not available the following are two simple substitutes, in descending order of cost and efficiency:

(i) A large pressure-cooker. In general, 15 min steaming at 15 lb above atmospheric pressure, or 20 min 10 lb will suffice.

(ii) A double (steaming) saucepan. Vessels are placed in the upper compartment and steamed for 30 min on three successive days, the lid being left undisturbed and the pan allowed to cool meanwhile.

(*c*) *Containers for media for bacteria and fungi.*

(i) Test-tubes may be the most readily obtainable. They occupy much space. After being partly filled with the medium they must be plugged with a long, tightly-fitting, rolled piece of cellulose wadding or cotton-wool. The end of the plug should project from the tube for ease of removal and, meanwhile, should be covered with a piece of cellophane held in position by a rubber band.

(ii) Glass bottles fitted with thick rubber washers and aluminium screw-top lids are the most convenient. For bacteria use the 14 ml size; for yeasts use the 28 ml size; for fungi use the 170 ml size.

* The author is greatly indebted to Dr. J. Gay, Imperial College of Science and Technology, London, and to R. F. Crowther, The Grammar School, Burton-on-Trent, for much of the information under this heading.

(*d*) *Water.* Unless otherwise stated, the water used for making up culture media must be distilled (preferably in glass apparatus, because some organisms are allergic to metallic salts), or de-ionized.

(*e*) *Aeration*. Some cultures must be aerated during their preparation. A cheap, simple and effective aerator can be made as shown in Fig. 7.1.

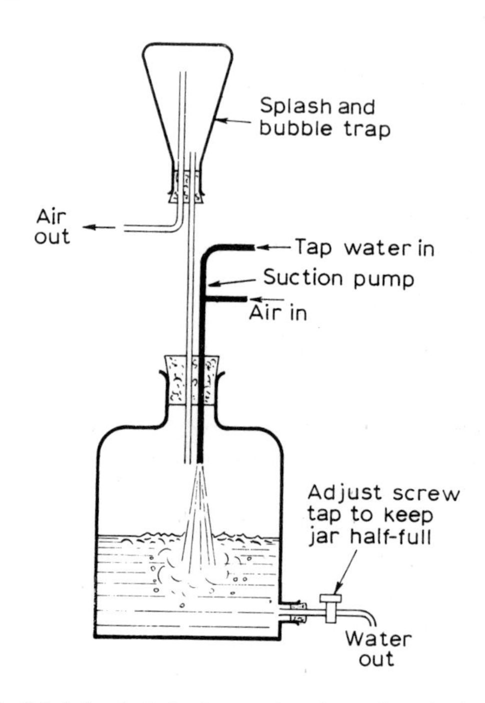


Fig. 7.1 A simple device for aeration of aquaria and cultures.

(*f*) *Preparation of 'slopes', 'stabs' and 'plates'.* The molten culture medium is poured into the container so that it is about one-quarter full. The tube is plugged, or the bottle is sealed, and the whole sterilized at 10 lb above atmospheric pressure for 20 min. The pressure is allowed to subside slowly. On removal, the tubes, or bottles, are allowed to cool, either tilted at an angle (for 'slope' cultures of *aerobic* organisms); or stood vertically (for 'stab' cultures of *anaerobic* organisms) and in 170 ml bottles (for tall-growing fungi); or laid horizontally (for 'plate' cultures of larger quantities if in 170 ml bottles).

(*g*) *Films, smears and inoculations.* These are best made with pieces of nichrome wire (No. 26 gauge) about 19 cm long and mounted in long handles. Some wires should be straight; some should have the free end turned into a *smooth* flat loop about 2 mm diam; some should have the free end turned into a little hook.

Wires for stabbing are preferably made of a stouter gauge (say No. 22) and rather shorter (say 5 cm). In default of a supply of nichrome wire the ready-glass-mounted basal wires from a broken electric-light bulb are not to be despised.

(*h*) Notes on the culture of many organisms will be found in Chapter 6, Methods for Specific Material.

## 2. COMPOSTS

*For growing angiosperms*

*Note:* The horticultural world is accustomed to dealing with rather larger quantities than is the laboratory technician and tends to use English rather than metric measures. The author has found it convenient to use a 1-gallon oil can, with one side removed, as a measure of volume when making up composts.

(*a*) *John Innes Seed Compost.**

Mix the following:

| | |
|---|---|
| Good loam . . . . . | 2 parts by volume |
| Peat (coarse texture; granules 3–10 mm) . . | 1 " " " |
| Sand (*coarse* texture; granules up to 3 mm) . | 1 " " " |

To every bushel (= 8 gallons) (= 36.4 l approx.) of this mixture, *add:*

| | |
|---|---|
| Superphosphate of lime (16% phosphoric acid) . | 1.5 oz (= 43 g approx.) |
| Chalk (ground chalk or limestone) . . . | 0.75 oz (= 21 g approx.) |

(*b*) *John Innes Potting Compost*

Mix the following:

| | |
|---|---|
| Good loam . . . . . | 7 parts by volume |
| Peat (as above) . . . | 3 " " " |
| Sand (as above) . . . | 2 " " " |

To every bushel (= 8 gallons) (= 36.4 l approx.) of the above mixture, *add:*

| | |
|---|---|
| John Innes Base (see below) . . . . . . | 4.0 oz (= 113 g approx.) |
| Chalk (as above) . . . | 0.75 oz (= 21 g approx.) |

*John Innes Base*

| | |
|---|---|
| Hoof and horn (1 cm grist) (13% nitrogen) . . . | 2 parts by weight |
| Superphosphate of lime (16% phosphoric acid) . | 2 " " " |
| Sulphate of potash (48% pure potash) . . . . | 1 " " " |

*Note:* The J. I. Base is slow-acting. If prolonged growth is required or if the angiosperms are vigorous growers, the quantity of J. I. Base added to the potting compost may be doubled or trebled, but this will not accelerate growth over that obtained with the normal mixture.

* Formulae reproduced by kind permission of the Director of the John Innes Horticultural Institution, Bayfordbury, Hertfordshire.

## 3. CULTURE MEDIA AND NUTRIENT SOLUTIONS

(*a*) *Agar*

Agar (or agar-agar) is the dried hydrophilic colloidal material obtained from a mucilaginous polysaccharide occurring in the cell-walls of certain red marine algae, e.g. *Gelidium corneum*. It is used as a combined substrate and carrier of added nutrients for the culture of various organisms. There are many varieties of agar and their clarity and setting quality vary considerably. For most purposes the variety sold as 'Oxoid No. 3' will be found quite satisfactory. For a good 'set' use from 1.0% to 1.5% (mass/volume). When preparing acid media such as malt agar and potato dextrose agar (PDA) use a rather higher proportion (1.5%–2.0%).

(i) *Czapek-Dox's Agar*

*For fungi*

| | |
|---|---|
| Agar . . . . . . . . . . . | 15.0 g |
| Ferrous sulphate . . . . . . | A trace |
| Magnesium sulphate . . . . . | 0.5 g |
| Potassium chloride . . . . . | 0.5 g |
| Potassium dihydrogen phosphate. | 1.0 g |
| Sodium nitrate . . . . . . . | 2.0 g |
| Sucrose . . . . . . . . . . | 30.0 g |
| Distilled water . . . . . . . . | 1000 ml |

(ii) *Dox's Agar*

*For bacteria and fungi*

| | |
|---|---|
| Agar | 15.0 g |
| Ferrous sulphate | 0.01 g |
| Magnesium sulphate | 0.05 g |
| Potassium chloride | 0.05 g |
| Potassium dihydrogen phosphate | 1.0 g |
| Sodium nitrate | 2.0 g |
| Sucrose | 15.0 g |
| Distilled water | 1000 ml |

(iii) *Dung Agar*

*For fungi*

Dung (cow, horse, or rabbit) . . 1000 g

**1** Soak the dung in cold water . . . (3 days)
**2** Decant and dilute till straw-coloured.
**3** Mix,

| | |
|---|---|
| Agar | 2.5 g |
| Diluted dung extract | 100 ml |

(iv) *Glucose Peptone Agar*

*For fungi*

| | |
|---|---|
| Agar | 1.5 g |
| Glucose | 1.0 g |
| Peptone bact. | 1.0 g |
| Sodium chloride | 1.0 g |
| Distilled water | 100 ml |

(v) *For Eremothecium Ashbyi*

As iv (above), but omit sodium chloride;
add yeast extract . . . . . . . 0.3 g

(vi) *Malt Agar*

*For fungi*

| | |
|---|---|
| Agar | 15.0 g |
| Malt extract (Boot's) | 20.0 g |
| Distilled water | 1000 ml |

*Note:* Malt extract may be increased up to 10% or more; yeast extract may be added, up to 0.1%; according to the organism being cultured.

(vii) *Mannitol-Salt-Yeast-Agar*

*For Rhizobium trifolium*

| | |
|---|---|
| Agar | 15.0 g |
| Calcium chloride | 0.2 g |
| Ferric chloride | 0.01 g |
| Magnesium sulphate | 0.1 g |
| Mannitol | 10.0 g |
| Potassium hydrogen phosphate | 0.5 g |
| Sodium chloride | 0.2 g |
| Yeast water extract [see 3 (*y*) (p. 208)] | 100 ml |
| Distilled water | 900 ml |

(viii) *Nutrient Agar*

*For bacteria*

| | |
|---|---|
| Agar | 1.5 g |
| Beef extract 'Lemco' | 1.0 g |
| Peptone bact. | 1.0 g |
| Sodium chloride | 0.5 g |
| Distilled water | 100 ml |

*Note:* Yeast extract may be added . . . 0.1–0.3%.

(ix) *Potato Agar*

*For fungi*

| | |
|---|---|
| Potatoes | 250 g |
| Tap water | To 1000 ml |

**1** Wash the potatoes thoroughly.
**2** Dice, but do not peel them.
**3** Place the diced potatoes in a muslin or jelly-bag.
**4** Tie the neck of the bag, but leave plenty of loose string to form a hanger later.
**5** Steam for 1 h.
**6** Suspend the bag above the steamer and allow the liquid to drip from the bag *without squeezing it*, till drainage is complete.
**7** Make the extract up to 1000 ml with tap water, in a double saucepan.
**8** Add the agar and warm till dissolved.
**9** Sterilize.

(x) *Potato Dextrose Agar (PDA)*

*For fungi*

As ix (above), but at **7** *add:*
Glucose . . . . . . . . . . 20 g

(xi) *Prune Agar*

*For fungi*

| | |
|---|---|
| Agar | 50 g |
| Prunes | 25 g |
| Sucrose | 400 g |
| Distilled water | 500 ml |

**1** Boil the prunes in the water (1 h).
**2** Decant the liquid.
**3** Make up with distilled water to . . 1000 ml
**4** Add the agar and sucrose.

(xii) *'V 8' Agar*

*For fungi*

'V 8' is the proprietary name for a canned mixture of vegetable juices.

| | |
|---|---|
| Agar | 30 g |
| 'V 8' | Contents of $12\frac{1}{2}$ oz (= 355 g approx.) can |
| Water | To make up to 1500 ml |

Warm the agar and 'V 8' together. Sterilize at 15 lb for 15 min. Cool. Inoculate.

*Note:* Some fungi grow better if the pH value is adjusted to 5.5–6.0 with alkali. Alternatively, powdered calcium carbonate may be added, but it will remain as a sediment in the bottom. For buffer solutions see pages 194–195.

(*b*) *Astasia Longa Medium*

| | |
|---|---|
| Beef extract 'Lemco' | 0.1 g |
| Calcium chloride | 0.001 g |
| Sodium acetate | 0.1 g |
| Tryptone | 0.2 g |
| Yeast extract 'Oxoid' | 0.2 g |
| Distilled water | 100 ml |

Sterilize. Inoculate.

(*c*) *Bread*

*For Mucor*

1 Sterilize some bread.
2 Wet it (but do *not* soak it).
3 Place under a bell-jar and leave for about one week.

(*d*) *Bristol's Solution*

*For fresh-water algae*

| | |
|---|---|
| Calcium chloride | 0.1 g |
| Ferric chloride | A trace |
| Magnesium sulphate | 1.3 g |
| Potassium dihydrogen phosphate | 1.0 g |
| Sodium chloride | 0.1 g |
| Sodium nitrate | 1.0 g |
| Distilled water | 1000 ml |

(*e*) *Broth, Nutrient*

*For bacteria*

As 'Nutrient Agar viii' (p. 204), but omit the agar.

(*f*) *Brown's Medium*

*For fungi*

| | |
|---|---|
| Agar | 2.0 g |
| Asparagine | 0.02 g |
| Glucose | 0.2 g |
| Magnesium sulphate | 0.075 g |
| Starch | 1.0 g |
| Tribasic potassium phosphate | 0.125 g |
| Distilled water | 100 ml |

(*g*) *Chalkley's Medium*

*For Amoebae*

| | |
|---|---|
| Calcium chloride | 0.06 g |
| Sodium chloride | 1.0 g |
| Potassium chloride | 0.04 g |
| Distilled water | 1000 ml |

Dilute 10 times before use.

(*h*) *Chilomonas Paramecium Medium*

| | |
|---|---|
| Beef extract 'Lemco' | 0.1 g |
| Sodium acetate | 0.1 g |
| Distilled water | 100 ml |

Sterilize. Cool. Inoculate.

(*i*) *Dung*

(i) *Cow, Horse, Rabbit*

*For Moulds,* e.g. *Mucor, Rhizopus, Pilobus; Ascomycetes, especially Discomycetes,* e.g. *Ascophanus* (*small type of Peziza*); *Basidiomycetes, especially Coprinus.*

Incubate fresh dung under a bell-jar in the laboratory.

(ii) *Cow, Fowl*

*For Euglena*

Soak the dung in cold water and decant the extract.

(iii) *Swan*

*For Euglena*

Mix partially decayed dung with silt.

(*j*) *Egg Yolk*

*For Amoeba, Daphnia*

1 Shake up some egg yolk with water.
2 Leave in a warm place for several d.
3 Add a few drops of the pabulum to the *Daphnia* culture *twice per week.*

(*k*) *Elm Leaves*

*For Daphnia*

Place a few old elm leaves in the vessels containing the *Daphnia* culture.

(*l*) *Hay Infusion*

*For bacteria; Colpidium; Paramecium*

1 Boil some chopped hay in water.
2 Add to the cooled liquid a little dry, chopped hay.
3 Avoid breaking the surface scum.
4 Sub-culture *twice every* 3 *months.*

*Note:* Organisms appear in the order indicated above.

(*m*) *Knop's Solution*

*For algae*

*Solution* (*i*)

| | |
|---|---|
| Magnesium sulphate | 1 g |
| Potassium nitrate | 1 g |
| Potassium phosphate | 1 g |
| Distilled water | 1000 ml |

*Solution* (*ii*)

| | |
|---|---|
| Calcium nitrate | 4 g |
| Distilled water | 1000 ml |

Add solution (*i*) to solution (*ii*).

*Note:* Better results may sometimes be obtained by diluting the final solution two, three, or four times. This is a matter for experiment.

(*n*) *Malted Milk* (*Horlick's*)

*For Daphnia*

Add malted milk powder to water, and supply the mixture to the culture occasionally.

(*o*) *Oscillatoria Medium*

*For the blue-green alga Oscillatoria animalis.*

| | |
|---|---|
| Agar | 10.5 g |
| Ammonium chloride | 0.05 g |
| Boric acid | 0.0001 g |
| Calcium nitrate | 0.025 g |
| Copper sulphate | 0.00001 g |
| Ferric sulphate | 0.004 g |
| Magnesium sulphate | 0.25 g |
| Manganese chloride | 0.0001 g |
| Molybdic acid | 0.0001 g |
| Potassium hydrogen phosphate | 1.0 g |
| Potassium nitrate | 1.0 g |
| Sodium carbonate | 1.50 g |
| Zinc sulphate | 0.00001 g |
| Distilled water | 1000 ml |

Autoclave at 15 lb for 15 min.
After sterilization the solution may be brown.

(*p*) *Pasteur's Solution*

| | |
|---|---|
| Ammonium tartrate | 1.0 g |
| Calcium phosphate | 0.02 g |
| Cane sugar | 15.0 g |
| Dipotassium hydrogen pnosphate | 0.2 g |
| Magnesium phosphate | 0.02 g |
| Distilled water | 100 ml |

(*q*) *Pond Water*

(i) *Pond Water and Bristol's Medium*

*For Chlorococcales; Volvocales; and Diatoms.* Bristol's medium (p. 205). Sufficient to give a shallow layer on the bottom of a conical flask.

| | |
|---|---|
| Pond water | 1 ml |

Incubate under a 25 watt lamp.

(ii) *Pond Water and Fowl Dung*

*For Daphnia; Cyclops; Cladocera; Vorticella.*

| | |
|---|---|
| Fowl dung | 3 g |
| Water | 1000 ml |

**1** Boil the above mixture.
**2** Filter.
**3** Mix.

| | |
|---|---|
| Filtered pond water | 900 ml |
| Filtrate from **2** | 100 ml |

**4** Keep the organisms in this mixture.

(iii) *Pond Water and Hemp Seed*

*For Pythium and allied types,* e.g. *Saprolegnia, Achlya.*

**1** Boil some hemp seed (obtainable from any shop selling bird foods) until the seed coats split.
**2** Place 20 ml pond water in a Petri dish.
**3** Add two or three boiled hemp seeds. No further culture necessary.

(iv) *Pond Water and Knop's Solution*

*For the same organisms as* (*q*) i (above). Method as (*q*) i, but using Knop's Solution. Better results sometimes obtained by diluting the Knop's Solution two, three or four times.

(v) *Pond Water and Soil*

*For the same organisms as* (*q*) i (above). Method as (*q*) i but substitute a few grains of soil for the nutrient solution.

(vi) *Pond Water and Wheat*

*For Amoeba*

Method as (*q*) i but substitute a few grains of wheat for the hemp seeds.

(*r*) *Pringsheim's Solution*

*For Amoeba*

*Stock Solution* (*i*)

| | |
|---|---|
| Potassium hydrogen phosphate | 0.2 g |
| Sodium chloride | 0.2 g |
| Distilled water | 500 ml |

1 Distribute the solution equally between 10 flasks.
2 Plug the flasks and sterilize them.

*Stock Solution (ii)*

| | |
|---|---|
| Calcium nitrate | 2.0 g |
| Ferrous sulphate | 0.02 g |
| Magnesium sulphate | 0.2 g |
| Distilled water | 500 ml |

*Working Solution*

| | |
|---|---|
| Solution (i) | 50 ml |
| Solution (ii) | 5 ml |
| Distilled water | 945 ml |

*Note:* Store solutions in brown glass, stoppered, bottles.

(*s*) *Raisin Gelatin*

*For bacteria*

| | |
|---|---|
| Gelatin | 120.0 g |
| Raisins | 30.0 g |
| Distilled water | 1000 ml |

1 Cut up the raisins.
2 Boil in the water for 15 min.
3 Strain off the liquid.
4 Add the gelatin, and heat the liquid until the gelatin is dissolved.
5 Filter through paper.
6 Pour into tubes [as 1 (*f*) (p. 202)].
7 Sterilize.

(*t*) *Rice Grains*

*For Amoeba* spp.

Add about six grains of polished rice to Chalkley's medium [(*g*) (p. 205)] or to Pringsheim's solution [(*r*) (p. 206)] in a shallow, transparent, lidded polythene dish.

(*u*) *Sewage Sludge (Activated)*

*For Protozoa* spp.

1 Place 500 ml activated sewage sludge (from aeration channels), in a vessel.
2 Suspend in it some coarse-mesh cotton-muslin.
3 Aerate for 1 or 2 days. (For a suitable aerator see Fig. 7.1, p. 202.)
4 Cut the muslin into 12 mm squares.
5 Place a muslin square on a glass slide.
6 Use sufficient sewage supernatant as a mountant.

*Note:* Stalked forms have a food platform. Swimming forms are trapped. Amoebae move out on to the glass surrounding the muslin.

(*v*) *Soil*

*Note:* Unless otherwise specified, for the term 'soil', read 'good garden loam', i.e. a well-balanced mixture of humus, sand, silt and clay particles. Very sandy soil will be short of organic matter, may be short of nutrient materials and may hence be short of native organisms. Heavy clay soils may be short of organic matter and will introduce unwanted problems peculiar to themselves. A *marl* is a calcareous clay soil.

(i) *Soil and Bristol's Solution*

*For the same organisms as* (*q*) i (p. 206).
Bristol's medium (p. 205). Sufficient to give a shallow layer in the bottom of a conical flask.

| | |
|---|---|
| Soil | A few grains of surface soil. |

Incubate under a lamp.

(ii) *Soil and Knop's Solution*

*For the same organisms as* (*q*) i (p. 206).
As (*v*) i (above), but substitute Knop's solution (p. 206). Better results may sometimes be obtained by diluting the Knop's solution 2, 3 or 4 times.

(iii) *Soil and Water*

*For green Algae and certain Protozoa*

| | |
|---|---|
| Soil | 1.0–2.0 g |
| Water (tap or distilled, to be found by experiment) | 7.0–10.0 ml |

1 Place the soil in a test-tube and add water.
2 Plug the tube with cotton-wool.
3 Steam for one *hour* at atmospheric pressure on two successive days.
4 Place the tubes near a window, but out of direct sunlight.
5 Stand for two days before inoculation.

*Note:* The pH value should be about 7.4.

(iv) *Marl and Water*

As (*v*) iii (above), but use marl instead of soil.

(v) *Soil and Calcium*

*For Chlamydomonas pulsatilla; Gonium pectorale; Hydrodictyon reticulatum; Pandorina morum; Spirogyra varians; Vaucheria sessilis; V. woroniniana; Zygnema* sp.
As (*v*) iii (above), but before putting the loam in the test-tube place 0.01–0.02 g of calcium carbonate in the bottom.

(vi) *Soil, Calcium and Barley*

*For Paramecium* spp.
As (*v*) v (above), but place with the calcium carbonate a grain of barley, before adding the soil.

(vii) *Soil, Nitrogen, Magnesium and Phosphorus*

*For Euglena viridis*
As (*v*) iii (above), but place 0.01–0.02 g of magnesium ammonium phosphate in the bottom of the tube before adding the soil.

(viii) *Marl, Nitrogen, Magnesium, and Phosphorus*

As (*v*) vii (above), but substitute marl for loam.

(ix) *Soil, Nitrogen, Magnesium, Phosphorus, and Yeast Extract*

*For Euglena* spp.
As (*v*) vii (above), but add also 0.001 g yeast extract.

(x) *Soil and Starch*

As (*v*) iii (above), but place 0.01–0.02 g of starch in the bottom of the tube before adding the soil.

(xi) *Marl and Starch*

*For Astasia longa, Chilomonas paramecium*
As (*v*) x (above), but substitute marl for soil.

(xii) *Soil and Wheat*

*For Spirostomum*
As (*v*) iii (above), but place a grain of wheat in the bottom of the tube before adding the soil.

*Note:* Tubes should not be more than half-full and lightly plugged with cotton-wool. There must be a concentration of carbon-dioxide above the water.

(*w*) i *Soil Extract* *

*For Eudorina; Paramecium bursaria; Pleodorina; Volvox*

1 Place good garden loam in the inner pan of a double saucepan to a depth of about 2.5 cm.
2 Add water to give a final depth of about 7.5 cm of the mixture.
3 Steam for three h.
4 Allow to settle.
5 Decant and filter the liquid, and measure its volume.

* After E. A. George, The School of Botany, University of Cambridge.

6 Make a stock solution as follows:

| | |
|---|---|
| *n*-Butyl chloride . . . . . . | 10 ml |
| *o*-Chlorobenzene . . . . . . | 5 ml |
| Ethylene dichloride . . . . . | 5 ml |
| Filtrate from **5** . . . . . . | 1000 ml |

*Note:* Do *not* breathe the vapours from the added liquids. This stock solution will keep for several months.

7 To prepare the culture fluid for use:

| | |
|---|---|
| Stock soln. from **6** . . . . . | 100 ml |
| Distilled water . . . . . . . | 900 ml |

8 Place the liquid in the culture vessels.
9 Sterilize up to 20 lb pressure and then remove the heat.
*Note:* The vapours are removed on sterilizing. pH value should be about 7.4.
10 Inoculate with the organism to be cultured.

(ii) *Soil Extract and Beef Extract*

As (*w*) i (above), but add 1 ml Beef Extract 'Lemco' to the mixture at **7**.

(iii) *Soil Extract and K, Mg, N, P, and S*

*For Paramecium bursaria fed on Yeast Extract.*
As (*w*) i (above), but at **7** make up the culture solution as follows:

| | |
|---|---|
| Stock soln. from **6** . . . . . | 100 ml |
| Magnesium sulphate . . . . . | 0.02 g |
| Potassium hydrogen phosphate . | 0.02 g |
| Potassium nitrate . . . . . . | 0.02 g |
| Distilled water . . . . . . . | 900 ml |

(*x*) *Soil Suspension and Agar*

*For spore-forming bacteria*

1 Make a suspension of soil and water.
2 Boil for 10 min.
3 Sub-culture to an agar medium, e.g. Dox's agar [(*a*) ii (p. 204)].

(*y*) *Yeast Water Extract*

| | |
|---|---|
| Baker's or brewer's yeast . . . | 100 g |
| Distilled water . . . . . . . . | 900 ml |

1 Steam the yeast and water together for one h. Shake occasionally.
2 Allow to settle.
3 Decant and filter the liquid through paper.
4 Sterilize at 15 lb for 15 min.

## 4. HANGING DROP CULTURES

(*a*) *For observing the growth and motility of bacteria, the growth of fungi, pollen tubes, yeast, etc.*

1 Sterilize a slide and a cover-slip by passing them through a flame.
2 Build a narrow ring of 'Plasticine', in diameter rather less than that of the cover-slip and about 3 mm high, in the centre of the slide (Fig. 7.2).
3 Place a drop of the culture medium containing the organism on the sterilized cover-slip. If necessary, smear the drop evenly with a sterilized wire.
*Note:* When examining bacteria a *very small* drop of culture medium should be used, otherwise focusing will be difficult.
4 Hold the sterilized cover-slip by its edge in a pair of sterilized forceps and quickly invert it on the 'Plasticine' ring. Press it down very gently to ensure a gas-tight fit.
5 Place the whole in a large Petri dish, and cover to keep free from dust.

(*b*) *To observe the effect of gases on a culture*

In lieu of the 'Plasticine' ring mentioned in 4 (*a*) (above) the necessary piece of apparatus may either be purchased (when proceed from **5**, below), or made as follows:

1 From a piece of glass tubing of diameter rather less than that of the cover-slip it is proposed to use, cut a ring about 4 mm long.
2 Grind the rough ends of the ring flat and parallel with each other on a stone.
3 Either drill or blow two small holes opposite each other in the ring.
4 Into each hole seal a small glass tube.
5 By means of D.P.X., seal the prepared ring to a sterilized slide. Smear the upper edge of the ring, very thinly, with 'Vaseline'.
6 To keep the preparation moist, place a drop of water on the slide, within the glass ring.
7 Proceed as in 4 (*a*) **3** and **4** above.
8 Connect the two tubes, respectively, to a gas-producer and a gas-exhauster, making sure that the cover-slip is a gas-tight fit on the ring.

5. JAR CULTURES

*For green algae.*

1 Cover the floor of a 1-lb or 2-lb (0.45–0.90 kg) size jam-jar with calcium carbonate (marble chips or precipitated).
2 Add garden soil to a depth of 2.5 cm.
3 Add distilled water sufficient to reach a level just below the shoulder of the jar.
4 Cover with a lid, e.g. the lid of a tobacco tin.
5 Sterilize by steaming for 20 min. Allow to cool.
6 Inoculate with the organism.
7 Place on a window sill. Shade from direct light in summer.
8 About once per week add 'Liquinure', or other compound fertilizer in solution, at about one-third the strength recommended for angiosperms.
9 Subculture twice during the 4 winter months; and about every 6 weeks (and certainly if the culture begins to go yellowish) during the 8 spring/summer/autumn months.

6. SLIDE-CULTURE OF FUNGI

See 'Fungi **S/C** vi'(p. 130).

7. SPLIT-AGAR DISC CULTURE OF FUNGI

See 'Fungi **S/C** vii' (p. 131).

**D.P.X. Mounting Medium** (Kirkpatrick and Lendrum, 1939, J. Path. Bact. **49**, 592)

This is commercially available, but may be made up as follows:

| | |
|---|---|
| Xylene . . . . . . . . . . | 100 ml |
| Tri *p* tolyl phosphate . . . . | 18.75 ml |
| 'Distrene 80' . . . . . . . . | 25 g |

'Distrene 80' is the trade name of a polymer of polystyrene.

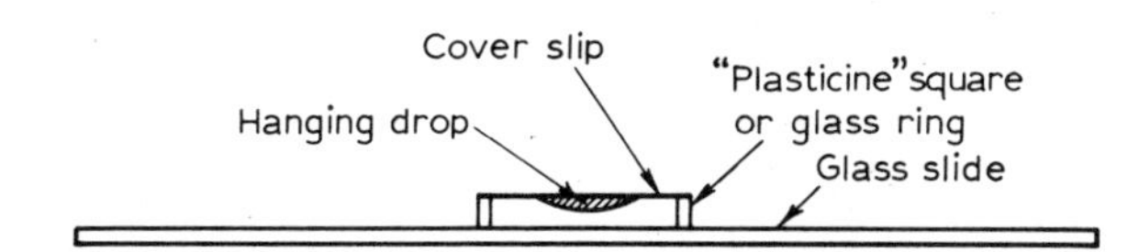


Fig. 7.2 The arrangement of a hanging drop culture (side elevation).

**Dacie's Fluid**

*For dilution of blood sample when making a count of erythrocytes* (p. 224).

| | |
|---|---|
| Formaldehyde (40%) . . . . | 1 ml |
| Sodium citrate . . . . . . . | 3 g |
| Distilled water . . . . . . . . | 100 ml |

*Note:* The erythrocytes can be stained by adding to the above solution:

| | |
|---|---|
| Eosin Y (1% aq.) . . . | Sufficient to tinge the solution. |

**Decalcifying Fluid**

(i) *For General Work*

(*a*) E.D.T.A. (Ethylene diamine tetra-acetic acid)

A 10% solution of the tetrasodium salt in water decalcifies effectively but rather slowly, due to the power of this salt to chelate with metal ions. Concentrated sodium hydroxide solution should be added until the E.D.T.A. solution is approximately neutral. The stainability of the tissues is very good.

| | |
|---|---|
| (*b*) Formaldehyde (5% aq.) . . . | 100 ml |
| Nitric acid (1.4 sp gr) . . . | 7.5 to 15 ml |

Wash in sodium sulphate (aq.), (p. 249).

(ii) *For Starfish*

| | |
|---|---|
| Alcohol (70%) . . . . . . . | 99 ml |
| Hydrochloric acid (conc.) . . . | 1 ml |

(iii) *For Shelled Protozoa*

First fix, and then decalcify in acid-alcohol, viz.:

| | |
|---|---|
| Nitric acid (conc.) . . . . . | 1 ml |
| Alcohol (70%) . . . . . . . | 99 ml |

**Detergents**

Modern detergents are based on either alkyl benzene sulphonate, or a mixture of equal parts of a soft alkyl benzene sulphonate with 'tallow alcohol sulphonate'; detergents made from it give the least trouble, later, from foam on rivers and streams carrying sewage effluent.

To avoid carry-over of undissolved detergent used in powder form it is better to use a liquid detergent for cleaning laboratory glassware.

Thorough rinsing in tap water, followed by distilled water, is *essential* after using any detergent.

*'Crystalex* 4' (supplied by T. Gerrard & Co.) is a combined detergent and wetting agent. *'Swarfega'*, a jelly, has been found by the author to be extraordinarily effective for cleaning very greasy and dirty hands. *'Teepol'* and *'R.B.S. 25'* are other very effective liquid detergents commercially available.

**Dilution of Liquids, Formula and Table for**

1. *Formula:*
   To prepare an '$x$% solution' from a '$y$% solution'; Dilute $x$ ml of the '$y$% solution' to $y$ ml.

2. *Table for Dilution of Liquids* (see p. 211)

*Notes* (to Table opposite, p. 211):

(i) The figures in this table take no account of any possible change in volume due to the mixture of the two liquids.

(ii) Heavy type indicates strengths of alcohols in most common use.

(iii) Italics indicate strengths of formaldehyde in most common use. [Formalin = formol = formaldehyde (40%).]

(iv) Intermediate figures in the table may be calculated by using the formula given at 1 (above), or as follows:

From the percentage strength of the original liquid subtract the percentage strength of the liquid required. The difference is the number of volumes of diluent which must be added to that number of volumes of original liquid which is indicated by the same number as denotes the percentage strength of the liquid required.

| | | |
|---|---|---|
| e.g. | Strength of original liquid . . . | 84.7% |
| | Strength of liquid required . . . | 33.5% |
| | Volumes of diluent to be added . | 51.2 vols. |
| | Volumes of original liquid to be taken . . . . . . . . . . | 33.5 vols. |

*Table for dilution of liquids,* see 2, *Notes* p. 210

| Percentage Strength of Liquid Required and Volumes of Original Liquid to be taken. | Percentage Strength of Original Liquid | | | | | | | | | | | | | | | | | | |
|---|---|---|---|---|---|---|---|---|---|---|---|---|---|---|---|---|---|---|---|
| | 100 | 96 | **95** | **90** | 85 | 80 | 75 | **70** | 60 | **50** | *40* | **30** | 20 | 15 | *10* | 8 | *5* | 4 | *3* |
| | Volumes of Diluent to be added | | | | | | | | | | | | | | | | | | |
| 95 | 5 | 1 | – | – | – | – | – | – | – | – | – | – | – | – | – | – | – | – | – |
| **90** | 10 | 6 | 5 | – | – | – | – | – | – | – | – | – | – | – | – | – | – | – | – |
| 85 | 15 | 11 | 10 | 5 | – | – | – | – | – | – | – | – | – | – | – | – | – | – | – |
| 80 | 20 | 16 | 15 | 10 | 5 | – | – | – | – | – | – | – | – | – | – | – | – | – | – |
| 75 | 25 | 21 | 20 | 15 | 10 | 5 | – | – | – | – | – | – | – | – | – | – | – | – | – |
| **70** | 30 | 26 | 25 | 20 | 15 | 10 | 5 | – | – | – | – | – | – | – | – | – | – | – | – |
| 60 | 40 | 36 | 35 | 30 | 25 | 20 | 15 | 10 | – | – | – | – | – | – | – | – | – | – | – |
| **50** | 50 | 46 | 45 | 40 | 35 | 30 | 25 | 20 | 10 | – | – | – | – | – | – | – | – | – | – |
| 40 | 60 | 56 | 55 | 50 | 45 | 40 | 35 | 30 | 20 | 10 | – | – | – | – | – | – | – | – | – |
| **30** | 70 | 66 | 65 | 60 | 55 | 50 | 45 | 40 | 30 | 20 | 10 | – | – | – | – | – | – | – | – |
| 20 | 80 | 76 | 75 | 70 | 65 | 60 | 55 | 50 | 40 | 30 | 20 | 10 | – | – | – | – | – | – | – |
| 15 | 85 | 81 | 80 | 75 | 70 | 65 | 60 | 55 | 45 | 35 | 25 | 15 | 5 | – | – | – | – | – | – |
| *10** | 90 | 86 | 85 | 80 | 75 | 70 | 65 | 60 | 50 | 40 | 30 | 20 | 10 | 5 | – | – | – | – | – |
| 8 | 92 | 88 | 87 | 82 | 77 | 72 | 67 | 62 | 52 | 42 | 32 | 22 | 20 | 7 | 2 | – | – | – | – |
| *5†* | 95 | 91 | 90 | 85 | 80 | 75 | 70 | 65 | 55 | 45 | 35 | 25 | 15 | 10 | 5 | 3 | – | – | – |
| 4 | 96 | 92 | 91 | 86 | 81 | 76 | 71 | 66 | 56 | 46 | 36 | 26 | 16 | 11 | 6 | 4 | 1 | – | – |
| *3* | 97 | 93 | 92 | 87 | 82 | 77 | 72 | 67 | 57 | 47 | 37 | 27 | 17 | 12 | 7 | 5 | 2 | 1 | – |
| 1 | 99 | 95 | 94 | 89 | 84 | 79 | 74 | 69 | 59 | 49 | 39 | 29 | 19 | 14 | 9 | 7 | 4 | 3 | 2 |

* To make 'Strong formol-saline' use sodium chloride solution (0.85% aq.) as the diluent for formaldehyde (10%).
† To make 'Weak formol-saline' use sodium chloride solution (0.85% aq.) as the diluent for formaldehyde (5%).

**Eau de Javelle**

(i) Bleaching Powder . . . . . . . 20 g
Water . . . . . . . . . . . 100 ml
Stand *for some hours* and *add:*

Potassium or sodium carbonate . 15 g
Water . . . . . . . . . . . 100 ml
Filter. If a film forms on the surface on exposure to air, add more potassium carbonate solution and filter.

(ii) *Formula for use with Debenham's method for xylem* (p. 180).
Bleaching powder . . . . . . . satis.
Water . . . . . . . . . . . 100 ml
Allow the bleaching powder to dissolve for at least 24 h. Filter off undissolved solid.
To the solution add the following, freshly made:
Potassium oxalate (conc. soln. in distilled water), until no further precipitate is formed.
Filter off the eau de Javelle as required.

**Eau de Labarraque**

*For nematode fixation* (p. 150).
Sodium hypochlorite . . . . 2–3 g
Distilled water . . . . . . . . 100 ml
The commercial solution varies in strength as shown.

**Embalming Fluid (Frog)**

Alcohol (60%) . . . . . . . . 100 ml
Formaldehyde (40%) . . . . 5 ml
Inject in body cavity and immerse animal in solution. Tends to remain flexible and is satisfactory for dissections for up to one year.

**Eosin, Ethyl**

See Ethyl Eosin (p. 213).

**Eosin–Haematoxylin**

See Haematoxylin, Eosin- (Renaut's) (p. 222).

**Eosin, Methyl**

See Methyl Eosin (p. 233).

**Eosin Y (i.e. Yellowish)** C.I. No. 45380

*Syn.: C.I. Acid Red* 87; *Bromo Acid J* (etc.); *Bromofluorescein; Bronze Bromo ES; Eosin, Water Soluble; Eosin WS.*

An acid dye.

A cytoplasmic stain. For general animal and plant histology. Aleurone grains – with crystalloids (use alc. soln.); bacteria-containing tissue; blood; cell walls – unlignified (counterstain to Delafield's haematoxylin); connective tissue; cytoplasm (→ red); protoplasm (especially plant); May be used as a counterstain to Delafield's haematoxylin, iodine green, and Loeffler's methylene blue.

*This dye* [to be distinguished from ethyl eosin and methyl eosin (for *both* of which *alcohol-soluble eosin* is a synonym)] *is soluble in either water or alcohol.*

(*a*) *Alcoholic solution*

| | |
|---|---|
| Eosin Y . . . . . . . . . . | 1 g |
| Alcohol (75%) . . . . . . . . | 99 ml |

(*b*) *Aqueous solution*

| | |
|---|---|
| Eosin Y . . . . . . . . . . | 1 g |
| (As counterstain to Carazzi's haematoxylin, use only 0.5 g eosin Y.) | |
| Distilled water . . . . . . . . | 99 ml |

(*c*) *As counterstain after a basic dye.*

| | |
|---|---|
| Eosin Y . . . . . . . . . . | 0.5 g |
| Alcohol (95%) . . . . . . . . | 25 ml |
| Distilled water . . . . . . . | 75 ml |

(*d*) *In clove oil*

Clove oil with eosin Y to saturation.

(*e*) *For use after treating with potassium ferrocyanide for iron* (p. 141).

| | |
|---|---|
| Eosin Y . . . . . . . . . . | 1.0 g |
| Alcohol (30%) . . . . . . . . | 100 ml |

(*f*) See also, Mann's stain (p. 233); haematoxylin-eosin (p. 222).

*Note:* Eosin is rapidly washed out by 70% and 90% alcohol: overstain sections slightly and, if alcohol is used for dehydration, dehydrate for 1 min in alcohol (96%), and 1 min in alcohol (100%).

**Erythrosin Bluish** C.I. No. 45430

*Syn.: C.I. Acid Red* 51; *Dianthine B; Eosin J; Erythrosin B* (etc.); *Iodeosin B; Pyrosin B.*

An acid dye.

Cell walls (counterstain to Delafield's haematoxylin); cytoplasm; protoplasm (esp. plant). May be counterstained with iodine green.

(*a*) *Alcoholic soln.*

| | |
|---|---|
| Erythrosin bluish . . . . . . . . | 1 g |
| Alcohol (90%) . . . . . . . . | 99 ml |

(*b*) *Aqueous soln.*

| | |
|---|---|
| Erythrosin bluish . . . . . . . | 1 g |
| Distilled water . . . . . . . . | 99 ml |
| Formaldehyde (40%) . . . . | 4–5 drops |

**Erythrosin-Glycerol**

*For staining sections of alcohol-preserved fungi.*

| | |
|---|---|
| Potassium acetate . . . . . . . | 1.0 g |
| Distilled water . . . . . . . . | 50 ml |

Dissolve the potassium acetate.

*Add:*

| | |
|---|---|
| Alcohol (95%) . . . . . . . . | 30 ml |
| Glycerol . . . . . . . . . . | 20 ml |

*Add:*

| | |
|---|---|
| Copper acetate . . | Sufficient to colour slightly |
| Add: | |
| Erythrosin bluish . . | Sufficient to colour deep red |

**Ethanol**

See p. 51 and also 'Alcohol, Ethyl' p. 186.

**2 Ethoxy Ethanol (Ethylene Glycol Monoethyl Ether)**

(*Formerly known as 'Cellosolve'*)

This substance is miscible with water, with alcohol, with clove oil and with xylene. Hence it is used as a dehydrating agent (or, to use the term suggested by J. R. Baker, an 'antemedium') in preparing tissues for treatment with clove oil or xylene for improving their transparency by virtue of changing their refractive index.

The great advantage of the use of 2 ethoxy ethanol as a dehydrating agent is that it is not necessary to 'grade up', as it is with alcohol. Consequently the dehydration process can be carried through much more quickly than with alcohol.

On the other hand, the 2 ethoxy ethanol method is not entirely fool-proof and should not be regarded as an instantaneous process. The diffusion currents produced when 2 ethoxy ethanol is mixed with water are very strong. It is advisable, therefore, to place the tissue in dilute alcohol (either as a single section on a slide, or in quantity in a watch-glass) and add 2 ethoxy ethanol *a little at a time* (drop-by-drop, if the tissue is on a slide). Finally, the diluted liquid should be replaced by 2 ethoxy ethanol (100%) and the tissue then transferred to clove oil or, preferably, xylene-phenol before being mounted in D.P.X.

**Ethyl Eosin** C.I. No. 45386

*Syn.: C.I. Solvent Red* 45; *Alcohol Soluble Eosin; Eosin, Alcohol Soluble; Eosin* S.

This dye is a useful counterstain for haematoxylin, but holds no special advantages for the elementary student.

**F.A.A.**

See 'Formol-Acetic-Alcohol' (p. 215).

**Farmer's Fluid**

A modification of Clarke's Fluid (p. 199).

| | |
|---|---|
| Acetic acid (glacial) | 25 ml |
| Ethyl alcohol (absolute) | 50 ml |

**Farrants' Medium**

| | |
|---|---|
| White gum arabic | 30 g |
| Distilled water | 30 ml |

Do not heat. Stir occasionally.

*Add:*

| | |
|---|---|
| Arsenious oxide | 0.01 g |
| Glycerol | 15 ml |

Strain through clean flannel if necessary.
Keep in stoppered bottle with pieces of camphor.
Material should be soaked for *a few minutes only.*

**Fast Green FCF** C.I. No. 42053

*Syn.: C.I. Food Green* 3.

An acid dye.

A cytoplasmic stain. Plant tissue. Counterstain to alum carmine (Grenacher's); haematoxylin; safranin O; Feulgen's technique for D.N.A. [Cellulose (→ green); cell-walls (unlignified) (→ green); cytoplasm (→ green); *Paramecium* (nuclear detail).]

This stain possesses all the advantages of light green SF yellowish, (which it has largely superseded) without the disadvantage of fading. It is therefore recommended in preference to light green SF yellowish for use in all preparations in which that stain was formerly used. It gives a blue-green compared with the leafy-green of light green SF yellowish. Fast green FCF is soluble in alcohol, clove oil, 2 ethoxy ethanol, and water.

(i) *In benzyl alcohol*

*As a counterstain to safranin* O. *See* III (*b*) (p. 160).

| | |
|---|---|
| Benzyl alcohol | 100 ml |
| Fast green FCF | 0.5 g |

(ii) *In ethyl alcohol*

| | |
|---|---|
| Ethyl alcohol (90%) | 100 ml |
| Fast green FCF | Satis. |

Filter when sufficient time has been allowed to make a saturated solution.

(iii) *In clove oil*

(*a*)

| | |
|---|---|
| Clove oil | 100 ml |
| Fast green FCF | Satis. |

Filter when sufficient time has been allowed to make a saturated solution.

(*b*) *For use in Method* III (α) (γ), *'Plant Tissue'* (p. 160).

| | |
|---|---|
| Clove oil | 50 ml |
| Ethyl alcohol | 50 ml |
| Fast green FCF | 0.2 g |

(iv) *In 2 ethoxy ethanol*

| | |
|---|---|
| 2 ethoxy ethanol | 100 ml |
| Fast green FCF | 3 g |

Heat together in a flask on a water-bath for 30 min. Stir occasionally. Cool. Filter.

(v) See also iv (p. 188), for solution in lacto-phenol.

**Fast Green FCF — Safranin O in 2 Ethoxy Ethanol**

See 'Safranin O — Fast Green FCF in 2 ethoxy ethanol' (p. 244).

**de Faure's Fluid (Gum Chloral)**

*For mounting delicate insects, eggs of helminthes in faeces, moulds.*

| | |
|---|---|
| Chloral hydrate . . . . . . . | 50 g |
| Glycerol . . . . . . . . . . | 20 ml |
| Gum arabic . . . . . . . . | 30–40 g |
| Distilled water . . . . . . . . | 50 ml |

1 Dissolve the chloral hydrate in the water.
2 Add the glycerol. Stir thoroughly.
3 Pulverize the gum arabic and place it in a muslin bag suspended in the chloral hydrate/glycerol mixture.

*Note:* As far as possible, air should be excluded while the gum arabic is being dissolved. The mixture should not be filtered.

**Fehling's Solutions**

*For tests for reducing sugars. See 'Sugars. Tests for, (b) Dextrose* ii' (p. 173).

*Solution A*

| | |
|---|---|
| Copper sulphate (crystalline) . . | .34.6 g |
| Distilled water, to make up to . | 500 ml |

If necessary to clarify, *add:*

| | |
|---|---|
| Sulphuric acid (conc.) . . . . | 2 drops |

*Solution B*

| | |
|---|---|
| Sodium hydroxide . . . . . | 77 g |
| Sodium potassium tartrate . . . | 175 g |
| Distilled water, to make up to . | 500 ml |

*Note:* For use: Mix equal volumes of solutions A and B. *In store the solutions must be kept separate.*

**Ferric Chloride**

(i) *As a blood coagulant*

Ferric chloride aq. at 'bench strength' is a blood coagulant and can be used in an emergency when, for example, a blood vessel is accidentally cut during the dissection of a freshly killed animal, but the practice is not to be encouraged.

(ii) *For use in Weigert's iron-haematoxylin* (p. 222).

| | |
|---|---|
| Ferric chloride (anhydrous) . . | 30 g |
| Distilled water . . . . . . . . | 65 ml |

Allow to dissolve. *Add:*

Distilled water. To make volume up to 100 ml.

*Note:* The solution must be freshly made.

**Feulgen Stain**

See Schiff's reagent (p. 245).

**Field's Stain**

*For malaria parasite in thick blood films* ['Blood vii' (p. 110)].

*Solution A*

| | |
|---|---|
| Azure I . . . . . . . . . . | 0.5 g |
| Methylene blue . . . . . . | 0.8 g |
| Phosphate buffer solution (p. 239) | 500 ml |

*Note:* First grind the azure I with a small quantity of the buffer solution. Mix the ingredients. Allow to stand for 24 h. Filter.

*Solution B*

| | |
|---|---|
| Eosin Y . . . . . . . . . . | 1 g |
| Phosphate buffer solution (p. 239) | 500 ml |

**Filter Paper**

(i) Use technical quality and buy in sheets 62 cm x 62 cm.
(ii) Cut into pieces 7.5 cm x 5 cm for irrigation, etc.

**Flemming's Fluid (Chrome-osmium-acetic)**

*A good fixative for cytological work.* Penetration poor; therefore fix *small* pieces of tissue (2–3 mm thick) for 1–48 h (the longer period for medullated nerve fibres) in the dark. Wash in running water for 24 h.

*Note:*

(i) The *weak* solution should be used for fungi and rotifers.
(ii) The *strong* solution should be used for cytological purposes.
(iii) *The solution should be freshly made just before use.*

| | *Weak solution* | *Strong solution* |
|---|---|---|
| (*a*) Acetic acid (glacial) . . . | 0.1 ml | 5 ml |
| Chromium trioxide (1%) . | 25 ml | 75 ml |
| Osmium tetroxide (2%) . | 5 ml | 20 ml |
| Distilled water . . . . | 70 ml | – |

(*b*) See also 'Navashin's Fluid' (p. 237).

**'Flemmings Without Acetic' (F.W.A.)**

| | |
|---|---|
| Chromium trioxide (0.25%) . . | 90 ml |
| Osmium tetroxide (1%) . . . . | 10 ml |

**Formaldehyde**

(i) 'Formalin' and 'Formol' are commercial names for a saturated solution (40%) of formaldehyde in distilled water.
(ii) To neutralize the formic acid produced on oxidation either, keep a lump of calcium carbonate at the bottom of the formaldehyde bottle, or, neutralize with sodium carbonate before use.
(iii) For use as preservative of animal tissue, use a 3% aq. soln.
(iv) For use as fixative, use a 4% soln. in isotonic saline.
(v) For dilutions, see 'Dilution of Liquids, Formula and Table for' (p. 210).

**'Formalin'**

| | |
|---|---|
| Formaldehyde . . . . . . . | 40 ml |
| Distilled water . . . . . . . | 60 ml |

'Formalin' is the commercial name for a saturated aqueous solution of formaldehyde.

**Formalin-Alcohol**

See 'Alcohol-Formalin' (p. 187).

**Formalin-Dichromate**

*For hardening brains.*

| | |
|---|---|
| Formaldehyde (8% aq.) . . . . | 50 ml |
| Potassium dichromate (1% aq.) . | 50 ml |

Leave the brain in the mixture for 2–3 weeks.
Wash in running water for 1 d.
Preserve in formalin (5%).

**Formol**

A commercial name for a saturated aqueous solution (i.e. 40%) of formaldehyde.

See 'Formaldehyde' and 'Formalin' (above).

**Formol-Acetic-Alcohol (F.A.A.) (Kahle's Fluid) (Bles's Fluid)**

*Especially useful for fixation of botanical material for anatomical purposes* and where highly critical fixation of cell contents is *not* required; for fixation and preservation of algae; and for plant histology generally.

| | (i) *Kahle's* | (ii) *Bles's* |
|---|---|---|
| Acetic acid (glacial) . . . . | 5 ml | 3 ml |
| Alcohol (70%) [(50%) for delicate tissues] . . . . . | 90 ml | 90 ml |
| Formaldehyde (40%) . . . | 5 ml | 7 ml |

*Note:* Formula (i) is a further modification by Johansen of Kahle's modification of Cardowsky's original formula.

**Formol-Propionic-Alcohol**

*A useful fixative for general plant histology.*

| | |
|---|---|
| Alcohol (70%) . . . . . . . . | 100 ml |
| Formaldehyde (40%) . . . . | 10 ml |
| Propionic acid . . . . . . . | 6.5 ml |

**Formol-Saline**

*A good fixative for routine work;* fixation takes from a few h to 3–4 d; penetrates well; hardens; preserves fat; most stains can be used after it; after fixation, wash and store tissue in alcohol (70%).

*Note:*
(i) See footnotes (*), (†) and note iii under 'Dilution of Liquids, Formula and Table for' (p. 210), and use sodium chloride (0.85% aq.) as the diluent for formaldehyde.
(ii) Neutralize the formaldehyde with sodium carbonate before making up the formol-saline.

**Fuchsin, Acid** C.I. No. 42685

*Syn.: C.I. Acid Violet 19; Acid Magenta; Acid Rubin; Fuchsin S* (etc.).

An acid dye.

A good general stain. Blood; cellulose (counterstain with iodine green); connective tissue (fresh) (dilute 20 times with Ringer's soln.); cytoplasm; chromatophores; yeast (iv, p. 181). May be used as a counterstain for iodine green, methyl green, aniline blue WS, and malachite green.

May be used in alcoholic or in aqueous solution:

(*a*) Acid fuchsin . . . . . . . . . 1 g
Alcohol (50%), (or distilled water) . 100 ml

(*b*) *For use in staining parasitic hyphae of rust fungus in leaf.*
Acid fuchsin . . . . . . . . . 2 g
Alcohol (70%) . . . . . . . . 98 ml

(*c*) See also van Gieson's stain (p. 218), orange

fuchsin (p. 237) and Mallory's triple stain (p. 232).

**Fuchsin, Acid, Anilin- (Altmann's)**

*For use in the Champy-Kull method for mitochondria* (p. 146).

| | |
|---|---|
| Acid fuchsin . . . . . . . . | 7 g |
| Aniline water . . . . . . . . | 100 ml |

**Fuchsin, Acid, Orange-**

See 'Orange-Fuchsin' (p. 237).

**Fuchsin, Acid, Picro-**

See 'van Gieson's stain' (p. 232).

**Fuchsin, Basic** (C.I. No. not allocated)

*Syn.: Anilin Red; Basic Rubin; Fuchsin RFN; Magenta.*

Basic fuchsin is a basic dye. It is a mixture of pararosanilin, rosanilin and magenta II. Details of these dyes are as follows:

Pararosanilin C.I. No. 42500

*Syn.: C.I. Basic Red 9; Basic Rubin; Parafuchsin; Paramagenta.*

Rosanilin C.I. No. 42510

*Syn.: C.I. Basic Violet 14; Magenta I.*

Magenta II (C.I. No. not allocated)

Unless made in the laboratory this member of the basic fuchsin mixture is not found pure. A near relation of magenta II is:

New Fuchsin C.I. No. 42520

*Syn.: C.I. Basic Violet 2; Magenta III.*

*Uses of basic fuchsin:*

*General nuclear stain.* Bacteria; *Chara* (temp. with iodine); hyphae protoplasm (with iodine); lignin (→ red); *Nitella* (with iodine); *Protococcus* (with iodine); *Vorticella;* Yeast (with malachite green, see iv, p. 181).

| | |
|---|---|
| Basic fuchsin . . . . . . . . | 0.1 g |
| Alcohol (70%) . . . . . . . . | 1 ml |
| Distilled water . . . . . . . . | 160 ml |

**Fuchsin, Basic, Ammoniacal**

*Bundle ends;* lignified tissue (→ red) (counterstain with fast green FCF).

(i) Basic fuchsin . . 5.0% soln. in alcohol (95%)
Ammonium hydroxide . . . 0.88 sp. gr.
Add the basic fuchsin to the ammonia until a permanent straw colour is obtained. Filter.

(ii) *Special formula for Debenham's method for xylem* [iii (p. 180)].
Basic fuchsin (Gurr's Special). Filtered sat. soln. in alcohol (100%).
Ammonium hydroxide . . . 0.88 sp. gr.
Add the ammonium hydroxide from a dropping funnel, in a steady stream, into the basic fuchsin solution until the liquid is a pale yellow. Shake continuously while mixing. *Use within* 24 h.

**Fuchsin. Basic, Anilin-water (Ehrlich's)**

*Bacteria spores.*

| | |
|---|---|
| Distilled water . . . . . . . . | 100 ml |
| Anilin oil . . . . . . . . . | 5 ml |

Shake up, and stand for 5 min. Filter through a paper wetted with distilled water. Filtrate must be water clear.

*Add:*

| | |
|---|---|
| Sodium hydroxide (1%) . . . | 1 ml |

then,

| | |
|---|---|
| Basic fuchsin . . . . . . . . | 5 g |

Shake. Stand for 24 h. *Use within* 2 d.

*Note:* Methyl violet 2B, crystal violet or methylene blue may be used in place of basic fuchsin in the above formula.

**Fuchsin, Basic, Phenol- (Carbol-Fuchsin) (Weigert's)**

Elastin (→ blue-black); cartilage; connective tissue.

| | |
|---|---|
| Basic fuchsin . . . . . . . . | 1 g |
| Phenol . . . . . . . . . . . | 2 g |
| Distilled water . . . . . . . . | 100 ml |

Dissolve and bring to boiling point in a large bowl.

When boiling, add, in small amounts, to precipitate the dyestuff,

| | |
|---|---|
| Ferric chloride (30% aq.) . . . | 12.5 ml |

Boil and stir, for another 10 min.

Cool. Filter.

Wash precipitate on filter till runnings are colourless. Dry precipitate.

To make the solution:

Dry precipitate . . . . . . . 0.75 g
Alcohol (90%) . . . . . . . . 100 ml

Boil under reflux condenser for 20 min.
Cool. Filter. *Add:*

Hydrochloric acid (conc.) . . . 2 ml

**Fuchsin, Basic, Phenol- (Carbol-Fuchsin) (Ziehl's)**

*A nuclear stain.* Bacteria and their spores; fungi; yeast and yeast spores.

Basic fuchsin . . . . . . . . 1 g
Ethyl alcohol (100%) . . . . 10 ml
Phenol (crystals) . . . . . . . 5 g
Distilled water . . . . . . . . 100 ml

Stand for 24 h. Filter. Keeps well.

**Fuchsin, Basic, Resorcin- (Weigert's)**

*For elastic fibres.*

Distilled water . . . . . . . . 200 ml

Bring almost to the boil in a large evaporating basin.
*Add:*

Basic fuchsin . . . . . . . . 1 g

Stir until dissolved. *Add:*

Resorcin . . . . . . . . . 2 g

Boil until dissolved. *Add:*

Ferric chloride (30% aq.) . . . 25 ml
Boil and stir. (2–5 min)

Filter off the precipitate. Wash the precipitate into:

Alcohol (95%) . . . . . . . 200 ml

Boil. Cool. Filter. *Add:*

Alcohol (95%). To make filtrate up to . . . . . . . . . . 200 ml

*Add:*

Hydrochloric acid (conc.) . . . 4 ml

**Fuchsin, Basic, -Sulphurous Acid**

See Schiff's reagent (p. 245).

**Fuchsin, Basic, -Violet (Rosanilin-Violet) (Hanstein's)***

Chlorophyll cell-wall stratification; stem-sections (esp. monocots.); amyloid substances, nucleus, gums (→ red shades); protoplasm (→ bluish violet); resins (→ blue); tannin (→ foxy-red); cellulose (→ pale violet); lignin (→ reddish); bast-fibres (→ deep red); sieve-tubes and bast parenchyma (→ hardly stained); zoophytes.

Alcohol (70%) . . . . . . . satis.
Basic fuchsin . . . . . . . 1 part by wt.
Methyl violet 2B . . . . . . 1 part by wt.

* After Strasburger, 1930, *Handbook of Practical Botany* (English edn.), Allen and Unwin, London.

**Gelatine**

| | (i) For attaching gelatine-embedded sections to slide | (ii) For attaching frozen sections to slide | (iii) For gelatine impregnation and embedding |
|---|---|---|---|
| Gelatine<br>Cut into small pieces.<br>*Add:* | 1 g | 2 g | 25 g |
| Distilled water<br>Allow the gelatine to dissolve. (3 h approx.)<br>*Add:* | 25 ml | 50 ml | 50 ml |
| Distilled water<br>Heat to not more than 60°C.<br>Stir. Cool.<br>Add 0.2 g sodium *p* hydroxybenzoate to inhibit moulds. | 75 ml | 50 ml | 50 ml |

*Note:* The solutions are best made up just before use.

**F.W.A.**

See 'Flemming's Without Acetic"(F.W.A.)', (p. 214).

**Gatenby's Fluid***

For removal of albumen from eggs of *Rana*.

| | |
|---|---|
| Chromium trioxide (1%) . . . | 100 ml |
| Nitric acid (conc.) . . . . . | 6 ml |
| Potassium dichromate (2%) . . | 100 ml |

**Giemsa's Stain†**

*Blood and blood parasites.*
See 'Blood v' (p. 109) for use and results.

(i) *Lillie's modification of Giemsa's formula.*†

| | |
|---|---|
| Azure A eosinate . . . . . . | 0.5 g |
| Azure B eosinate . . . . . . | 2.5 g |
| Methylene blue eosinate . . . | 2.0 g |
| Methylene blue chloride . . . | 1.0 g |
| Glycerol . . . . . . . . . . | 375 ml |
| Methyl alcohol, reagent . . . . | 375 ml |

*Note:* Reagents used in the preparation must be strictly acid-free.

(ii) If not prepared in the laboratory, the stain may be purchased from a reputuble biological supplier.

**van Gieson's Stain (Picro-Acid Fuchsin)**

Cartilage; blood vessels; connective tissue (a specific stain) (→ red); elastic fibres (→ yellow); epithelia (→ yellow); muscle (→ yellow); see also results when used as a counterstain to Weigert's iron haematoxylin ['Animal Tissue II (*j*)' (p. 101)].

| | |
|---|---|
| Acid fuchsin (1% aq.) . . . . . | 5 ml |

Boil well. Filter. *Add:*

| | |
|---|---|
| Picric acid (aq. satd.), (see p. 240) . . . . . . . . . | 100 ml |

* Bolles-Lee, 1937, *Microtomist's Vade-Mecum*, Churchill London.
† After Conn, *Biological Stains*, 7th Edn., Williams & Wilkins.

**Glassware**

1 *Adhesive for:* See 'Adhesives' (p. 185).
2 *To clean.*

(i) *Slides, cover slips and small apparatus.*

**1** Soak in
either (*a*) A mixture of old xylene . . 50%
Methylated spirits . . . . 50%
or (*b*) Sodium hydroxide (conc. aq.).
or (*c*) Nitric acid (conc.).
or (*d*) A mixture of sulphuric acid (conc.), or nitric acid (conc.) . . . 10%
Potassium dichromate (3% aq.) . . . . . . 90%
**2** Wash in running tap water.
**3** Rinse in distilled water.
**4** Rinse (store if desired) in acid alcohol.
**5** Dip in alcohol (90%).
**6** Wipe dry on a *dry, clean, lint-free* cloth.
**7** Before using for bacterial, fungal and agar work dip in alcohol (95%) and pass through a flame to dry.

(ii) *To remove grease.*

Either, (*a*) Soak in a mixture of:
Sulphuric acid (conc.) . . satis.
Potassium dichromate . . excess
or, (*b*) Wash with 'Crystalex 4', 'Teepol', or any other liquid detergent.

Subsequent treatment after (*a*) and (*b*) as (i) **2** and **3**, and, if for microscopic work, **4–6** or **7** above.

(iii) *To remove white deposit.*
Soak in sodium metasilicate (5% aq.).

(iv) *Blood pipettes.*
Attach by pressure tubing to a filter pump and dip the ends successively in distilled water, alcohol (100%), and ether.

(v) *Microscope lenses.* See p. 12.

3 *To lubricate*

Lubricants for glassware (taps, desiccator lids, etc.) consist generally of mixtures of pale crêpe rubber and petroleum jelly 'Vaseline', with or without paraffin wax. The proportions of the ingredients vary according to the particular properties required of the lubricant. If pale crêpe rubber is not easily obtainable, the pure rubber tape from the inside of old golf balls is a satisfactory substitute. In making the mixtures the rubber is first melted, the wax (if any) added in *small* pieces, followed by the petroleum jelly and the whole well mixed and maintained at the temperature and for the length of time stated.

(i) Pale crêpe rubber . . . . . . . 10 g
Petroleum jelly . . . . . . . . 100 g
Heat at 125°C to 150°C for three d.

(ii) Pale crêpe rubber . . . . . . . 40 g
Petroleum jelly . . . . . . . . 80 g

(iii) Pale crêpe rubber . . . . . . . 40 g
Petroleum jelly (white) . . . . 72 g
Paraffin wax (m.pt. 30°C) . . . 4 g

(iv) Pale crêpe rubber . . . . . . . 42 g
Petroleum jelly (white) . . . . 49 g
Paraffin wax . . . . . . . . . 7 g
Mix at 155°C and maintain at that temperature for 190 h. Chill in ice and allow to settle for 3 or 4 d before use.

(v) Pale crêpe rubber . . . . . . . 62 g
Petroleum jelly (white) . . . . 48 g
Paraffin wax (m.pt. 36°C) . . . 10 g

(vi) Aluminium stearate . . . . . 25 g
Viscous oil (Standard Oil Co. No. 32) . . . . . . . . . . 100 g
Heat to 150°C until homogeneous. Cool rapidly.
*Note:* This gives a very sticky grease.

(vii) Bentonite
Glycerol
The proportions of the two ingredients can be varied through a wide range in order to obtain any desired consistency.
*Note:* This lubricant can be used at high temperatures.

4 *To sterilize*

In the absence of an autoclave or special sterilizing apparatus the simplest piece of equipment is a household pressure cooker. In general, 15 min steaming at 15 lb above atmospheric pressure, or 20 min steaming at 10 lb above atmospheric pressure will suffice.

5 *To write on*

(i) 'Chinagraph' pencil

(ii) *Foertsch's grease pencil.* *
Tallow . . . . . . . . 20% (by weight)
White wax . . . . . . 80% (by weight)
Melt the tallow and wax together (care) and stir in prussian blue until the required intensity of colour is obtained. Cool. When nearly cold, roll into pencils of suitable size on a slab. Cover with a paper case.

(iii) Gurr's glass ink

(iv) *Formula for glass ink*
Borax (13% soln. in distilled water) . . . . . . . . . . 50 ml
Shellac (13% soln. in cold alcohol (96%)) . . . . . . . . . . 30 ml
Mix the two solutions a drop at a time. If necessary, heat gently to dissolve any precipitate. When solution is complete, add methylene blue or other dye to give the depth of colour required.
*Note:* Felt pen nibs with a reservoir are very useful for applying glass ink.

(v) Felt ink markers (various colours).

(vi) *Isinglass*
Isinglass . . . . . . . . . . A 'pinch'
Distilled water . . . . . . . . 500 ml
Boil. Filter. Apply to the glass by means of a pipette. When quite dry, use Indian black or coloured ink.

**Glucose**

*For comparative study of effects of temperature upon the respiratory rate of yeast* (pp. 166, 167).
Glucose . . . . . . . . . . 10 g
Distilled water . . . . . . . 100 ml

**Glycerol (Glycerine)**

(i) *For use as a temporary mountant.*
Glycerol . . . . . . . . . 50 ml
Distilled water . . . . . . . 50 ml
Thymol (conc. soln.) . . . . 1 ml

* After Geoffrey Martin (Ed.), *Dyestuffs and Coal Tar Products,* Crosby Lockwood.

(ii) *Acid-glycerol for use as a temporary mountant for botanical preparations after staining with anilin blue-picric acid.*

| | |
|---|---|
| Glycerol . . . . . . . . | 50 ml |
| Hydrochloric acid (conc.) . . . | 5 ml |
| Distilled water . . . . . . | 50 ml |

*Note:* Mix the glycerol with the water before adding the hydrochloric acid.

(iii) See also 'Glycerol/alcohol (p. 58) and 'Calcium Chloride' (p. 193).

### Glycerol-Jelly

*For method of use, refer to 'Mounting – Some Special Techniques,* ii' (p. 59).

| | |
|---|---|
| Gelatine . . . . . . . . . . | 10 g |
| Distilled water . . . . . . | 60 ml |

Leave for 2 h. *Add:*

| | |
|---|---|
| Glycerol . . . . . . . . | 70 ml |
| Phenol (crystalline)* . . . . | 0.25 g |

Warm and stir for 15 min until the flakes produced by the phenol have disappeared.

### Glycerol Substitute (for mounting)

See 'Calcium chloride' (p.193).

### Gold Chloride (Merck's Reagent)

*Toning solution for use in the silver method for nerve axons* (p. 151), *and in Wilder's method for reticulin fibrils* (p. 120).

| | |
|---|---|
| Gold chloride . . . . . . . | 0.2 g |
| Distilled water . . . . . . | 100 ml |

### Guiacum Resin

*For experiments on respiration in plant tissues.*

| | |
|---|---|
| Alcohol (95%) . . . . . . | 100 ml |
| Charcoal (absorbent) . . . . | A little |
| Guiacum resin (freshly broken) . | 1.5 g |

Heat together on a water-bath for 5 min. Filter.

### Gum Arabic

*To restrict movements of spermatozoids.*

10% aq. filtered.

* Phenol appears to cause fading of chlorophyll and haematoxylin. A suggested alternative preservative is 0.01 g thymol.

### Gum Chloral (Faure's)

*For mounting insects, helminth eggs, moss leaves, moulds.*

| | |
|---|---|
| Chloral hydrate . . . . . . | 50 g |
| Glycerol . . . . . . . . | 20 ml |
| Gum arabic . . . . . . . | 40 g |
| Distilled water . . . . . . | 50 ml |

1 Dissolve the chloral hydrate in the water.
2 Add the glycerol.
3 Break up the gum.
4 Suspend the gum, in a bag made of gauze, in the liquid, and exclude air as far as possible.
5 Avoid filtering if possible.

### Haemalum, Mayer's

*Bulk and section staining of animal tissue. Small entire animals; nuclei.*
*used). After staining wash in potassium alum* (1% *aq.*) (24 h *after bulk staining) and then wash thoroughly in tap water. Tissue may be bleached in 'Parozone'* (p. 239). *Do* not *use clove-oil for clearing. Mount in D.P.X.*

| | |
|---|---|
| Haematoxylin . . . . . . . | 1 g |
| *Distilled* water . . . . . . | 1000 ml |

Dissolve. *Add:*

| | |
|---|---|
| Potassium alum . . . . . . | 50 g |
| Sodium iodate ($NaIO_3$) . . . | 0.2 g |

Dissolve. Filter.

### Haemalum, Acid (Mayer's)

*Bulk and section staining of animal tissue. Small entire animals; nuclei.*

| | |
|---|---|
| Haematoxylin . . . . . . | 1 g |
| Distilled water . . . . . . | 1000 ml |

Dissolve, and *add:*

| | |
|---|---|
| Potassium alum . . . . . . | 50 g |
| Sodium iodate . . . . . . | 0.2 g |

Dissolve, and *add:*

| | |
|---|---|
| Acetic acid (glacial) . . . . . | 20 ml |
| Chloral hydrate . . . . . . | 50 g |
| Citric acid . . . . . . . . | 1 g |
| Phenol . . . . . . . . . . | 1 crystal |

### Haematal 8*

A haematein dye; stable; quick-acting; suitable for progressive staining; dispenses with the necessity

* After J. R. Baker (with his kind permission), *School Science Review*, **XLV**, 156, 401, March 1964.
'Dr. Baker considers that haematal 8 replaces Mayer's haemalum and all other haemateins and haematoxylins with aluminium as mordant. (*Private communication to the Reviser.*)'

for differentiation or 'blueing'; can be used after any of the usual fixatives (if used after Zenker's fluid, restrict fixation to a maximum of 6 h). Counterstain with Biebrich scarlet WS; or with eosin Y.

*Solution A*

| | |
|---|---|
| Aluminium sulphate (crystalline) | 7.88 g |
| Distilled water, to make up to . | 500 ml |

*Note:* This makes a dM/4 aqueous soln.

*Solution B*

Ethylene glycol (ethane-diol) . . 250 ml

*Add:*

Distilled water, to make up to . 500 ml

*Add:*

Haematein (See 'Haematoxylin', below) . . . . . . . . . 0.94 g

*Note:* This makes a dM/16 soln. of haematein in dilute ethylene glycol.

*Solution C – the staining solution*

| | |
|---|---|
| Solution A . . . . . . . . . | 50 ml |
| Solution B . . . . . . . . . | 50 ml |

*Note: Stain sections:* 2–15 min. Wash in running tap water.

*Stain whole mounts:* Overstain and then remove excess stain by soaking in aluminium sulphate (dM/8 aq.) (made by diluting solution A, above, with an equal volume of distilled water). Wash thoroughly in running tap water.

**Haematein, Ammonia-**

*Cladophora* sp. (after picric acid fixation).

(i) 1 Place a few crystals of haematoxylin (below) in a few ml of distilled water.
2 Pass ammonia vapour through the liquid until the haematoxylin dissolves to give a violet solution.
3 Dilute the solution considerably with distilled water.

(ii) *Use:*
1 Stain the tissue in this solution for several hours (until the tissue is slightly overstained).
2 Then wash in distilled water until the preparation is of the desired colour.

**Haematoxylin** C.I. No. 75920

*Syn.: C.I. Natural Black* 1 *and C.I. Natural Black* 2.

Haematoxylin is obtained from logwood. It is not, itself, a dye but, on oxidation, it is converted into the coloured substance ***haematein.*** For biological purposes, however, the staining substance is usually referred to as haematoxylin.

Haematoxylin has a great affinity for metals and most formulae include a mordanting material containing either aluminium, or iron, or potassium, often supplied by way of one of the alums.

The colour resulting from staining with haematoxylin depends on the mordant used. Iron alum gives a black colour; potassium alum gives a purple-blue.

Haematoxylin is a basic stain and is of great use in histology and cytology. Properly differentiated preparations can show gradations of colour from red to blue. Various mixtures are given under 'Haemalum', 'Haematal 8', 'Haematein' and 'Haematoxylin'. See also 'van Gieson's Stain' (p. 218).

**Haematoxylin, Alcoholic**

| | |
|---|---|
| Haematoxylin . . . . . . . . | 1 g |
| Alcohol (100%) . . . . . . . | 70 ml |
| Distilled water . . . . . . . | 30 ml |

**Haematoxylin, Alum-**

For section staining after fixation in Flemming's solution.

| | |
|---|---|
| Alum (ammonium or potassium) | 5 g |
| Haematoxylin . . . . . . . | 0.25 g |
| Thymol . . . . . . . . . . | 0.25 g |
| Distilled water . . . . . . . | 100 ml |

*Note:* This solution will not keep satisfactorily for longer than 3 months.

**Haematoxylin,* Carazzi's**

May be counterstained with eosin Y (0.5% aq.).

| | |
|---|---|
| Haematoxylin . . . . . . . . | 0.75 g |
| Potassium alum . . . . . . . | 37.50 g |

* Langeron, M., 1925, *Précis de Microscope*, Masson, Paris.

| | |
|---|---|
| Potassium iodate | 0.15 g |
| Glycerol | 250 ml |
| Distilled water | 600 ml |

Do not heat to dissolve.
There is no need to allow to ripen.

*Note:* (i) Stain sections 20 min.
(ii) After staining wash in tap water or alkaline water to blue the stain.

**Haematoxylin, Delafield's**

A basic dye.

A good general stain for nuclei. Cellulose (counterstain to safranin O) (→ purple); cell walls (unlignified) (counterstain with eosin Y, or erythrosin bluish); chromatin (→ purple); epithelia; *Fasciola; Hydra; Lumbricus* (entire); mitotic figures; mosses; mycelia in wood; nuclei (animal and plant) (→ blue); plant tissue [fresh sections; fixed sections (with safranin O); thick objects; whole mounts; general histology]; ovary; pituitary; protozoa; sieve plates; spinal cord; suprarenal body; testis; thyroid; *Trypanosoma;* yeast. May be followed by picric acid where chitin or horn is to be stained.

| | |
|---|---|
| Ammonium alum (aq. satd.) | 400 ml |
| Haematoxylin [16% in alcohol (100%)] | 25 ml |

Stand 4 d (in a flask plugged with cotton wool) exposed to light.
Filter. *Add:*

| | |
|---|---|
| Glycerol | 100 ml |
| Methyl alcohol | 100 ml |

Place in a warm, light situation for 6 *weeks.* Ripening more rapid by adding a small quantity of hydrogen peroxide. Improves with age. As it ripens, dilute with ammonia alum (aq. satd.). If the haematoxylin is *very* old it will not 'blue' with tap water. If in this red condition, add a few drops of ammonium hydroxide to the stock.

**Haematoxylin, Ehrlich's**

A basic dye.

For general animal histology. Kidney, liver, testis [all counterstained with eosin Y (alc.)]; *Monocystis.*

| | |
|---|---|
| Haematoxylin | 2 g |
| Alcohol (100%) | 100 ml |

*Add:*

| | |
|---|---|
| Distilled water | 100 ml |
| Glycerol | 100 ml |
| Acetic acid (glacial) | 10 ml |
| Potassium alum | excess |

Leave the whole in a large bottle in sunlight. Remove stopper for *a few min.* Replace. Shake. Leave open. Repeat this *over several weeks.*

**Haematoxylin, Eosin- (Renaut's)**

*For nuclei (plant).*

| | |
|---|---|
| Eosin Y (1% aq.) | 30 ml |
| Haematoxylin (*satd.* alc.), Potash alum (satd. soln. in glycerol) | 130 ml |

Leave unstoppered *for several weeks until alcohol has evaporated.*
Filter.

**Haematoxylin, Iron- (Weigert's)**

*For general and cytological work.*

*Solution A*

| | |
|---|---|
| Haematoxylin | 1 g |
| Alcohol (95%) or (96%) | 100 ml |

*Solution B*

| | |
|---|---|
| Ferric chloride (30% aq.), (ii, p. 214) | 4 ml |
| Hydrochloric acid (s.g. 1.124) | 1 ml |
| Distilled water | 95 ml |

Allow solution A to ripen for a few days, but use it within 6 months. Just before use, mix equal volumes of solutions A and B.
Mixture will keep for a few days.
Stain sections 10–15 min. If necessary, differentiate with acid alcohol.

**Haematoxylin, Iron Alum- (Anderson's)**

General animal histology; *Paramecium* (nuclear detail); *Vorticella* (with orange G).

*Note:* Haemoglobin has a great affinity for iron haematoxylin: do not mistake red blood corpuscles for nuclei.

*Solution A*

| | |
|---|---|
| Haematoxylin | 0.5 g |
| Alcohol (50%) | 100 ml |
| Calcium hypochlorite (2% aq.) | 3 ml |

*Solution B* (the mordant)

| | |
|---|---|
| Iron alum | 4 g |

Distilled water . . . . . . 100 ml
Sulphuric acid (conc.) . . . . 3 ml

Just before use, mix two parts of solution A with one part of solution B. Mixture keeps for *a few hours only.*
Iron alum can be used to differentiate under the microscope.

**Haematoxylin, (Hansens)**

Haematoxylin . . . . . . 0.75 g
Ferric alum . . . . . . . 4.5 g
Water . . . . . . . . . 100 ml

Dissolve the iron alum in 65 ml of the water. Dissolve the haematoxylin in the remainder of the water. Mix the two, boil, cool and filter.

**Haematoxylin, Iron-alum- (Heidenhain's)**

A useful nuclear stain. Algae; cell walls (→ light blue); cytology; mitotic figures (→ black); nuclei (plant and animal) (→ dark blue); skin, thymus, and suprarenal body (all counterstained with van Gieson's).

Haematoxylin . . . . . . . 0.5 g
Alcohol (100%) . . . . . . 10 ml

Dissolve the haematoxylin. *Add:*

Distilled water . . . . . . 90 ml

The stain ripens and is ready for use in a few days.

*Suggested method for sections:*

1 Mordant in iron alum (3% aq.) in the warm. (10–20 min)
2 Wash in distilled water.
3 Overstain in Heidenhain's haematoxylin in the warm. (10–20 min)
4 Wash in distilled water.
5 Differentiate in iron alum (3% aq.) under the microscope.
6 Wash in water.
7 Dehydrate successively in alcohol (50%), (70%), (90%), (100%).
8 Clear in xylene.
9 Mount in D.P.X.

**Haemocytometer***

1. DESCRIPTION

A haemocytometer, or blood-counting chamber, of which there are several types, consists essentially of a microscopic slide carrying a small glass chamber of known depth whose base is marked in squares of known size, and which is covered, during use, with a special cover-slip.

Some haemocytometers have a double (or quadruple) counting-chamber so that two (or four) counts may be taken from the same sample, or two (or four) different samples investigated almost simultaneously. The cover-slips are usually 0.4 mm thick. Those for a single chamber measure 22 mm x 16 mm, and those for a double chamber 22 mm x 23 mm.

The instrument can, of course, be used not only for blood cell counts but also for population counts of algae, protozoa, yeast suspensions and the like.

Whatever the type of haemocytometer, the principle involved in its use is the same. It is obviously essential to know the conversion factor for the particular ruling used on the base of the chamber.

(*a*) *In the improved Neubauer haemocytometer* the base of the (single) chamber is marked with a square of side 3 mm (Fig. 7.3). This square is sub-divided into 9 squares, each of side 1 mm. Each of the corner 1 mm squares is sub-divided into 16 squares, each of side $\frac{1}{4}$ mm. The centre 1 mm square is sub-divided into 400 squares, each of side $\frac{1}{20}$ th mm. By means of a triple ruling (shown as a darker single line in Fig. 7.3) the smallest ($\frac{1}{20}$ mm) squares are conveniently grouped into 25 blocks, each of 16 squares (Fig. 7.4). The centre line of the triple ruling is the delineator.

As the chamber is $\frac{1}{10}$ mm deep, the volume of liquid held above each $\frac{1}{20}$ mm square (when the cover-slip is in place) $= \frac{1}{10} \times \frac{1}{20} \times \frac{1}{20}$ mm$^3$ $= \frac{1}{4000}$ mm$^3$.

As the single counting chamber is 3 mm square its volume is thus $\frac{1}{4000} \times 60 \times 60$ mm$^3$ $= 0.9$ mm$^3$.

(*b*) *In the Fuchs Rosenthal haemocytometer* the chamber holds a larger sample and is thus useful for making counts of larger bodies such as yeast cells in suspension. The counting chamber is $\frac{1}{5}$ mm deep and its base is marked with a square of side 4 mm (Fig. 7.5).

This square is sub-divided into squares of side 1 mm, each marked by a triple ruling of which the centre line is the delineator. Each 1 mm square is sub-divided into 16 squares, each of side $\frac{1}{4}$ mm. As the chamber is $\frac{1}{5}$ mm deep the

* I am indebted to D. Shaw of the Pathological Laboratory, Gloucestershire Royal Hospital, for information and suggestions about the use of the haemocytometer.

volume of fluid held over each of the smallest ($\frac{1}{4}$ mm) squares (when the cover-slip is in place) $= \frac{1}{5} \times \frac{1}{4} \times \frac{1}{4} \text{mm}^3 = \frac{1}{80} \text{mm}^3$.

The volume of the counting chamber is thus $\frac{1}{80} \times 16 \times 16 = 3.2 \text{ mm}^3$.

## 2. DILUTION OF THE SAMPLE

Unless the suspension of cells is extremely dispersed it must first be diluted to a known extent. When blood counts are being taken the nature of the diluent varies according to whether erythrocytes or white cells are being counted.

The precise dilution is made by the use of special micro-pipettes known as Thoma pipettes. Those for use in making counts of erythrocytes have graduations marked 0.5, 1, and 101. If the pipette is filled to the 0.5 mark with blood and then to the 101 mark with diluent, the dilution is 1 in 200. If it is filled with blood to the 1 mark (as is usual when a low count is likely) and then to the 101 mark with diluent, the dilution is 1 in 100. Thoma pipettes graduted 0.5, 1, and 11 are used when making counts of leucocytes. If the pipette is filled with blood to the 0.5 mark, and with diluent to the 11 mark, the dilution will be 1 in 20; if filled to the 1 mark with blood, and to the 11 mark with diluent, the dilution will be 1 in 10.

## 3. TECHNIQUE OF MAKING A COUNT OF ERYTHROCYTES

*Note: All apparatus, and particularly the counting-chamber and the cover-slip, must be scrupulously clean.*

*Haemocytometer used:* Improved Neubauer.
*Pipette:* Thoma, graduated 0.5, 1 and 101.
*Diluent:* Dacie's fluid (p. 210).

(*a*) *Technique of dilution*

1 By means of the attached rubber tubing, suck blood into the pipette to the 0.5 mark.
2 Quickly wipe the point of the pipette.

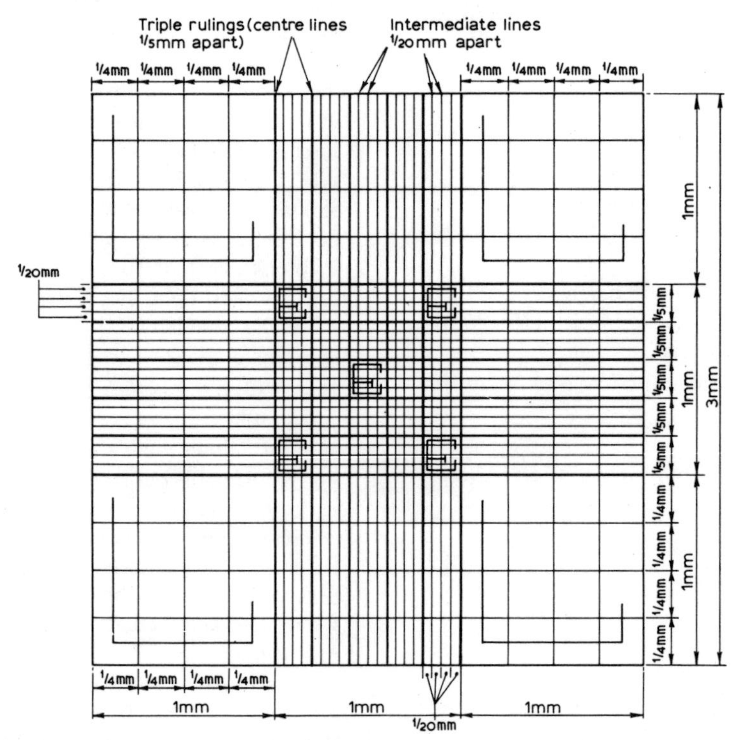


Fig. 7.3 Rulings on base of counting chamber of the improved Neubauer haemocytometer. The five blocks of sixteen $\frac{1}{20}$ mm squares marked E in the figure are used for counting erythrocytes; the four blocks of $\frac{1}{4}$ mm squares marked L are used for counting leucocytes.

3 Suck the diluent (Dacie's fluid, p. 210) up to the 101 mark, *avoiding bubbles.*
4 Use the finger-tip to close the lower end of the pipette.
5 Thoroughly mix the contents to ensure even distribution of the erythrocytes by holding the pipette between the tips of the thumb and second finger and turning it backwards and forwards through 180°. (2 min)
*Note:* The dilution is 1 in 200.

(*b*) *Technique of filling the counting chamber*
1 Place a piece of moist filter-paper in a Petri dish (with cover) large enough to contain the haemocytometer.
2 Slide the cover-slip in position on the counting-chamber, using slight pressure from both thumbs until not more than six interference fringes (Newton's rings) are seen where the cover-slip rests on the glass at the sides of the counting-chamber.
*Note:* This part of the technique is essential
(*a*) to ensure that the counting-chamber holds the correct volume of blood; and
(*b*) to ensure adhesion of the cover-slip to the counting-chamber.
3 Remove the rubber tubing from the pipette.
4 Shake the contents of the pipette.
5 Discard about one-third of the fluid from the bulb of the pipette by placing the tip of the pipette on filter-paper.
*Note:* This ensures that the sample investigated is of the stated dilution and not mixed with additional diluent that might have remained unmixed in the lower stem of the pipette.
6 Remove the finger from the pipette; let the tip of the pipette touch the grooved edge of the cover-slip and allow sufficient fluid to flow into, and just fill, the counting-chamber by capillary attraction.
7 If a small drop of fluid remains outside the cover-slip when the chamber is full, sweep it away quickly with a piece of filter-paper.

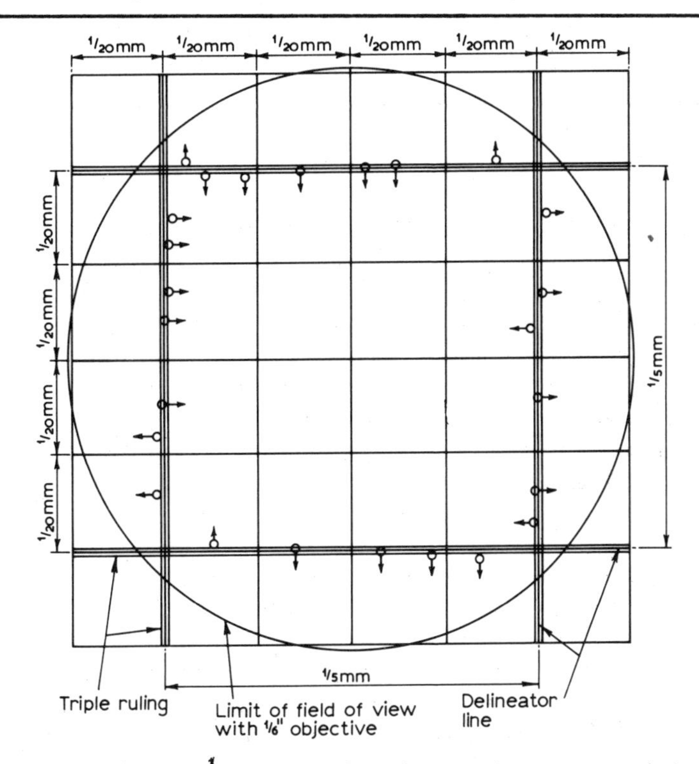


Fig. 7.4 Enlarged view of a group of sixteen $\frac{1}{20}$ mm squares from the centre 1 mm square on the base of the counting chamber of the improved Neubauer haemocytometer. The large circle indicates the field of view seen under a $\frac{1}{6}''$ objective; the small circles represent erythrocytes. Arrows pointing inward to the group of sixteen $\frac{1}{20}$ mm squares indicate erythrocytes to be included in the count; arrows pointing outwards indicate erythrocytes to be excluded from the count. [See (*c*) **3**, p. 226.]

**8** If it is desired to make a second count in the unused portion of a double-chambered instrument:

(*a*) Discard a little more fluid from the pipette (as in process **5**, above).

(*b*) Fill the second chamber in like manner to the first.

**9** Place the haemocytometer in the Petri dish and keep it covered. Allow the erythrocytes to settle. (3 min)

(*c*) *Technique of counting the erythrocytes*

*Note:* At least 5 groups of 16 of the smallest ($\frac{1}{20}$ mm) squares must be counted. One group of 16 squares should be taken from each corner, and one from the centre of the ruled area of the base of the chamber (as shown by the letter B in Fig. 7.3).

**1** Focus under low-power ($\frac{2}{3}$″ i.e. 16mm objective), with the light much reduced.

**2** Turn over to high-power ($\frac{1}{6}$″ i.e. 4mm objective).

**3** Count the erythrocytes, starting from the middle (delineator) line of the triple ruling at one side of the group of 16 $\frac{1}{20}$ mm squares and proceeding to the middle (delineator) ruling at the other side of the group of squares. *Include* erythrocytes touching the delineator line *at the top and one adjacent side* of the group of 16 squares, but *do not include* erythrocytes touching the bottom and the other side of the group of 16 squares. [See Fig. 7.4 where the direction of the arrows attached to the (diagrammatic) cells indicates whether they are to be included or excluded from the count.]

It will be found convenient to start counting at the top of the top left-hand square of the block of 16 squares, then to proceed downwards through the 4 squares, then upwards through the next adjacent 4 squares, downwards through the next, and finally upwards through the 4 squares on the right-hand side of the block. In this way less confusion is likely to arise over which erythrocytes are to be excluded or included.

**4** Repeat the count either in another haemocytometer, or in the second chamber if a double-chambered instrument is being used.

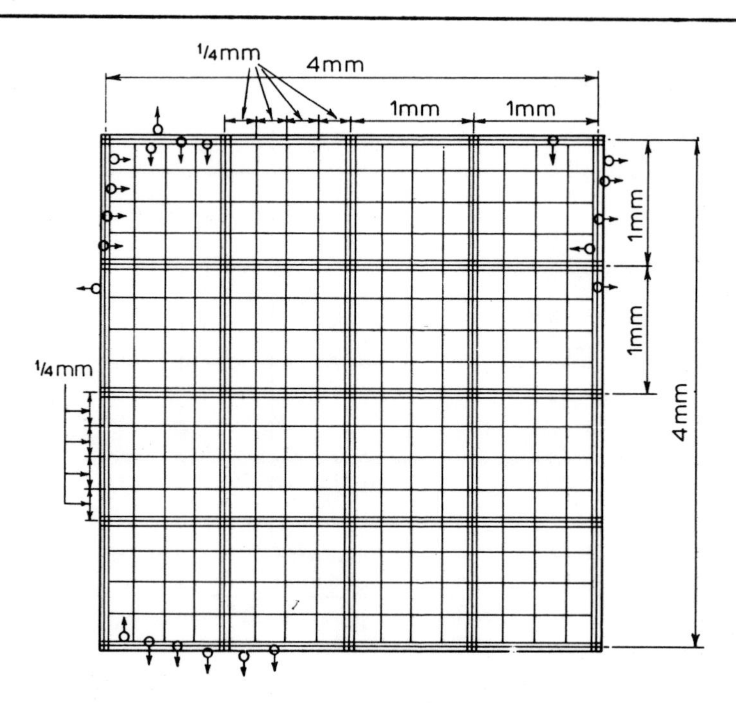


Fig. 7.5 Rulings on the base of the counting chamber of the Fuchs Rosenthal haemocytometer. The middle line of each triple ruling delineates the boundaries of each 1 mm square. The same rules for counting are used as with the improved Neubauer instrument.

(*d*) *Calculation of number of erythrocytes per mm*$^3$.

(i) *Long method*

*Erythrocytes per mm*$^3$ =

$$\frac{\text{Number of erythrocytes counted x dilution x 4000}}{\text{Number of the smallest } (\frac{1}{20}\text{mm}) \text{ squares counted.}}$$

(ii) *Short method*

*Data:*

*Squares counted:* Five groups, each of 16 of the smallest ($\frac{1}{20}$mm) squares.

∴ *Area counted* = $\frac{1}{20} \times \frac{1}{20} \times 16 \times 5 = \frac{1}{5}\text{mm}^2$.

*Let number of erythrocytes counted in this area* = E

*Depth of chamber* = $\frac{1}{10}$mm

*Dilution of sample* = 1 in 200

*Then,*

*Erythrocytes per mm*$^3$ = E x 5 x 10 x 200 = E x 10 000;

i.e. E with four cyphers added.

(*e*) *Degree of error in an erythrocyte count.*

*Probable error:* 2% minimum.

*Significant difference:* Probable error x 4.

*Insignificant difference:* 400 000.

(*f*) *Sources of error*

Failure to carry out *all* the instructions with meticulous care; inaccurate counting; uneven distribution in the counting chamber; sampling from a cyanosed area; squeezing the sampling area.

4. TECHNIQUE OF MAKING A COUNT OF LEUCOCYTES IN BLOOD

*Note: The rule of scrupulously clean apparatus applies.*

*Haemocytometer used:* Improved Neubauer, *with double chamber.*

*Pipette:* Thoma, graduated 0.5, 1, and 11.

*Diluent:* Acetic acid (1% aq.), (ii, p. 184).

(*a*) *Technique of dilution*

Proceed as in 3 (*a*) (p. 225). Fill the pipette with blood to the 0.5 mark, and with diluent to the 11 mark. The dilution will be 1 in 20.

(*b*) *Technique of filling the counting chamber*

Proceed as in 3 (*b*) (p. 225).

(*c*) *Technique of counting the leucocytes*

Using the same rules of delineation as in 3 (*c*) 3 (p. 226), count the leucocytes in the four corner 1 mm squares (marked L in Fig. 7.3).

(*d*) *Calculation of number of leucocytes per mm*$^3$

(i) *Long method*

*Leucocytes per mm*$^3$ =

$$\frac{\text{Number of leucocytes counted x dilution x 10}}{\text{Number of 1 mm squares counted.}}$$

(ii) *Short method*

*Data:*

*1 mm squares counted* = 4

*Area counted* = 4 mm$^2$

*Let number of leucocytes counted in this area* = L

*Depth of chamber* = 10 mm

*Dilution of sample* = 1 in 20

*Then:*

*Leucocytes per mm*$^3$ = L/4 x 10 x 20 = L/2 x 100

i.e. halve L and add two cyphers.

*Note:* If a double-chambered instrument is available it is best to take two counts in order to reduce possible error.

**Helly's Fluid**

| | |
|---|---|
| Mercuric chloride | 5 g |
| Potassium dichromate | 2.5 g |
| Sodium sulphate | 1 g |
| Distilled water | 100 ml |

To 20 ml, add 1 ml neutralized formalin immediately before use. Wash out fixative overnight in running water. Carmine does not stain well after this fixative.

**Hofmann's Blue**

See 'Anilin Blue WS, Acetic-' (p. 189).

**Hofmann's Violet** C.I. No. 42530

*Syn.: Dahlia; Hofmann's* WS *violet; Iodine violet; Primula* R *water soluble; Red violet; Violet* R (etc.).

*Note:* Mixtures of basic fuchsin and methyl violet are sometimes sold under the name 'Hofmann's violet' and may vary in shade from red to blue.

A basic, vital dye.

Fresh animal tissue; vital dye for cytoplasmic inclusions; lipid globules; *Lumbricus* (seminal vesicles); nuclei (plant); protozoa; spermatozoa.

| | |
|---|---|
| Hofmann's violet | 0.25 g |
| Distilled water | 100 ml |

**Hydrochloric Acid**

(i) *For use in the Feulgen technique for chromosomes* (p. 115).

*Note:* The hydrochloric acid (*a*) liberates aldehyde groups of the nucleic acid of the chromosomes. (The freed aldehyde groups react with Schiff's reagent in the staining process); (*b*) loosens the middle lamella of plant tissues prior to the squashing process.

| | |
|---|---|
| Hydrochloric acid (conc.) | 10 ml |
| Distilled water, to make final volume | 100 ml |

This makes an approx N/1 soln.

(ii) *Alcoholic – for preliminary treatment of plant tissue for maceration.*

| | |
|---|---|
| Alcohol (industrial) (95%) | 75 ml |
| Hydrochloric acid (bench) | 25 ml |

**Hydrogen Peroxide**

(i) *For bleaching after fixation with osmium tetroxide* (*'osmic acid'*) (*liquid or vapour*).

| | |
|---|---|
| Alcohol (80%) | 75 ml |
| Hydrogen peroxide (20 vol. soln.) | 25 ml |

(ii) *For use in the ortho-toluidine test for blood stains* (p. 108).

| | |
|---|---|
| Hydrogen peroxide ('A.R.') | 20 vols. soln. |

*Note:* It is essential to use 'A.R.' quality.

**Hydroquinone**

*Reducing fluid after treatment with silver nitrate.*

(i) *For use in modified Cajal's method for Golgi bodies* (p. 137).

| | |
|---|---|
| Formaldehyde (40%) | 15 ml |
| Hydroquinone | 2 g |
| Sodium sulphite (anhydrous) | 0.15 to 0.5 g |
| Distilled water | 100 ml |

(ii) *For use with the silver method for nerve axons* (p. 151).

| | |
|---|---|
| Hydroquinone | 1 g |
| Sodium sulphite (crystals) | 10 g |
| Distilled water | 100 ml |

*Note:* This reducing solution may be used repeatedly, but it will not keep for more than a few days.

**β-Hydroxyquinoline**

*For pre-treatment of root tips, before fixation, to inhibit clumping of chromosomes.*

| | |
|---|---|
| β-hydroxyquinoline | 0.3 g |
| Distilled water | 1000 ml |

This solution is 0.002 M.

**Injection Fluid (for blood vessels)**

(i) *Guyer's*

| | |
|---|---|
| Carmine | 5 g |
| Water | 10–12 ml |

Grind up carmine in the water and add drops of ammonium hydroxide until the solution becomes transparent. Soak 50 g gelatine (best sheet) in cold water (24 h). Pour off water and melt gelatine at 40°C. Pour in colouring matter. Stir. While cooling add drops of acetic acid (25% aq.) *till the injection mass is opaque and smells faintly acid.*

If a blue colour is desired, add anilin blue WS (instead of carmine) to the molten gelatine.

(ii)

| | |
|---|---|
| Gelatine (powdered) | 10 g |
| Distilled water | 200 ml |

Dissolve the gelatine in the distilled water. Then add

| | |
|---|---|
| Lead acetate | 50 g |

When dissolved add gradually

| | |
|---|---|
| Potassium chromate (powdered) | 25 g |

(iii)

| | |
|---|---|
| Gelatine | 10 g |
| Chloral hydrate | 10 g |
| Water | 100 ml |

If the gelatine is in sheets, use a jacketed heater to assist solution. Otherwise, use powdered gelatine.

When solution is complete, add: Chrome yellow (powdered), till the desired depth of colour is obtained.

The chloral hydrate delays setting of the gelatine. Once the gelatine has set, the action is irreversible.

*Note:* These injection masses must be kept warm during injection.

(iv) Rubber latex. Obtainable from suppliers.

**Iodine**

*A temporary stain for:*

Cellulose (→ yellow) or, + sulphuric acid (40%) (→ blue); *Chara* (with basic fuchsin); glycogen; hyphae (protoplasm) (with basic fuchsin); *Nitella* (with basic fuchsin); protein cell contents in plant tissue (→ brown); *Protococcus* (with basic fuchsin); protoplasm (→ brown); starch (→ blue); *Vorticella* (with basic fuchsin).

Potassium iodide . . . . satd. aq. soln.

*Add:*

Iodine . . . . . . . . . to saturation

Filter. Dilute with distilled water to a medium sherry colour.

**Iodine. Alcoholic**

(i) Iodine . . . . . . . . . . . 1 g
Potassium iodide . . . . . . . 1 g
Alcohol (70%) [or (80%) according to requirements] . . . . . 100 ml

(ii) *For washing tissue fixed with mercuric chloride.*
Iodine . . . . . . . . . . . 2 g
Potassium iodide . . . . . . . 3 g
Alcohol (70%) or (96%) (as required) . . . . . . . . . 100 ml

**Iodine, Gram's**

Bacteria; nuclei (plant) (counterstain with crystal violet and orange G in clove oil).

Iodine . . . . . . . . . . . 1 g
Potassium iodide . . . . . . . 2 g
Distilled water . . . . . . . 300 ml

**Iodine, Herzberg Stain**

See 'Schulze's Solution (Chlor-zinc-iodine)' (p. 246).

**Iodine, Lugol's**

Iodine . . . . . . . . . . . 4 g
Potassium iodide . . . . . . . 6 g
Distilled water . . . . . . . 100 ml

**Iodine, Melzer's**

Chloral hydrate . . . . . . . 22.0 g
Iodine . . . . . . . . . . . 0.5 g
Potassium iodide . . . . . . . 1.5 g
Distilled water . . . . . . . 20 ml

**Iodine Green** C.I. No. 42556

*Syn.: Hofmann's Green (Grün).*
A basic dye.

Lignin (counterstain with acid fuchsin, Mayer's carmalum, eosin Y, erythrosin bluish, or magdala red).

Iodine green . . . . . . . . 1 g
Alcohol (70%) (or distilled water) 100 ml

**Iodine Green, Acetic-**

Acetic acid (glacial) . . . . . 1 ml
Iodine green . . . . . . . . 99 ml

**Janus Green B** C.I. No. 11050

*Syn.: Diazin green S; Union green B.*
A basic, vital, dye.
Living organisms (especially fungi and protozoa); mitochondria; certain plastids;

Janus green B . . . . . . . . 0.1 g
Isotonic saline . . . . . . . . 1000 ml

**Kahle's Fluid**

See 'Formol-acetic-alcohol' (p. 215).

**Kaiserling-Gelatine***

*For preservation of animal tissue in bulk.*

1 Heat to boiling point in a suitable vessel (stirring to prevent burning):
Kaiserling's solution (below) . . 3000 ml
Gelatine . . . . . . . . . . 200 g
2 When the temperature reaches 55°C stir in:
The whites of three eggs.
Acetic acid, sufficient to make strongly acid to litmus paper. (This helps clarification and subsequent colour conservation.)
3 Allow to boil for a *few minutes.*
4 Filter through two thicknesses of paper into stock jars. (Use ribbed funnels and a hot-water filter, or fix the whole in a steam sterilizer to prevent solidification of jelly.)
5 If the jelly is required for stock purposes, after it has set place a crystal of thymol on the top of the jelly (to prevent the growth of fungi) and close the vessel.
6 Before use for mounting, remove the thymol crystal.
7 Melt jelly (45°C–50°C) by placing the container on a water-bath.

* Adapted from information supplied by the Pathological Department, Cheltenham General Hospital.

8 To every 1000 ml of melted jelly stir in:

| | |
|---|---|
| Formaldehyde (40%) | 27.5 ml |

The jelly is now ready for use.

**Kaiserling's Solution***

| | |
|---|---|
| Glycerol | 200 ml |
| Potassium acetate | 100 g |
| Water | 1000 ml |

**Killing Animals**

(i) See Chapter 6, 'Methods for Specific Material' (p. 93), under animal required.
(ii) Arthropods. See 'Killing bottle' (below).

**Killing Bottle**

(i) *For terrestrial arthropods.*

(*a*) Ammonium carbonate. Place some crystals in a wide-mouthed, glass-stoppered bottle and cover them with a sheet of cellulose wadding. This is effective without being dangerous.

(*b*) Potassium cyanide (*Poison*) — 28 g. Break up the cyanide and place it in a 280 ml wide-mouthed bottle with an air-tight bung. Plaster-of-Paris — Mix sufficient with water to a thickness that will just allow of its running from the mixing vessel and covering the cyanide to a depth of from 3.5 cm—5 cm. Soon sets hard and dry if properly mixed.

(ii) *For most aerial arthropods.* (*Except bumble-bees and larger beetles.*)

Cut cherry laurel (*Prunus laurocerasus*) leaves into narrow strips and pack them fairly tightly in a tin or wide-mouthed bottle. Cover with muslin.

(iii) *For mosquitoes, flies, bees.*

(*a*) Chop rubber tubing into pieces and place them in the bottom of a specimen tube (say 7.5 cm x 2.5 cm). Add chloroform until the rubber is soaked. Over the rubber pieces place a 'platform' of cotton wool. Properly corked, this tube remains effective for a month.†

(*b*) In the bottom of a specimen tube (7.5 cm x 2.5 cm) place a wad of cotton wool covered with a piece of perforated zinc cut to size. Damp the cotton wool with ethyl acetate [or, in an emergency, petrol, benzene, xylene (care), or chloroform]. See that the cork is a good fit. The ethyl acetate keeps the muscles relaxed, and insects may be stored in this liquid. If carried in the pocket, it is well to provide this killing tube with a protective case. Standing insects (e.g. mosquitoes) may be caught by inverting the open tube over them.

(iv) *For relaxing animals killed with cyanide.*

Use chopped cherry laurel (*Prunus laurocerasus*) leaves.

**Labels**

Bottles and tubes of plant and animal specimens should bear a label *inside* as well as outside.

(i) *Inside labels.* Use plain white paper. Write in pencil, and state, not only the name of the tissue, but also the treatment received up to the time of bottling and the name and strength of the preservative. A knowledge of such information may influence the course of future treatment.

(ii) *Outside labels.* Use good quality paper and good quality gum or alternatively suitable self-adhesive labels. Write legibly in Indian ink. After fixing label to bottle, brush over with a thin layer of molten paraffin wax if the specimen is likely to be kept for a long time. The wax covering is effective against an over-dry or an over-damp atmosphere. Alternatively, cover the label with transparent plastic tape.

(iii) See also 'Adhesive for Labels' (p. 185); 'Glass, To Write on' (p. 219).

**Lacmoid**

This substance is sometimes *erroneously* referred to as resorcin blue. It is, in fact, the unbrominated homologue of resorcin blue. In acetic acid solution it is used for staining chromosomes. In conjunction with martius yellow it is used for staining pollen tubes in styles (see p. 231).

**Lacmoid, Acetic-**

*A stain-fixative for chromosomes.* [See Method (ii), p. 116.]

| | |
|---|---|
| Acetic acid (glacial) | 100 ml |
| Lacmoid | 2.2 g |

* Adapted from information supplied by the Pathological Department, Cheltenham General Hospital.
† Suggested by G. S. Sellick, Highgate School.

*For use:*

| | |
|---|---|
| Stock solution (as above) . . . | 10 ml |
| Distilled water . . . . . . | 12 ml |

*Note:*

(i) The stain tends to decompose in diluted acid solution and only sufficient of the diluted stain, which is approximately 1% in acetic acid (45%), should be made up for immediate use.

(ii) In acetic acid solution lacmoid stains only the chromosomes. It remains red if acid and mounted in cedar-wood oil. It turns blue if mounted in neutral D.P.X. or other resin. In alkaline solution lacmoid stains the cytoplasm blue, as in the pollen-tube technique.

**Lacmoid- Martius Yellow**

*For pollen tubes in styles.*

| | |
|---|---|
| Lacmoid . . . . . . . . . | 0.05 g |
| Martius yellow. . . . . . . | 0.05 g |
| Distilled water . . . . . . | 100 ml |

*Add:* Ammonium hydroxide (1%) sufficient to adjust pH value to 8 (a few *drops* will suffice). (Pollen tubes → blue.)

**Lacto-Phenol**

See 'Amann's Medium' (p. 188), and 'Polyvinyl Alcohol — Lactophenol' (p. 241).

**Leishman's Stain**

(i) *For blood and blood parasites.* See 'Blood v (p. 109).

(*a*) The dry stain may be purchased.

(*b*) *Alternatively:*

| | |
|---|---|
| Methylene blue . . . . . . | 1 g |
| Distilled water . . . . . . | 100 ml |
| Sodium carbonate (0.5% aq.) . . | 200 ml |

Heat together for 12 h. Stand for 10 d.

*Add:*

| | |
|---|---|
| Eosin Y (use the shade known as 'Eosin B Extra') (0.1% aq. soln.) . . . . . . | 300 ml |

Stand for 12 h. Filter. Wash the precipitate with distilled water until the washings are colourless. Dry.

*To make the stock solution of Leishman's stain:*

| | |
|---|---|
| Leishman's stain . . . . . . | 0.15 g |
| Methyl alcohol (100%) (neutral and acetone free) . . . . . . . | 100 ml |

(ii) *For sections of blood-forming tissues* (p. 110).

| | |
|---|---|
| Leishman's stain (stock solution). | 10 ml |
| Distilled water . . . . . . | 20 ml |

**Light Green S.F. Yellowish** C.I. No. 42095

*Syn.: C.I. Acid green* 5; *Acid green; Fast green* N; *Licht Grün; Light green* 2G (etc.).

An acid dye.

Plant tissue (counterstain with haematoxylin or safranin O); cellulose (→ green); cell walls (unlignified) (→ green); cytoplasm (→ green); *Paramecium* (nuclear detail).

(*a*) Saturated solution in alcohol (90%).

(*b*) *In clove oil.*

| | |
|---|---|
| Light green SF yellowish (powdered) . . . . . . . . | 0.2 g |
| Alcohol (100%) . . . . . . | 50 ml |
| Clove oil . . . . . . . . | 50 ml |

*Note:* Although this stain has long been used as a counterstain to safranin O it is liable to fade and should be regarded as superseded by fast green FCF for botanical purposes. (See p. 213.)

**Liquor Ferri***

Used as a mordant for Heidenhain's haematoxylin, especially when staining algae.

| | |
|---|---|
| Ferrous sulphate . . . . . . | 8.5 g |
| Distilled water . . . . . . | 4.5 ml |
| Nitric acid (conc.) . . . . . | 1.8 ml |
| Sulphuric acid (conc.) . . . . | 1.5 ml |

Dilute each ml of this solution with 25 ml of distilled water to make the stock solution. For use, dilute this stock solution to a very pale straw colour with distilled water.

**Lithium Carbonate**

| | |
|---|---|
| Alcohol (70%) . . . . . . | 100 ml |
| Lithium carbonate . . . . | To saturation |

Filter.

* With acknowledgements to C. F. Bause.

*For removal of picric acid after fixation.*
Sections should be treated for 2 min.

**Macerating Fluids**

*Note:* Before using any of the following fluids see 'Techniques of Maceration of Plant Material' (pp. 46–47).

(i) *For herbaceous tissues*

(*a*) Sodium hydroxide (5–8%), or potassium hydroxide (5–8%).

| | | |
|---|---|---|
| (*b*) | Alcohol (95%) | 75 ml |
| | Hydrochloric acid (2N) | 25 ml |

(*c*) Chromium trioxide (5%).

(ii) *For root tips*

Hydrochloric acid (N/1).

(iii) *For woody tissues*

(*a*) *Schulze's fluid.* [*Note:* Not to be confused with Schulze's *solution* (chlor-zinc-iodine) used as a microchemical test for cellulose.]

| | | |
|---|---|---|
| | Nitric acid (conc.) | 50 ml |
| | Potassium nitrate | 1 g |
| (*b*) | Chromium trioxide (10%) | 50 ml |
| | Nitric acid (10%) | 50 ml |

Soak tissue for 24 h and wash in water very thoroughly.

**Magdala Red** C.I. No. 50375

*Syn.: C.I. Basic Red* 6; *Naphthalene Pink; Naphthalene Red; Naphthylamine Pink; Sudan Red.*

A basic dye.

Algae (with anilin blue WS); cellulose; elastin; mosses (with anilin blue WS); nuclei.

| | | |
|---|---|---|
| (*a*) | Magdala red | 2 g |
| | Distilled water | 98 ml |
| (*b*) *For algae* | | |
| | Magdala red | 0.2 g |
| | Alcohol (95%) | 100 ml |

**Malachite Green** C.I. No. 42000

*Syn.: C.I. Basic green* 4; *Diamond green B* (etc.); *Light green N; Malachite green A, B* (etc.); *New Victoria green extra O* (etc.); *Solid green O; Victoria green B* (etc.).

A weakly basic dye.

Nuclear stain. Epidermal cells of onion (vital); lignin; yeast (with basic fuchsin), (p. 181).

| | | |
|---|---|---|
| (*a*) | Malachite green | 1 g |
| | Distilled water | 99 ml |

(*b*) See also Pyronin/malachite green technique for RNA and DNA (p. 91).

**Mallory's Triple Stain***

*Ascaris;* cartilage; connective tissue (→ blue); cytoplasm (→ red); elastic fibres are unstained; erythrocytes (→ red); *Fasciola; Hirudo;* intestine; lymph glands; neuroglia (→ red); nuclei (→ red); ovary; pancreas; pituitary; salivary glands; *Taenia;* testis; thymus; thyroid.

A triple stain giving good results for routine work *after fixation in Zenker's solution and dehydration in alcohol.*

For method of use see Method 20 (p. 86).

*Solution A*

| | |
|---|---|
| Acid fuchsin | 0.1 g |
| Distilled water | 100 ml |

*Solution B.* Phosphomolybdic acid (1% aq.).

*Solution C*

| | |
|---|---|
| Anilin blue WS | 0.5 g |
| Orange G | 2 g |
| Oxalic acid | 2 g |
| Distilled water | 100 ml |

**Mann's Fixative**

*For small pieces of animal tissue.*
Penetration poor. Fix 3–4 h.

*Stock solution*

| | |
|---|---|
| Picric acid | 1 g |
| Mercuric chloride | 2.5 g |
| Distilled water | To make up to 100 ml |

*Before use, add:*

Formaldehyde (40%), 15 ml to every 100 ml of stock solution.

*Note:*

(i) Wash in lithium carbonate [satd. alcohol (70%)] to remove picric acid.
(ii) Wash in iodine [1% in alcohol (70%)] to remove mercuric chloride.
(iii) Wash sections in sodium thiosulphate (i, p. 249), to remove iodine colouration.

* After Green, *School Science Review*, **XV** 406; March 1934.

**Mann's Stain**

*A good double stain for sections.*

| | |
|---|---|
| Methyl blue (1% aq.) | 35 ml |
| Eosin Y (1% aq.) | 35 ml |
| Distilled water | 100 ml |

**Martius Yellow** C.I. No. 10315

*Syn.: C.I. Acid yellow* 24; *Manchester yellow; Naphthol yellow.*

An acid dye.

Used in conjunction with lacmoid for pollen tubes in styles (see 'Lacmoid-Martius Yellow', p. 231).

**Mercuric-Acetic ('Corrosive-Acetic')**

*A useful fixative for small animals.*
*Note:* Poisonous.

(*a*) *For general animal histology.*

| | |
|---|---|
| Acetic acid (glacial) | 5 ml |
| Mercuric chloride (aq. satd.) | 95 ml |

For fixing small animals. (3–5 min)
For fixing larger pieces of tissue. (10–15 min)

(*b*) *For smears of seminal vesicles of Lumbricus.*

| | |
|---|---|
| Acetic acid (glacial) | 1 ml |
| Mercuric chloride (aq. satd.) | 100 ml |

(*c*) *For desmids*

| | |
|---|---|
| Acetic acid (glacial) | 3 ml |
| Alcohol (50%) | 100 ml |
| Mercuric chloride | 3 g |

Use hot solution.

*Note:*

(i) Wash in alcoholic iodine (ii, p. 229). If colour disappears add more iodine. (2 min for small tissues)

(ii) Iodine may be removed by washing tissues in sodium thiosulphate soln. (i, p. 249).

**Mercuric Chloride ('Corrosive Sublimate')**

*Fixative for animal histology and plant cytology.*
*Note:* Poisonous.

For fixation use a saturated aqueous solution.

After fixation tissues must be treated in accordance with *Notes* (i) and (ii) under 'Mercuric-Acetic' (above).

**Mercuric-Formaldehyde ('Corrosive-formaldehyde')**

*Fixative for animal histology.*
*Note:* Poisonous.

| | |
|---|---|
| Formaldehyde (40%) | 10 ml |
| Mercuric chloride (aq. satd.) | 90 ml |

**Mercuric Sulphate**

*For stopping action of triphenyl tetrazolium chloride during experiments on respiratory rates of cells* (p. 166).

| | |
|---|---|
| Mercuric sulphate | Satis. |
| Distilled water | 100 ml |

*Note:* 'Basic' mercuric sulphate ($HgSO_4 . 2H_2O$) is soluble in cold water only to the extent of 0.002 g in 100 ml of water.

**Metanil Yellow** C.I. No. 13065

*Syn.: C.I. Acid yellow* 36; *Acid yellow* R; *Jaune Metanil; Orange* MN; *Orange* MNO; *Soluble yellow* OL; *Tropaeolin* G; *Yellow* M.

An acid dye.

Connective tissue (counterstain to haematoxylin and acid fuchsin); mucin (counterstain to Mayer's mucicarmine, p. 197).

| | |
|---|---|
| Metanil yellow | 1 g |
| Distilled water | 100 ml |

**Methyl Blue** C.I. No. 42780

*Syn.: C.I. Acid blue* 93; *Cotton blue; Helvetia blue.*

An acid dye.

*Note:* According to Conn (*Biological stains*) this dye is sometimes sold under the label 'anilin blue WS' instead of C.I. No. 42755.

A good counterstain for carmine, eosin Y, picric acid, and safranin O.

(*a*)

| | |
|---|---|
| Methyl blue | 1 g |
| Distilled water | 99 ml |

(*b*) See 'Mann's stain' (above).

**Methyl Eosin** C.I. No. 45385

*Syn.: C.I. Solvent red* 44; *Alcohol soluble eosin; Eosin, alcohol soluble.*

This dye is not used by biologists. It is mentioned here because of confusion with the use of the synonym 'alcohol soluble eosin'. If an alcohol-soluble eosin is required, ethyl eosin, C.I. No. 45386 should be specified.

**Methyl Green** C.I. No. 42585

*Syn.: C.I. Basic blue* 20; *Double green* SF; *Light green.*

A basic dye.

A nuclear stain. Bast (→ blue); fresh tissue (temp.); lignin (→ green) living organisms; nuclei (→ green); protozoa [especially if previously fixed with Ripart's and Petit's fluid (p. 243)] ; small entire objects (temp.); *Vorticella;* yeast. May be counterstained with acid fuchsin.

| | |
|---|---|
| Methyl green | 1 g |
| Alcohol | 99 ml |

**Methyl Green, Acetic-**

Protozoa (kills and stains).

| | |
|---|---|
| Methyl green (see above). | Sufficient to make a clear, weak green-blue solution when added to |
| Acetic acid (glacial) | 1.5 ml |
| Distilled water | 98.5 ml |

**Methyl Violet 2B** C.I. No. 42535

*Syn.: C.I. Basic violet* 1; *Dahlia; Gentian violet; Methyl violet* B, BO, R (etc.); *Paris violet; Pyoktaninum coeruleum.*

A basic dye.

A nuclear stain. Gives a reddish shade (cf. crystal violet, p. 201). Amyloid (animal) (→ reddish); bacteria; blood; leaf and stem transparencies.

*Alcoholic* (*or Aqueous*) *soln.*

| | |
|---|---|
| Methyl violet 2B | 1 g |
| Alcohol (70%) (or distilled water) | 99 ml |

Do *not* use any alcohol after using the aqueous soln., otherwise the stain will be washed out.

**Methyl Violet 2B-Anilin**

*For use in Weigert's method for bacteria and fibrin* [Bacteria iv (*b*), (p. 106)] .

*Solution A*

| | |
|---|---|
| Alcohol (100%) | 33 ml |
| Anilin oil | 9 ml |
| Methyl violet 2B | Excess. |

*Solution B*

| | |
|---|---|
| Methyl violet 2B | Satis. |
| Distilled water | 100 ml |

*To make up the stain*

| | |
|---|---|
| Solution A | 3 ml |
| Solution B | 27 ml |

*Note: The made-up stain will not keep for more than* 14 *days.*

**Methylene Azure** C.I. No. 52010

This dyestuff is a mixture of the dyes azure A and azure B (p. 190). It is one of the components of polychrome methylene blue (p. 235), the dyestuff resulting from the oxidation of methylene blue. It has been given the same C.I. No. as azure B.

**Methylene Blue** C.I. No. 52015

*Syn.: C.I. Basic blue* 9; *Methylene blue* B (etc.); *Methylene blue chloride; Swiss blue.*

A basic dye.

*Note:* Methylene blue is not to be confused with new methylene blue N (p. 237), nor with polychrome methylene blue (below).

A nuclear stain. Bacteria; blood; epithelia; mucin (→ purple); nerve tissue (nuclei, axons, dendrons in spinal cord); protozoa; yeast.

Counterstain for Ziehl's phenol-fuchsin and Ehrlich's anilin-water fuchsin.

To display general features of crustacean organization, inject *Artemia* with methylene blue.

| | | |
|---|---|---|
| (*a*) | Methylene blue | 0.3 g |
| | Alcohol (95%) | 30 ml |
| | Dissolve, and add | |
| | Distilled water | 100 ml |

(*b*) *For living organisms*

| | | |
|---|---|---|
| (i) | Methylene blue | 1 g |
| | Sodium chloride | 0.6 g |
| | Distilled water | 100 ml |

(ii) See also 'Methylene Blue, Intra-Vitam' (below).

(*c*) For other formulae and combinations see below.

**Methylene Blue, Acetic-**

*Hydra* (discharges nematocysts).

| | |
|---|---|
| Acetic acid (glacial) | 1 ml |
| Methylene blue (see above) | 0.2 g |
| Distilled water | 99 ml |

**Methylene Blue, Borrel's**

Nerve tissue; mucin.

Silver nitrate (1%). Precipitate by dil. sodium hydroxide soln. Filter and wash precipitate thoroughly. Add silver precipitate to

Methylene blue (1% aq.). Boil 10 min until colour goes dark *violet.* Cool. Filter. Dilute with 4 times its vol. of distilled water.

**Methylene Blue — Eosin**

See Giemsa's stain (p. 218); Leishman's stain (p. 231); Wright's stain (p. 252).

**Methylene Blue, Intra-Vitam (Reduced Methylene Blue)**

Vital staining of individual nerve cells of, e.g. tube feet of *Astropecten;* ganglia of *Hirudo;* nerve net of *Hydra;* palps of *Nereis.*

*Soln.* (*a*) Methylene blue (0.5% aq. dest.) . . . . . . . . . 100 ml
Hydrochloric acid (24% aq. dest.) . . . . . . . . . 3 drops
Mix thoroughly. Filter.

*Soln.* (*b*) Solution (*a*) . . . . . . 10 ml
Rongalite C (p. 243) (12% aq. dest.) . . . . . . . 2 ml

Warm over a *small* flame. Do *not* boil. Stir constantly. When the colour changes from deep blue to a yellowish-brownish-green remove the vessel from the flame *but continue stirring.* When the liquid has become almost clear but with a yellow precipitate stop stirring. Cool. Filter. Allow to stand 24 h–36 h. Solution remains usable for 8–10 d.

(Nerve cells → purplish tinge.)

**Methylene Blue, Löffler's**

A nuclear stain. Bacteria; lignin (counterstain with eosin Y or erythrosin bluish); nuclei.

(i) *Solution A*

Methylene blue . . . . . . 0.3 g
Alcohol (95%) . . . . . . 30 ml

*Solution B*

Potassium hydroxide (0.01% aq.) 100 ml

Mix solutions *A* and *B*. (The potassium hydroxide is an accentuator.)

(ii) See also 'Methylene Blue, Polychrome'.

**Methylene Blue N, New**

See 'New Methylene Blue N' (p. 237).

**Methylene Blue,* Nissl's**

*Nerve tissue* (nuclei, axons, dendrons in spinal cord).

Use after fixation in alcohol (95%) without subsequent hydration.†

Venetian soap . . . . . . . 1.75 g
Distilled water . . . . . . . 1000 ml

Dissolve, and add:

Methylene blue . . . . . . . 3.75 g

Shake vigorously from time to time and do not use *till four months old.* Filter into the stock bottle any of this stain left after staining sections.

*Note:* After using Nissl's methylene blue every care must be taken to remove all traces of alcohol used in dehydration, by thorough clearing with benzene or xylene.

**Methylene Blue, Phenol- (Carbol-Methylene Blue)**

*Bacteria*

Methylene blue . . . . . . . 1.5 g
Phenol . . . . . . . . . 5 g
Alcohol (100%) . . . . . . . 10 ml
Distilled water . . . . . . . 100 ml

**Methylene Blue, Polychrome**

This dye is *not* identical with methylene blue C.I. No. 52015. It is a mixture of methylene blue with the reddish dye methylene azure formed as a slow oxidation product of methylene blue as, for example, when the methylene blue is kept in half-filled bottles for a year. The presence of an alkali hastens the reaction, hence its production in Löffler's methylene blue.

Methylene blue . . . . . . . 1 g
Potassium carbonate . . . . 1 g
Alcohol (100%) . . . . . . . 20 ml
Water . . . . . . . . . . 100 ml
Evaporate this solution down to . 100 ml

*For staining cell-granules*

Use either as prepared or dilute with an equal volume of anilin-water.

* After Lee, 1937, *Microtomist's Vade-Mecum,* Churchill, London.
† See 'Nerve Tissue iii' (p. 152).

**Methylene Blue, Reduced-**

See 'Methylene Blue, Intra-Vitam' (p. 235).

**Meve's Fixative**

| | |
|---|---|
| Chromium trioxide 1% . . . . | 7.5 ml |
| Osmium tetroxide 2% . . . . | 4 ml |
| Acetic acid (glacial) . . . . . | 3–4 drops |
| Sodium chloride . . . . . . | 0.15 g |
| Distilled water . . . . . . . | 7.5 ml |

This is a modification of Flemming's fluid and is useful for impregnation studies of the Golgi bodies.

**Micromanipulation**

Although elaborate pieces of apparatus can be purchased for purposes of micromanipulation and microdissection it is often possible to make do with simpler things, e.g.:

(i) *Arm rests:* The manipulator's hands are likely to tremble unless the fore-arms are supported on some rests. These may take the form of wooden wedges having their sloping surface about 10 cm x 13 cm and their height at the thick, front, end cut to suit the height of the stage carrying the object that is being manipulated. If manipulations are likely to be prolonged it is more comfortable if the arm-rests are padded with sponge-rubber fixed with 'Bostik No. 2'.

(ii) *Mounting:* Specimens for dissection may be suitably mounted on wood, or on a halved cork, or on a block of wax. Arrangements should be made to hold such a base firmly.

(iii) *Lifters:* Very small objects under the microscope may conveniently be lifted up by means of:

(*a*) a fine nylon bristle (from a tooth-brush) mounted and fixed (with 'Araldite') in a fine slit in a good-quality (cedar-wood) pencil.

(*b*) a human eye-lash similarly mounted.

(iv) *Probes:* These may take the form of glass rod drawn out into fine glass needles. Such probes may also sometimes conveniently be used as cutters.

(v) *Scalpels:* Small scalpels of various sizes may be made from pieces of safety-razor blade, mounted and fixed (with 'Araldite') in a fine slit made in a good-quality (cedar-wood) pencil. The whole blade may be placed in a vice, or in a slot in a firmly-held piece of wood, with the portion of blade to be snapped off projecting. This portion is then bent over, by pressure from another piece of wood, until the blade snaps.

(vi) *Sectioning very small and delicate objects:* Objects such as nematode worms and filamentous algae, of which it is desired to make transverse sections, but which cannot easily be handled in an embedding bath, may be cross-sectioned after they have been rolled up in some thin, membraneous substance, such as onion scale epidermis, the ends of the bundle being tied with very fine thread. Transverse sections are made of the bundle thus formed.

**Microscope, Cover for**

When it is desired to leave a microscope out of its normal case, or cupboard, or both, for a short time, it is useful to have a cover made of polythene of ample size and suitable shape.

See 'Care of the Microscope' (p. 12) and 'Adhesive, for polythene' (p. 186).

**'Milton'**

*For differentiating chlorazol black E*, use a dilute soln. *Note.* 'Milton' *is a trade mark*, but no proprietary rights are claimed in the preparation itself:

| | |
|---|---|
| Sodium hypochlorite . . . . | 1.00% |
| Sodium chloride . . . . . . | 16.50% |
| Sodium chlorate . . . . . . | 0.13% |
| Sodium carbonate . . . . . | 0.05% |
| Sodium sulphate . . . . . . | 0.15% |
| Calcium chloride . . . . . . | 0.07% |
| Magnesium chloride . . . . . | Trace |
| Water . . . . . . . . . . | 82.10% |

**Moll's Solution**

*For clearing,* in Dawson's method for bone (p. 111).

| | |
|---|---|
| Glycerol . . . . . . . . . | 20 ml |
| Potassium hydroxide (1%) . . . | 80 ml |

**Muller's Fluid**

For hardening; dissolving intercellular substances prior to teasing; preserving brains; fixation of nervous tissue and eye. Hardens very slowly (small pieces of tissue take several weeks). During the first week the liquid should be changed daily.

Potassium dichromate . . . . 2.5 g
Sodium sulphate . . . . . . . 1 g
Distilled water . . . . . . . 100 ml

**Navashin's Fluid**

*A modification of Flemming's Fluid* (p. 214).
A fixative for plant chromosomes; parasitic fungi in plant tissue.

Acetic acid, glacial . . . . . . 1 ml
Chromium trioxide (1%) . . . 10 ml
Formaldehyde (40%)* . . . . 4 ml
Distilled water . . . . . . . 5 ml

**Neutral Red** C.I. No. 50040

*Syn.: C.I. Basic red* 5; *Toluylene red.*
A weakly basic, non-toxic, vital, dye. Turns yellow in solutions of pH less than 7.
Cytoplasmic inclusions; living organisms; nuclei (→ red); plasma (→ yellow); food vacuoles of living *Paramecium;* many lipid globules.

Neutral red . . . . . . . . . 0.1 g
Isotonic saline . . . . . . . . 1000 ml

**Neutral Violet** C.I. No. 50030

A weakly basic dye.
*For microscopical test for pectin.*

Neutral violet . . . . . . . . 0.01 g
Distilled water . . . . . . . 100 ml

**New Methylene Blue N** C.I. No. 52030

*Syn.: C.I. Basic blue* 24; *Methylene blue NN.*
A basic dye.
Cartilage by van Wijhe's method (p. 112); reticulocytes in human blood smears.

New methylene blue N . . . . 0.25 g
Alcohol (70%) . . . . . . . 100 ml
Hydrochloric acid (conc.) . . . 1 ml

**Nigrosin, Water Soluble** C.I. No. 50420

*Syn.: C.I. Acid black* 2; *Gray R* (etc.); *Indulin black; Nigrosin W* (etc.); *Silver gray; Steel gray.*
A mixture of dyes.
Cell contents; *Obelia;* Unlignified tissue.

Nigrosin, water soluble . . . . 1 g
Distilled water . . . . . . . 100 ml

* Either, the whole solution should be made up freshly, or, the formaldehyde should be added immediately before use.

**Nile Blue Sulphate** C.I. No. 51180

*Syn.: C.I. Basic blue* 12; *Nile blue A.*
A basic dye.

(*a*) *Amphibian eggs* (*living*); *Hydra; protozoa; yeast.*

Nile blue sulphate . . . . . 0.1 g
Distilled water . . . . . . . 100 ml

(*b*) *Bacteria and connective tissue* (*Drew-Murray method, 'Connective Tissue* iii' p. 120).

Nile blue sulphate . . . . . 2 g
Distilled water . . . . . . . 100 ml

(*c*) *Fat* (p. 128).

Nile blue sulphate . . . . . . 1 g
Distilled water . . . . . . . 100 ml

**Normal Solutions**

See page 254.

**Orange-Fuchsin**

Cytoplasm; connective tissue.

Orange G . . . . . . . . . 6 g
Acid fuchsin . . . . . . . . 1 g
Alcohol (100%) . . . . . . . 60 ml
Distilled water . . . . . . . 240 ml

**Orange G** C.I. No. 16230

*Syn.: C.I. Acid orange* 10; *Crystal orange GG; Orange GG* (etc.); *Wool orange* 2G.
An acid dye.
Cellulose (→ yellow); nuclei (counterstain to Gram's iodine and crystal violet); *Vorticella* (with iron haematoxylin).

(*a*) Satd. soln. aq.
(*b*) *In clove oil.*

Orange G . . . . . . . . . 1 g
Alcohol (100%) . . . . . . . 100 ml

Dissolve the orange G in the alcohol. Add:

Clove oil . . . . . . . . . 100 ml

Allow the alcohol to evaporate till 100 ml of solution remains.

(*c*) See also Mallory's triple stain (p. 232) and orange-fuchsin.

**Orcein** C.I. (1st edn.) No. 1242

*Syn.: C.I. Natural red* 28.

*Note:* This dye has not been allocated a C.I. No. in Part II of the 2nd Edn. of the Colour Index. It is a natural dye derived from certain lichens after treatment.

Elastic fibres [nuclei (→ blue); cytoplasm (→ pink); do *not* differentiate with acid alcohol]; inulin (→ orange-red).

(*a*) *Alcoholic soln.*

| | |
|---|---|
| Orcein | 1 g |
| Alcohol (100%) | 100 ml |
| Hydrochloric acid (conc.) | 1 ml |

(*b*) *Aqueous soln.*

| | |
|---|---|
| Orcein | 2 g |
| Acetic acid (glacial) | 2 ml |
| Distilled water | 100 ml |

**Orcein, Acetic-**

*A stain-fixative for chromosomes.* (See Methods 1 (*a*) (i), (iii) and (*b*), pp. 115, 116).

| | |
|---|---|
| Acetic acid (glacial) | 100 ml |
| Orcein | 2.2 g |

The above makes the stock solution.

*For use:*

| | |
|---|---|
| Stock solution | 10 ml |
| Distilled water | 12 ml |

*Note:* The stain tends to decompose in diluted acid solution (which is approximately 1% in acetic acid (45%) and only sufficient of the diluted stain for immediate use should be made up at any one time.

*ortho*-**Toluidine**

*For use in testing for blood stains.*
See 'Blood ii' (p. 108).
*Note:* It is essential to use A.R. quality materials.

| | |
|---|---|
| Acetic acid (glacial) (A.R. quality) | 90 ml |
| ortho-toluidine | 10 g |

*Note:* The stock solution should be stored at 0°C. It should be used from a dropping bottle, which should be stored at 0°C when not in use.

**'Osmic Acid'**

See 'Osmium Tetroxide'.

**Osmium Tetroxide**

(i) *For fixing protozoa.* 0.25% aq.
(ii) *For fixing animal tissue for cytological purposes.* 1% aq.
(iii) *For staining fats, etc., and for fixing plant tissue for histological purposes.* 2% aq.

*Note:*
(*a*) The solutions should be kept in an uncoloured glass bottle (to enable contents to be seen), but this *must* be kept free from dust (which acts as an oxidizing agent) and enclosed in a suitable light-tight box. One drop of mercuric chloride (satd. aq.) is said to prevent the reduction of 10 ml of osmium tetroxide (2%).* *Keep away from fingers, eyes, and mucous membrane.*
(*b*) The tetroxide is reduced to oxide by unsaturated fatty compounds. The oxide combines with the fatty substances to form black compounds. Fats; lipids (→ brown).

**Oxalic Acid**

*Solution for use in the silver method for nerve axons* (ii, p. 151).

| | |
|---|---|
| Oxalic acid | 2 g |
| Distilled water | 100 ml |

**Pampel's Fluid**

*For preservation of zoological specimens, especially insects.*
See 'Animal Tissue iii' (p. 98).

| | |
|---|---|
| Acetic acid (glacial) | 2 volumes |
| Alcohol (95%) | 15 " |
| Formaldehyde (40%) | 6 " |
| Distilled water | 30 " |

**Paradichlorbenzene**

(i) *For pre-treatment of root-tips, prior to fixation, to inhibit clumping of chromosomes.*

| | |
|---|---|
| Paradichlorbenzene | 5–10 g |
| Distilled water | 500 ml |

*Note:* Paradichlorbenzene is relatively very insoluble but sufficient will have dissolved if the liquid is allowed to stand overnight at 60°C. Filter before use.

* Baker, J. R., *Cytological Technique*, Methuen.

(ii) *For the destruction of insect pests* (e.g. ants, cockroaches, moths, etc.) *of garments, museum specimens and other stored products.*

*Dosage:*

3–4.5 kg per 28 $m^3$ of space,
for 24 h at temperatures above 29.5°C;
for 36 h at temperatures below 29.5°C.

*Note:* At temperatures above 23°C the vapour has a paralysing and intoxicating effect upon insects.

**'Parozone'**

*For bleaching after staining with Mayer's haemalum.*

| | |
|---|---|
| 'Parozone' . . . . . . . . . | 15 ml |
| Distilled water . . . . . . . | 100 ml |

*Note:* The above concentration should be regarded as approximate. If the solution is too concentrated the tissue may be caused to disintegrate. The finding of the best concentration for use with any particular tissue is a matter for trial and error.

**Perenyi's Fluid**

*For removing jelly, fixing and preserving amphibian spawn.*

| | |
|---|---|
| Alcohol (90%) . . . . . . . | 18 ml |
| Chromium trioxide . . . . . | 0.09 g |
| Nitric acid (60%) . . . . . . . | 4 ml |
| Distilled water . . . . . . . | 38 ml |

Jelly dissolved in *a few weeks.*

**Periodic Acid**

*For use in the Hotchkiss-McManus-Periodic acid-Schiff technique for fungal hyphae in host plant, fungi,* xi (*a*) *and for carbohydrates* (p. 112).

| | |
|---|---|
| Periodic acid . . . . . . . . | 1 g |
| Distilled water . . . . . . . | 100 ml |

**Phenol — Fuchsin**

See 'Fuchsin, Basic, Phenol-' (p. 217).

**Phenol — Thionin**

See 'Thionin, Phenol-' (p. 250).

**Phenylhydrazine Hydrochloride**

*For test for dextrose. See 'Sugars. Tests for,* (*b*) *Dextrose',* (p. 173).

| | |
|---|---|
| Phenylhydrazine hydrochloride . | 2 g |
| Sodium acetate (solid) . . . . | 4 g |
| Distilled water . . . . . . . | 20 ml |

To the above quantity of reagent, add for the test:

| | |
|---|---|
| Sugar . . . . . . . . . . | 1 g |

**Phloroglucin(ol)** (Symmetrical trihydroxybenzene)

Lignin (temp.) (soak tissues and add conc. hydrochloric acid) (→ violet-red) (this is a specific test for lignin); inulin (+ dil. hydrochloric acid) (→ orange-red).

| | |
|---|---|
| Phloroglucin(ol) . . . . . . . | 5 g |
| Alcohol (75%) . . . . . . . | 100 ml |

'Best results are obtained at this concentration. The evaporation rate is not too rapid and therefore crystallization is slow . . . the ligneous tissue should be well-flooded and staining continued for 4 min after which 1 drop of conc. hydrochloric acid is added.'*

**Phloxine B** C.I. No. 45410

*Syn.: C.I. Acid red* 92; *Cyanosine; Eosin* 10B; *Phloxine* TA (etc.).

An acid dye.

*Algae*

(i) *Counterstain to anilin blue* WS. (*See 'Algae, Chamberlain's method,* p. 95).

| | |
|---|---|
| Phloxine B . . . . . . . . . | 1 g |
| Alcohol (90%) . . . . . . . | 99 ml |

(ii) *For Spirogyra*

| | |
|---|---|
| Phloxine B . . . . . . . . . | 0.5 g |
| Distilled water . . . . . . . | 100 ml |

**Phosphate Buffer Solution**

*For use with Field's stain for blood films,* (p. 214).

| | |
|---|---|
| Disodium hydrogen phosphate (anhydrous) . . . . . . . . | 10 g |
| Potassium dihydrogen phosphate (anhydrous) . . . . . . . . | 12.5 g |
| Distilled water . . . . . . . | 1000 ml |

* Private communication from N. C. Peacock, M.A., Colorado Academy, Denver, Colorado, U.S.A.

**Phosphomolybdic Acid**

*For use in Wilder's method for connective tissue fibrils* (p. 120).

| | |
|---|---|
| Phosphomolybdic acid . . . . | 10 g |
| Distilled water . . . . . . . | 100 ml |

*For use in Masson's technique for connective tissues* (p. 121).

| | |
|---|---|
| Phosphomolybdic acid . . . . | 1 g |
| Distilled water . . . . . . . | 100 ml |

Make fresh each day.

**Picric Acid** C.I. No. 10305

A fixative which can also act as an acid dye.

Chitin (→ yellow); erythrocytes; hair; horn; lignified tissue; *Nereis* parapodia (preceded by borax carmine); nerve tissue (in dissections); trachea of insect (preceded by borax carmine); muscle; may be preceded by haematoxylin.

(i) *Alcoholic soln.:*
Alcohol (100%) [or (95%), or (50%), according to requirements] with picric acid to saturation. Decant.

(ii) *Aqueous soln.:*
Distilled water with picric acid to saturation. Decant.

**Picric-alcohol**

Alcohol (50%) with picric acid to saturation. Decant.

**Picric-anilin Blue**

See 'Anilin Blue WS – Picric acid' (p. 189).

**Picro-carmine**

See 'Carmine, Picro-' (p. 197).

**Picro-Clove Oil**

*Chitin* (→ yellow or brown) (preceded by borax carmine); crustacea (preceded by borax carmine).

Clove oil with picric acid to saturation.

**Picro-formol-acetic**

See 'Bouin's Fluid' (p. 191).

**Pith, Elder**

*For holding small pieces of tissue during sectioning.*

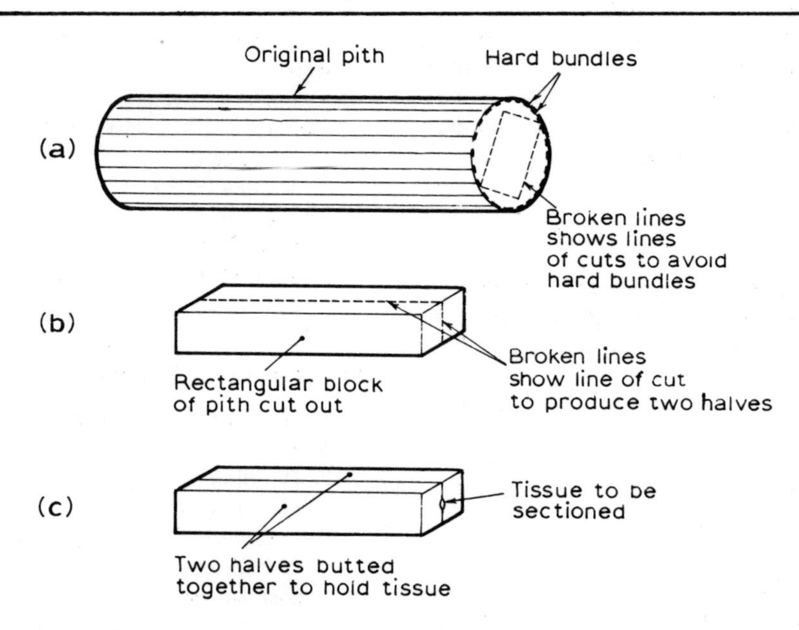


Fig. 7.6 How to cut a piece of elder pith to hold tissue for freehand sectioning. (Suggested by Professor H. Godwin, The School of Botany, University of Cambridge.)

Keep a small stock in alcohol (70%). Cuts more easily than when wetted just before use.

For method of cutting to avoid hard bundles see Fig. 7.6.

*Note:* All cuts must be made with a sharp scalpel blade held parallel with the long axis of the stem, otherwise the pith breaks as the blade goes through it.

**Polystyrene, expanded**

Pieces of expanded polystyrene, as sold for ceiling tiles, are an excellent alternative to elder pith for holding small pieces of tissue during freehand sectioning. A stock may be kept in 70% alcohol.

**Polyvinyl Alcohol — Lactophenol**

*A mountant for insect larvae* (p. 141); *and a wood softener* (p. 179).

| | |
|---|---|
| Lactic acid | 25 ml |
| Phenol | 22 g |
| Polyvinyl alcohol | 56 ml |

Dissolve the phenol crystals in the lactic acid. Add the polyvinyi cohol and stir vigorously. Heat on a water-bath to clear the solution.

**Potassium Acetate**

*For use in preparation of Erythrosin-glycerine.* Potassium acetate 0.5% aq. soln.

**Potassium Dichromate**

(i) *For fixation of animal tissue for cytological purposes.*
1.5% aq. soln.

(ii) *For cleaning glassware.*

| | |
|---|---|
| Potassium dichromate (3%) | 90 ml |
| Sulphuric acid (conc.) | 10 ml |

**Potassium Ferrocyanide**

*For staining iron compounds in sections.*
*Note: The solutions should be freshly made.*
See iron, *Method* i (p. 141).

| | |
|---|---|
| Hydrochloric acid (0.5% aq.) | 50 ml |
| Potassium ferrocyanide (1.5% aq.) | 50 ml |

**Potassium Hydroxide**

*To remove fats and roughen cuticle of nematodes.*

| | |
|---|---|
| Potassium hydroxide | 5 g |
| Distilled water | 100 ml |

**Potassium Metabisulphite**

*For use in Dring's Hotchkiss-McManus-Periodic Acid-Schiff (PAS) method for fungal hyphae in non-lignified tissues* (p. 135)* *and in the* PAS *technique for carbohydrates* (p. 112).

| | |
|---|---|
| Hydrochloric acid (N/1) | 5 ml |
| Potassium metabisulphite (10% aq.) | 5 ml |
| Distilled water | 90 ml |

*Note:* This solution must be kept in a tightly-stoppered bottle and is usable as long as it smells fairly strongly of sulphur dioxide.

**Pyridine**

(i) *For use in the silver method for nerve axons* (p. 151).

| | |
|---|---|
| Pyridine (pure) | 10 ml |
| Distilled water | 100 ml |

(ii) *For detaching tissue-paper which may adhere to sticky frozen sections when being attached to the slide.*

| | |
|---|---|
| Alcohol (50%) | 100 ml |
| Pyridine | 0.5 ml |

**Pyrogallol Solution**

*For absorption of oxygen.*

*Solution A*

| | |
|---|---|
| Pyrogallic acid | 5 g |
| Distilled water | 100 ml |

*Solution B*

| | |
|---|---|
| Potassium hydroxide | 25 g |
| Distilled water | 100 ml |

Mix equal volumes of the two solutions immediately before use.

**Pyronin/Malachite Green (for RNA and DNA staining)**

| | |
|---|---|
| Pyronin Y (4% aq.) | 40 ml |
| Malachite green (0.3% aq.) | 10 ml |
| Buffer solution at pH 4.8 | 50 ml |

* From information supplied by Dr. D. M. Dring, Royal Botanic Gardens, Kew.

Buffer solution is made by mixing 81 ml 0.2 N acetic acid with 119 ml of 0.2 M sodium acetate. Check pH on meter and adjust if necessary.

**Razor, to Sharpen**

(i) *Grinding.* This should never be attempted by amateurs.

(ii) *Honing.* This becomes necessary when the keen, angular edge of the razor has become rounded by constant stropping, or when a feather-edge remains after grinding.

*1 Use a Turkey stone. Thinly cover the working surface of the stone with olive oil.
2 Wedge a piece of folded paper between shank of razor and handle to keep the blade steady.
3 Sit at a table with the length of the stone arranged parallel with the edge of the table, in front of the body.
4 Place the razor blade *flat* on the left end of the stone with its *edge* pointing to the right and with its heel (i.e. the end nearer the handle) rather in advance of its toe (i.e. 'heel-to-toe').
5 With gentle pressure *pull* the razor to the right, *edge first*, 'heel-to-toe'.
6 At the end of the stroke turn the Razor over, ON ITS BACK, and *pull* it to the left, *edge first,* 'heel-to-toe'.
7 Gradually decrease the pressure and shorten the stroke.
8 It may be found necessary, finally, to tilt the razor on to its toe, and, with a circular motion, rub off the toe.

*Note:*
(*a*) Both wedge-shaped and hollow-ground (plano-concave) blades are honed in the same manner.
(*b*) Keep the Turkey stone covered and free from dust, and remove surplus oil after use.

(iii) *The 'Razor-Board': a substitute for honing.* * Although the art of honing is one that can be acquired with practice, it remains a process which, carelessly used, can lead to the ruin of a razor by alteration of the correct angle of the cutting edge.

The use of the 'razor-board' provides a safe and effective method for keeping razors in good condition, provided that their cutting edges have not already been hopelessly ruined by inexpert attempts at honing on a stone.

1 Cut a rectangular block of balsa wood, 20 cm x 10 cm x 1.5 cm.
2 Smooth the surfaces *plane* with very fine sand-paper.
3 By means of a small piece of cloth, apply 'Rolls Razor Paste' to one of the 20 cm x 10 cm surfaces. The paste must be applied evenly and gently all over this surface and *great care must be taken to use even pressure.* If, for example, too great pressure is applied by a thumb, the very soft balsa wood will be indented and the plane surface destroyed. Sufficient paste is applied to impregnate the surface of the 'board' thoroughly.
4 Use the 'razor-board' in precisely the same way as a *strop* is used [see iv, below].
*Note:* The *'razor-board'* should be used from time-to-time only, in order to keep the cutting edge in first-class condition. The *strop* should be used, as recommended, both before and after section-cutting.

(iv) *Stropping.* Razors should always be stropped immediately before and after use. It protects the razor-edge from corrosion and polishes it, at the same time correcting any wear or bluntness.

Amateurs sometimes have difficulty in keeping the correct angle between the edge of the blade and the strop. If the back of the blade is raised very slightly by placing over it a shield in the form of a bent piece of very thin sheet metal cut from a 'tin' can, the correct angle can be maintained. (See Fig. 7.7.)

When using the strop proceed as follows:

1 Before use, wipe the strop with the palm of the hand to remove any adhering dust or grit.
2 With one hand hold the strop taut, and with the other press the razor blade *flat* on the strop.
3 Draw the blade along the strop, away from the body, *back first,* 'heel-to-toe' [See ii **4** above].
4 At the end of the stroke turn the razor over, ON ITS BACK, and draw it, *back first*, 'heel-to-toe', towards the body.

* I am indebted to the late W. J. Clare for the instructions on honing; and to J. Blair for the information about the Razor-Board.

**5** Give about 8 strokes on the rough, followed by about 10 on the smooth side of the strop.
**6** Finally, using the palm of the hand as a strop, give about 8 strokes as directed in **3** and **4**.

(v) *General care.*
1 Always strop the razor before use.
2 Never lay the razor, with blade exposed, on the bench.
3 After use, clean the blade with xylene and draw it, edge first, away from the body, in the folds of a soft duster held between finger and thumb.
4 Always strop the razor after use.
5 If much section-cutting is being done, it is advisable to have three razors in use. Make use of each in rotation and rest each for two consecutive days.

**Reducing Solution**

*For use in Wilder's method for connective tissue fibrils* (iv, p. 120).

| | |
|---|---|
| Formaldehyde (40%) (neutralized by adding magnesium carbonate) | 0.5 ml |
| Uranium nitrate (1%) . . . . | 1.5 ml |
| Distilled water . . . . . . . | 50 ml |

**Refractive Indices**

See page 255.

**Resorcin**

*Test for sugars.* See 'Seliwanoff's Reagent' (p. 248).

**Resorcin-fuchsin (Weigert's)**

See 'Fuchsin, Basic, Resorcin- (Weigert's)' (p. 217).

**Ripart's and Petit's Fluid**

*A gentle fixative (and preservative) for protozoa either for immediate or for later examination.*

| | |
|---|---|
| Acetic acid (glacial) . . . . . | 1 ml |
| Copper acetate . . . . . . . | 0.3 g |
| Copper chloride . . . . . . . | 0.3 g |
| Camphor water (*not* satd.) . . . | 75 ml |
| Distilled water . . . . . . . | 75 ml |

A good stain to use after this fixative is methyl green.

**Rongalite C**

Rongalite C is the industrial name for sodium formaldehyde sulphoxylate, $HO.CH_2.OSONa.2H_2O$, a reducing agent used in the production of reduced methylene blue (intra-vitam methylene blue) (see p. 235). Formula for use in this process:

| | |
|---|---|
| Rongalite C . . . . . . . . | 12 g |
| Distilled water . . . . . . . | 100 ml |

*Note:* Rongalite C is sometimes erroneously referred to as 'Rongalit'.

**Rosaniline**

See 'Fuchsin, Basic-' (p. 216).

**Rossman's Fixative**

*For use when glycogen is to be preserved 'in situ'.*

| | |
|---|---|
| Picric acid [satd. soln. in alcohol (100%)] . . . . . . . . . | 90 ml |
| *Just before use, add:* | |
| Formaldehyde (40%) . . . . | 10 ml |

**Ruthenium Red** (Ammoniacal ruthenium oxychloride)

A mineral pigment.

*Pectic compounds* (mucilages and gums). Does not stain mucilage derived from cellulose. Stains chromatin well; cytoplasm feebly; cellulose not at all.

| | |
|---|---|
| Ammonium hydroxide (10% aq.) | 5 drops |
| Ruthenium red . . . . . . . | 0.01 g |
| Distilled water . . . . . . . | 100 ml |

Keep in the dark.

Fig. 7.7 Position of razor on strop.

**Safranin O** C.I. No. 50240

*Syn.: C.I. Basic red 2; Cotton red; Gossypimine; Safranin A; Safranin Y* (etc.).

A basic dye.

A nuclear stain. Chromatin (→ red); cutin (→ pink); elastic fibres; fresh animal tissue; fungi; lignin (→ cherry-red) (counterstain with Delafield's haematoxylin, anilin blue WS, picric-anilin blue WS, or light green SF yellowish in clove oil); nuclei (plant and animal) (→ red); *Opalina;* plant tissue (fixed sections) (counterstain with haematoxylin or fast green FCF); protozoa; sieve plates (temp.); spermatozoa; starch (→ pink); unlignified tissue (→ brown-red); xylem (→ cherry-red) (counterstain as for lignin).

(i) Ethyl alcohol (50%) . . . . . 99 ml
Safranin O . . . . . . . . . 1 g

(ii) *When benzyl alcohol is to be used later for dehydrating.*
Ethyl alcohol (70%) . . . . . 100 ml
Safranin O . . . . . . . . . Satis.

Filter before use.

**Safranin O — Anilin Blue WS in 2 ethoxy ethanol**

*A double stain for plant tissue.*

A. Anilin blue WS . . . . . . . 1 g
2 ethoxy ethanol . . . . . . 100 ml

B. Safranin O . . . . . . . . . 1 g
2 ethoxy ethanol . . . . . . 100 ml

*Mix:*
Solution A . . . . . . . . . 48 ml
Solution B . . . . . . . . . 52 ml

*Note:*

(i) The quality of safranin O is liable to vary and hence trial and error may indicate the necessity for some variation in the above proportions.

(ii) Fresh sections are transferred to the stain (approx. 10 min), differentiated in fresh 2 ethoxy ethanol, cleared in xylene and mounted in D.P.X.

**Safranin O, Babe's**

Safranin O . . . . . . . . . excess
Anilin oil . . . . . . . . . 2 ml
Alcohol (50%) . . . . . . . 100 ml

Warm the mixture to between 60°–80°C.
Filter through a wet filter. Will keep 1–2 months.

**Safranin O — Fast Green FCF in 2 ethoxy ethanol**

*A double stain for use with plant tissue.*

A. Fast green FCF . . . . . . . 3 g
2 ethoxy ethanol . . . . . . 100 ml
Heat together in a flask on a water-bath for 30 min. Stir occasionally. Cool. Filter.

B. Safranin O . . . . . . . . . 1 g
2 ethoxy ethanol . . . . . . 100 ml

*Mix:*
Solution A . . . . . . . . . 48 ml
Solution B . . . . . . . . . 52 ml

*Note:*

(i) As the quality of safranin O is variable, it may be necessary to vary the proportions of solutions A and B accordingly.

(ii) Fresh sections are placed in the stain (approx. 10 min), differentiated in fresh 2 ethoxy ethanol, cleared in xylene and mounted in D.P.X.

**Saline Solutions**

1. *Physiological saline solutions isotonic with the cell contents.*

*For temporary bathing of tissues for microscopic and other purposes.*

(i) *Ringer's solution*
Calcium chloride (anhydrous). . 0.03 g
Potassium chloride . . . . . 0.025 g
Distilled water . . . . . . 100 ml

*Add:*

(*a*) *For homiothermic animals.*
Sodium chloride . . . . . . 0.85 g

(*b*) *For poikilothermic animals.*
Sodium chloride . . . . . . 0.65 g

*Add,* to bring the pH value to 7.0–7.4 (approx.)
Sodium bicarbonate . . . . . 0.02 g

(ii) *Sodium chloride — Isotonic solutions.* *

| | *Sodium chloride aq.* |
|---|---|
| (*a*) For mammalian tissue, except blood . . . . . . . . . | 0.9% |
| (*b*) For avian tissue . . . . . | 0.75% |
| (*c*) For amphibian tissue, except blood . . . . . . . . . | 0.64% |

* Sometimes loosely and wrongly called 'Normal Salt Solutions'. The term 'normal' should not be used here as it may lead to confusion with its use in the chemical sense when solutions are being prepared.

(*d*) For Selachian tissue . . . 1.5%–2.6%
(*e*) For vertebrate blood . . . 0.6%
(*f*) For invertebrate tissue . . . 0.75%

(iii) *Insect saline.*

| | |
|---|---|
| Calcium chloride (anhydrous) . | 0.02 g |
| Sodium chloride . . . . . . . | 0.7 g |
| Distilled water . . . . . . . | 100 ml |

2. *To discharge nematocysts of Hydra.*
Sodium chloride . . . . . . . 5.0% aq.

3. *For fixing and preserving.*
Use formol-saline. See 'Dilution of Liquids – Formula and Table for, 2 *Note* iii' (p. 210) and footnotes (*) and (†) below Table (p. 211), and use sodium chloride (0.85% aq.) as the diluent for the formaldehyde.

**San Felice's Fluid**

| | |
|---|---|
| Chromium trioxide (1%) . . . | 64 ml |
| Acetic acid, (glacial) . . . . . | 4 ml |

To 17 ml, add 8 ml of formalin just before use. Fix 24 hours and wash out overnight in running water. This fixative is especially good for chromosomes which are to be stained with crystal violet.

**Schaudinn's Fluid**

*For fixing protozoa.*

| | |
|---|---|
| Acetic acid (glacial) . . . . . | A few drops |
| Alcohol (100%) . . . . . . . | 50 ml |
| Mercuric chloride (sat. aq.) . . | 100 ml |

**Schiff's Reagent**

(i) *Coleman's formula for use in the Feulgen technique for chromosomes,* (p. 115).

| | |
|---|---|
| Basic fuchsin . . . . . . . . | 0.5 g |
| Distilled water (boiling) . . . | 100 ml |

Dissolve the basic fuchsin by pouring the boiling water over it. Shake well. Cool to 50°C. Filter.
*Add to the filtrate:*

| | |
|---|---|
| Hydrochloric acid (N/1) . . . | 15 ml |
| Potassium metabisulphite (anhydrous) ($K_2S_2O_5$) . . . | 1.5 g* |

Leave for 24 h, in a stoppered bottle in the dark, to bleach.
*Add:*
Vegetable carbon (Norit) or animal charcoal . . . . . . . . . 0.25 g
Shake well (1 min). Filter rapidly through coarse paper. The resultant liquid should be light straw-coloured with no trace of red or purple.
Store in a tightly-stoppered bottle, in the dark, and preferably in a refrigerator. Will keep for at least 6 months.

(ii) *Schiff's formula, for use in Dring's Hotchkiss-MacManus-Periodic Acid-Schiff* (PAS) *method for fungal hyphae in non-lignified plant tissue* (p. 135)*.
As formula i above, but reduce the amounts of
Hydrochloric acid (N/1) to 10 ml
and Potassium metabisulphite (anhydrous) to 0.5 g
*Note:* It is now believed that the optimum pH value of the liquid for this technique is 2.4.

(iii) *Talboy's formula for use in staining the vascular system of plants* (p. 178).†

| | |
|---|---|
| Basic fuchsin . . . . . . . | 0.1 g |
| Distilled water . . . . . . . | 100 ml |
| Sodium metabisulphite . . . . | 10 g |
| Distilled water . . . . . . . | 100 ml |

Add about 5 ml of the sodium metabisulphite solution *slowly and with vigorous shaking* to 100 ml of the dye solution, until the dye is completely decolorized. A faint residual colour has no undesirable effect.

(iv) *Barger and De Lamater's formula*‡
Dissolve 1 g basic fuchsin in 400 ml boiling distilled water. Cool to 50°C and filter.
To the filtrate add 1 ml of thionyl chloride ($SO\ Cl_2$) *with great care*, in small amounts. Shake to mix and stand in the dark 12 hours or overnight. Add 2 g activated charcoal and shake well. Filter and store in the dark at 4°C.

* P. S. Fielden, Warwick School, substitutes 1.5 g of sodium bisulphite. (Private communication.)

* From information supplied by Dr. D. M. Dring of the Royal Botanic Gardens, Kew.

† From information supplied by Dr. P. W. Talboys of East Malling Research Station.

‡ Barger, J. D., and De Lamater, E. D. *Science,* **108**, 121, 1948.

**Schulze's Fluid**

*For maceration of woody tissues.*

| | |
|---|---|
| Nitric acid (conc.) | 50 ml |
| Potassium nitrate | 1 g |

**Schulze's Solution** (chlor-zinc-iodine) (Herzberg's stain)

*Micro-chemical test for cellulose.*

Cellulose – a specific stain (temp.) (→ blue-violet); cutin (temp.) (→ yellow-brown); hyphae (cell wall) (temp.); lignin (temp.) (→ yellow-brown); proteins (→ brown); starch (temp.) (→ blue); suberin (temp.) (→ yellow-brown).

Place sections in water for a few minutes before staining.

(*a*)

| | |
|---|---|
| Zinc chloride | 30 g |
| Potassium iodide | 5 g |
| Iodine | 1 g |
| Distilled water | 14 ml |

(*b*) *Leach's formula* *

Hydrochloric acid (conc.) . . . satis.
Zinc, add to the acid until effervescence ceases, and excess zinc remains.
Evaporate liquid until of consistency of conc. sulphuric acid. Now add

Potassium iodide . . . . to saturation
Allow liquid to stand.
Decant supernatant liquid. Add

Iodine . . . . . . . . to saturation
Decant supernatant liquid.
*Keep in the dark.* Make up freshly from time to time. Does not keep longer than two weeks.

**Sealing Media**

(i) *Apáthy's cement for glycerol mounts*†

| | |
|---|---|
| Canada balsam | 1 part |
| Paraffin wax (m.p. 60°C) | 1 part |

Heat in a porcelain vessel *until the mixture turns golden and no longer gives off turpentine vapours.* To use – give one application of the warmed cement on a glass rod or spatula.

* After Leach, 1949, *Textbook of Practical Botany*, Methuen.

† After Lee, 1937, *Microtomist's Vade-Mecum*, Churchill, London.

(ii) *Asphaltum black varnish* (*Bitume de Judée*).

Obtainable from opticians and suppliers.

(iii) *Bause's ringing varnish* *

Does not crack, 'run in', or 'spread', and is immersion-oil proof.

1 Place a quantity of ordinary flaked shellac in an earthenware or enamel vessel.
2 Cover the shellac with methylated spirit.
3 Place the vessel in a saucepan (whose rim should be lower than the rim of the inner vessel) and pour water into the saucepan until the levels of the liquids in inner and outer vessels are the same.
4 Heat the water and meanwhile keep the shellac and alcohol stirred with a glass rod or soft-wood stick. *Be ready to lift the saucepan off the source of heat as soon as the methylated spirit is on the point of boiling.* (CARE.)
5 Keep stirring until all the shellac is dissolved. Ignore any residue of stringy material.
6 Warm another earthenware or enamel vessel and filter the shellac solution into it, through several layers of muslin.
7 Add to the filtered shellac solution, 25% of its volume of Venetian turpentine. Reheat in the water in the saucepan and keep stirring till mixture is complete. On cooling, there will result a thick jelly which may be stored indefinitely in a tightly corked vessel.
8 When required for ringing, thin out a suitable quantity with methylated spirits until it is of the correct consistency for the purpose. *Note:* If a black varnish is required, add to every 110 ml of methylated spirit used for thinning, one salt-spoonful of 'spirit-black' (obtainable from oil and colour merchants).
9 Reheat the thinned varnish and allow to cool. (Reheating after thinning makes the varnish more tenacious.) The varnish is now ready for use.

(iv) *Brunswick black*

Obtainable from hardware merchants. Three coats necessary.

(v) *Canada balsam in xylene*

See p. 193.

(vi) *Cellulose black enamel*

Is immersion-oil-proof. Obtainable from

* Private communication to the author.

cycle-agents, and suppliers of motorists' sundries.
Three coats necessary.

(vii) *Cellulose varnish (clear)*

Use clear 'Brushing Belco'. Obtainable from cycle-agents and suppliers of motorists' sundries.
Three coats necessary.

(viii) *Glycerol-jelly*

A first seal for liquid mounts.
For formula see p. 220.

(ix) *Gold size*

Is soluble in oil of turpentine.
If necessary to dilute, do so with *raw* linseed oil.
Obtainable from opticians, decorators and other suppliers.

(x) *Gray's sealing medium for fluid mounts**

(*a*) Melt together

| | |
|---|---|
| Lanoline (anhydrous) . . . . | 4 parts |
| Resin . . . . . . . . . . | 8 parts |
| Canada balsam (dry) . . . . | 1 part |

(*b*) *To apply:*

($\alpha$) *To circular cover-slips*

1 Fit a handle on to a piece of brass-tubing of bore very slightly in excess of the diameter of the cover-slip.
2 Heat the tubing, dip into mixture, and apply over the cover-slip. The cement hardens immediately.

($\beta$) *To square cover-slips*

1 Heat a thick steel knitting needle and flatten one end to make a small spatula.
2 Bend to a convenient shape.
3 Apply cement by means of heated tool.

(xi) *Gum-mastic paraffin wax*

1 *Using care,* melt *powdered* gum-mastic in a porcelain dish.
2 Add paraffin wax in small pieces, stirring with a wooden or bone spatula until the whole is smooth and free from lumps.
3 Before the mixture cools, pour it into a suitable covered storage vessel.
4 Apply the seal to the edge of the cover-slip by means of a heated copper wire of suitable thickness.

* Adapted from *The Microscope Record*, No. 33; Sept. 1934. Messrs. W. Watson & Sons, Ltd.

(xii) *Krönig's Deckglaskitt**

(*a*) Wax . . . . . . . . . . . 2 parts
Melt, and add gradually,
Colophonium resin . . . . . 7–9 parts
Mix thoroughly, filter, and cool.

(*b*) *To apply.* Heat an L-shaped metal rod in a flame, dip into the vessel containing the medium and apply to the edge of cover-slip.

(xiii) *Marine glue in xylene*

Make a thick solution and build up in layers. Ring with gold size.

(xiv) *'Perspex', Cement for*

See 'Adhesives, for 'Perspex'' (p. 185).

(xv) *Pitch*

Forms a water-proof cement for sealing specimen jars. May be obtained from the tops of old accumulators and dry batteries. Melt the pitch (*care*) and apply and smooth off with an old scalpel, heated. Cover joints with 'passe-partout' paper strip.

(xvi) *'Plasticine'*

A useful seal for temporary mounts.

(xvii) *Rubber solution*

Obtainable from cycle dealers and motor accessory suppliers. Apply to the edge of the cover-slip by means of the nozzle of the supply-tube.

(xviii) *Shellac*

For sealing cover-slips and for making rings to form cavities on slides. Is immersion-oil-proof.

(*a*) Methylated spirit.
Shellac (flaked).
Dissolve shellac in methylated spirits until the solution has the viscosity of the liquid gum commonly sold by stationers.

(*b*) See also 'Bause's Ringing Varnish, iii' (p. 246).

(xix) *Tolu balsam cement*†

| | |
|---|---|
| Tolu balsam . . . . . . . . | 2 parts |
| Canada balsam . . . . . . . | 1 part |

* After Carleton, H. M. (1926), *Histological Technique,* University Press, Oxford.

† After Lee, 1937, *Microtomist's Vade-Mecum,* Churchill, London.

Shellac (satd. soln. in chloroform) 2 parts
Chloroform . . . To bring to a syrupy consistency.

(xx) *Venetian turpentine*

Useful for square cover-slips.

Carefully evaporate ordinary resinous turpentine (*not* 'white spirit', nor 'turpentine substitute') until the residue is brittle on cooling.

See 'Turpentine, Venetian' (p. 251).

To apply the seal, heat an L-shaped piece of wire and carry the medium to the edge of the cover-slip on the short arm of the L.

(xxi) *Water-proof cement for sealing specimen jars*

See XV, 'Pitch'.

(xxii) *Zinc white*

| | |
|---|---|
| Zinc oxide . . . . . . . . . | 10 parts |
| Turpentine . . . . . . . . . | 10 parts |

Rub up the zinc oxide with the turpentine and *add:*

| | |
|---|---|
| Gum damar in turpentine . . . | 80 parts |

The solution of gum damar should be of the consistency of treacle.

**Seliwanoff's Reagent**

*For test for laevulose. See 'Sugars. Tests for, (c) Laevulose* ii' (p. 173).

| | |
|---|---|
| Hydrochloric acid (conc.) . . . | 30 ml |
| Resorcin . . . . . . . . . | 0.5 g |
| Distilled water . . . . . . . | 30 ml |

**Silver Diaminohydroxide (Foot's formula)**

*For use in Wilder's method for connective tissue fibrils* (p. 120).

Silver nitrate (10.2% aq.) . . . 5 ml

*Add:*

Ammonium hydroxide (0.880 sp. gr.) — Drop by drop (Until precipitate dissolves)

*Add:*

Sodium hydroxide (3.1% aq.) . 5 ml

*Add:*

Ammonium hydroxide (0.880 sp. gr.) — Drop by drop (Until precipitate dissolves)

*Add:*

Distilled water. To make up to . 50 ml

**Silver Nitrate**

(*a*) Cell outlines; cement substance; chloride ions; stomata in pavement epithelium [see 'Epithelia' (p. 126)].

0.5% aq. soln.

(*b*) *For production of silver diaminohydroxide* (p. 248) *for use in Wilder's method for connective tissue fibrils* (p. 120).

| | |
|---|---|
| Silver nitrate . . . . . . . . | 10.2 g |
| Distilled water . . . . . . . | 100 ml |

(*c*) *For use in the silver method for nerve axons* (ii, p. 151).

(i) *For preliminary impregnation of tissue.*

| | |
|---|---|
| Silver nitrate (A.R. quality) . . | 20 g |
| Distilled water . . . . . . . | 100 ml |

(ii) *For final impregnation with buffered impregnation solution.*

($\alpha$) Silver nitrate . . . . . . 1 g
Distilled water . . . . . . 100 ml

($\beta$) *Buffered impregnating solution:*

| | |
|---|---|
| Boric acid buffer solution (p. 191) . . . . . . . . | 55 ml |
| Sodium borate buffer solution (p. 249) . . . . . . . | 45 ml |

Mix the above quantities in a 500 ml measuring cylinder and dilute to 494 ml with distilled water.

*Add:* silver nitrate [1% aq. (ii ($\alpha$), above)] 1 ml (from a pipette).

*Add:* pyridine [10% aq. (i, p. 241)] 5 ml (from another pipette).

Mix thoroughly.

*Note:* Silver solutions are very sensitive to light. Any cloudiness or precipitate indicates that the solution must be rejected as contaminated.

**Slide Holder***

Useful when dealing with quantities of slides in the same reagent. Stretch a light spiral spring of approximately 2 cm diameter until there is a permanent gap (slightly less than the thickness of a slide) between each coil. Cut the spring into lengths of convenient size to hold the required number of slides when placed in the containing vessel.

**Soap, Bécoeur's Arsenical (poison)**

*For preservation of skins*

* Modified from a suggestion by J. McCloy, *School Science Review*, **XX**, 80, 607; June 1939.

White soap . . . . . . . . . 4.4 kg
Cut up and boil. *Add*
Potassium carbonate (anhydrous) 340 g
Calcium carbonate ('whiting') 113 g
Mix thoroughly. When nearly cold add
Arsenious oxide . . . . . . 4.4 kg
Camphor . . . . . . . . . 142 g
(The camphor should be triturated with alcohol before addition.)
Pour into jars for subsequent use.

**Soap, Browne's**

*For preservation of skins*
White curd soap . . . . . . . 2.2 kg
Calcium carbonate ('whiting') . 6.6 kg
Boil together. Whilst still hot, add add
Bleaching powder . . . . . 42 g
(Avoid inhaling the fumes while the mixture is hot.)
When cold, add
Tincture of musk . . . . . . . 28 g

**Sodium Acetate**

*For micro-chemical test for glucose. See 'Sugars. Tests for, (b)* i *(α)'* (p. 173).
Sodium acetate . . . . . . . 1 g
Glycerol (*pure*) . . . . . . . 10 g
Heating will assist solution. Filter.

**Sodium Alginate**

*To retard movement of protozoa*
Sodium alginate . . . . . . . 1 g
Distilled water . . . . . . . 100 ml

**Sodium Borate**

*Formula for buffer solution for use in the silver method for nerve axons* (p. 151).
Sodium borate ($Na_2B_4O_7 . 10 H_2O$. – A.R. quality) . . . . . . 19 g
Distilled water . . . . . . . 1000 ml

**Sodium Chloride**

See 'Saline Solutions' (p. 244).

**Sodium Hydroxide**

*For use in Wilder's method for connective tissue fibrils* (p. 120).
Sodium hydroxide . . . . . 3.1 g
Distilled water . . . . . . . 100 ml

**Sodium Metasilicate**

*For cleaning the white deposit from glassware.*
5% aq. soln.

**Sodium Nitrate**

*For test for chloride ions.*
1.5% aq. soln.

**Sodium Sulphate**

*For washing after acid decalcification.*
5% aq. soln.

**Sodium Thiosulphate (Hypo)**

(i) *For removal of iodine after iodine-treatment of tissue fixed with mercuric chloride.*
Sodium thiosulphate . . . . 0.75 g
Alcohol (96%) . . . . . . . 10 ml
Distilled water . . . . . . . 90 ml
Thymol . . . . . . . . . . 1 crystal

(ii) *For use in Wilder's method for connective tissue fibrils* (p. 120).
Sodium thiosulphate . . . . 5 g
Distilled water . . . . . . . 100 ml

(iii) *For use in the silver method for nerve axons* (p. 151).
(*a*) *For removal of iodine after treatment of tissue fixed in mercuric chloride.*
Sodium thiosulphate . . . . 0.1 g
Distilled water . . . . . . . 100 ml
(*b*) *For photographic fixing*
Sodium thiosulphate . . . . 5 g
Distilled water . . . . . . . 100 ml

**Spirit Blue** C.I. No. 42775

*Syn.: C.I. Solvent Blue* 3; *Anilin Blue, alcohol soluble; Anilin Blue. spirit soluble; Light Blue; Lyon Blue; Paris Blue.*
A basic dye.
*Protozoa:* small animals and embryos; counter-stain to carmine when bulk-staining.
Spirit blue . . . . . . . . . 1 g
Alcohol (70%) . . . . . . . 99 ml

**Sudan Black B** C.I. No. 26150

*Syn.: C.I. Solvent Black* 3.
Fatty materials; cutin; suberin.

| | |
|---|---|
| Sudan black B . . . . . . . . | 5 g |
| Alcohol (70%) . . . . . . . | 100 ml |

Reflux for 20 min, cool and filter.

**Sudan III** C.I. No. 26100

*Syn.: C.I. Solvent Red* 23; *Cerasin Red; Fat Ponceau G; Oil Red AS* (etc.); *Scarlet B, fat soluble: Sudan G; Tony Red.*

A weakly acid dye.

Cutin (slow); endodermis of root, ii (p. 126); fat (→ red) [see 'Fats and Oils', (p. 128)].

| | |
|---|---|
| Acetone . . . . . . . . . . | 50 ml |
| Alcohol (70%) . . . . . . . | 50 ml |
| Sudan III . . . . . . . . . | 5 g |

Filter. Keep in a well-stoppered bottle.

*Note:* This dye has been largely superseded, as a stain for fats, by Sudan IV (below), which gives a deeper, more intense stain, and by Sudan Black B (above).

**Sudan IV** C.I. No. 26105

*Syn.: C.I. Solvent Red* 24; *Cerotin Ponceau 3B; Fat Ponceau LB or R; Fat Ponceau: Oil Red IV; Scarlet R (erroneous); Scarlet Red (erroneous); Scharlach R (erroneous); Scharlach Red (erroneous).*

Cutin; fat. (Fats and fatty acids → bright red; myelin → yellow to orange).

| | |
|---|---|
| Sudan IV . . . . . . . . . . | 5 g |
| Alcohol (70%) . . . . . . . | 95 ml |

**Sulphuric Acid**

*For destaining in the Ziehl-Neelsen method for tubercle bacilli* ['*Bacteria*, iv (*c*)' (p. 106)].

| | |
|---|---|
| Sulphuric acid (conc.) . . . . | 25 ml |
| Distilled water . . . . . . . | 75 ml |

*Note: Add the acid to the water, carefully, a little at a time, and stir constantly.*

**Sulphurous Acid Rinse (for Feulgen and PAS techniques)**

See Potassium metabisulphite (p. 241).

**'Susa' (Heidenhain's formula)**

*A good general fixative for animal tissue.* Does not harden unduly.

| | |
|---|---|
| Acetic acid (glacial) . . . . . | 4 ml |
| Formaldehyde (40%) . . . . | 20 ml |
| Mercuric chloride . . . . . | 4.5 g |
| Sodium chloride . . . . . . | 0.5 g |
| Trichloracetic acid . . . . . | 2 g |
| Distilled water . . . . . . . | 80 ml |

Do not use any metal apparatus or instruments when using this fixative.

Time for fixation may vary between 1 h and 24 h. Wash in alcohol (50%). To check that no mercuric chloride has been precipitated in the tissue, iodine solution, in sufficient quantity to give a dark sherry-colour, may be added to the alcohol. If the colour disappears after 12 h, further iodine must be added. Transfer to alcohol (70%) until required for use. In all probability the iodine treatment will not be required. Iodine may be removed from sections by washing them in sodium thiosulphate soln.

**Tannic Acid**

(i) *To discharge trichocysts of Paramecium.*
1.0% aq. soln.

(ii) *For use in staining yeast* (method iv, p. 181).
5% aq.

**Taxidermy**

*Preservatives for:*

| | | |
|---|---|---|
| (i) | Burnt alum . . . . . . . . . | 2.2 kg |
| | Potassium nitrate . . . . . . . | 113 g |

Mix thoroughly. See 'Skin, i' (p. 170).

(ii) See 'Soap, Bécoeur's Arsenical' and 'Soap, Browne's' (p. 249).

**Thionin** C.I. No. 52000

*Syn.: Lauth's violet.*
A strongly basic dye.
*For van Wijhe's method for cartilage* (p. 112).

| | |
|---|---|
| Thionin . . . . . . . . . . | 0.5 g |
| Alcohol (70%) . . . . . . . | 100 ml |
| Hydrochloric acid (conc.) . . . | 1 ml |

**Thionin, Phenol- (Carbol-thionin)**

*Fungal mycelium in host plant.* (Mycelium → violet purple; lignified tissue → blue.)

| | |
|---|---|
| Thionin | 1 g |
| Phenol | 5 g |
| Distilled water | 100 ml |

Filter; dilute before use 50/50 with distilled water.

### *ortho*-Toluidine

See p. 238.

### Toluidine Blue O — C.I. No. 52040

*Syn.: C.I. Basic Blue* 17; *Methylene Blue extra; Methylene Blue* T 50.

A basic dye.

(i) *For van Wijhe's method for cartilage* (p. 112).

| | |
|---|---|
| Toluidine blue O | 0.25 g |
| Alcohol (70%) | 100 ml |
| Hydrochloric acid (conc.) | 0.5 ml |

(ii) *For the Champy-Kull method for mitochondria* (p. 146); *and the Drew-Murray method for connective tissue* (p. 120).

| | |
|---|---|
| Toluidine blue O | 0.5 g |
| Distilled water | 100 ml |

### Triphenyl Tetrazolium Chloride

*For the comparative study of respiratory rates in plant tissues** (p. 166).

| | |
|---|---|
| Triphenyl tetrazolium chloride | 0.5 g |
| Distilled water | 100 ml |

*Note:* Triphenyl tetrazolium chloride is the chloride of a complex organic base which can be reduced to an insoluble red compound by living cells in the presence of a suitable hydrogen donor and enzyme system. The rate of development of the red colour is directly proportional to the rate of respiration of the cells. The substance is useful for investigating the distribution of respiratory activity in the tissues of higher plants, or the effect of environmental conditions on the respiration of micro-organisms.

### Trypan Blue — C.I. No. 23850

*Syn.: C.I. Direct Blue* 14; *Azidine Blue* 3B; *Benzamine Blue* 3B; *Benzo Blue* 3B; *Chlorazol Blue* 3B; *Congo Blue* 3B; *Dianil Blue* H3G; *Naphthamine Blue* 3BX; *Niagara Blue* 3B.

* After Dr. M. J. Merrett, University of Bradford.

An acid dye.

*A vital stain,* for lower vertebrate and insect tissues; anther smears; chlamydospores of fungi; nuclear stain for plant material. (Plant material is best fixed in formol-acetic-alcohol.)

(i) *Stock solution*

| | |
|---|---|
| Trypan blue | 1 g |
| Distilled water | 99 ml |

(ii) *For plant epidermis*

| | |
|---|---|
| Alcohol (100%) | 60 ml |
| Cresol | 10 ml |
| Hydrochloric acid (conc.) | 0.1 ml |
| Trypan blue (stock soln.) | 20 ml |
| Distilled water | 10 ml |

Differentiate in alcohol (50%)

(iii)

| | |
|---|---|
| Lactophenol | 100 ml |
| Trypan blue | 0.2 g |

*Note:* Tissue may continue to take up the stain for several h.

(iv)

| | |
|---|---|
| Alcohol (40%) | 100 ml |
| Trypan blue | 0.5 g |

### Turpentine, Phenol-*

*A clearing agent.*

| | |
|---|---|
| Phenol (melted) | 25 ml |
| Turpentine (rectified) | 75 ml |

### Turpentine, Venetian

(i) *As a mountant for filamentous algae*

Venetian turpentine resin is thinned with an equal volume of absolute alcohol and heated, in a flask fitted with a calcium chloride tube, on a water-bath. Filter in a desiccator. To 10 ml of the thick Venetian turpentine so obtained add, alcohol (100%), 90 ml.

*Note:* Venetian turpentine is very apt to take up water from the atmosphere and become cloudy. Preparations are best left in a desiccator containing soda-lime.

(ii) *As a sealing medium*

See 'Sealing Media, XX' (p. 248).

### Two BD (2 BD)

See 'La Cour's Fixatives' (p. 201).

* After Durand, E. J., *Phytopathologist,* I. 129, quoted by Strasburger, 1930, *Handbook of Practical Botany* (English Edition). Allen & Unwin, London.

**Two BE (2 BE)**

See 'La Cour's Fixatives' (p. 201).

**Two BX (2 BX)**

See 'La Cour's Fixatives' (p. 201).

**Uranium Nitrate**

*For use in Wilder's method for reticulin fibrils* (p. 120).

| | |
|---|---|
| Uranium nitrate | 1 g |
| Distilled water | 100 ml |

**Verhoeff's Stain (for elastic fibres)**

| | |
|---|---|
| Absolute alcohol | 60 ml |
| Haematoxylin | 3 g |
| Ferric chloride (10% aq.) | 0.25 ml |

Filter the above and add 25 ml of Lugol's iodine solution. (Iodine 6 g; potassium iodide 4 g dissolved in 10 ml water and diluted to 100 ml.)

**Water, Acid**

*For 'blueing' sections stained in haematoxylin.*

| | |
|---|---|
| Hydrochloric acid (conc.) | 0.5 ml |
| Distilled water | 100 ml |

**Water, Alkaline (Scott's Tap Water Substitute)***

*For 'blueing' sections stained in haematoxylin.*

*Solution A*

| | |
|---|---|
| Sodium bicarbonate | 3.5 g |
| Tap-water | 100 ml |

*Solution B*

| | |
|---|---|
| Magnesium sulphate | 20 g |
| Tap-water | 500 ml |

Mix equal volumes of solutions A and B.
*Add:*
A crystal of thymol to the stock solution.

**Water, Anilin-**

| | |
|---|---|
| Anilin oil | 5 ml |
| Distilled water | 100 ml |

Shake up and stand for 5 min. Filter through a paper wetted with distilled water. The filtrate must be water-clear.

**Wax, Paraffin, Acetone-**

| | |
|---|---|
| Paraffin wax (m.p. 50°C) | 50% |
| Acetone (anhydrous) | 50% |

**Wax, Paraffin, Xylene-**

| | |
|---|---|
| Paraffin wax (m.p. 50°C) | 50% |
| Xylene | 50% |

**Weigert's Stain**

See 'Fuchsin, Basic, Phenol- (Weigert's)' (p. 216) and 'Fuchsin, Basic, Resorcin- (Weigert's)' (p. 217).

**Wright's Stain**

*For blood films.* [See 'Blood, (p. 109).]
The stain is best purchased dry.
Alternatively:

| | |
|---|---|
| Methylene blue | 0.9 g |
| Sodium hydrogen carbonate (0.5% aq.) | 100 ml |

Dissolve the stain and heat the vessel containing the mixture in a pressure cooker (10 lb pressure for 1 h).
*Add:*

| | |
|---|---|
| Eosin Y (0.2% aq. soln.) | 500 ml |

Filter. Wash ppt. with distilled water until the washings are colourless. Dry.
*Stock solution of Wright's stain*

| | |
|---|---|
| Dry stain | 0.1 g |
| Methyl alcohol (100%) (neutral and acetone-free) | 60 ml |

**Xylene**

*A clearing agent.*

When used for clearing, shows 'milky' if there is the slightest trace of water remaining in the tissue. Replace in fresh alcohol (100%), and use xylene-phenol, or, better still, benzene-phenol.

**Xylene, Acetone-**

*For rapid clearing from alcohol* (90%).

| | |
|---|---|
| Acetone (anhydrous) | 20 ml |
| Xylene | 80 ml |

* After Carleton, H. M. (1926), *Histological Technique,* University Press, Oxford.

**Xylene-Alcohol**

| | |
|---|---|
| Alcohol (100%) . . . . . . . | 50 ml |
| Xylene . . . . . . . . . . | 50 ml |

**Xylene-Phenol**

Partly overcomes the trouble of 'milky' xylene due to the presence of water.

| | |
|---|---|
| Xylene . . . . . . . . . . | 100 ml |
| Phenol . . . . . . . . . . | 5 g |

**Yeast**

*For comparative study of effects of temperature upon respiratory rate* (p. 166).

| | |
|---|---|
| Yeast (brewer's or baker's) . . | 20 g |
| Distilled water . . . . . . . | 100 ml |

Shake together and make a suspension.

**Zenker-Formol**

*Fixative for use in animal histology.*

(i)

| | |
|---|---|
| Mercuric chloride . . . . . . . | 5 g |
| Potassium dichromate . . . . | 2.5 g |
| Sodium sulphate . . . . . . . | 1 g |
| Distilled water . . . . . . . | 100 ml |

*Just before use,* add:

| | |
|---|---|
| Formaldehyde (40%) . . . . | 5 ml |

*Note:*

(*a*) Fix for 12–14 h. See 'Zenker's Solution'. Wash out in running water.

(*b*) Do not use for plant material.

**Zenker's Solution (Modified)**

A useful fixative for fine detail of *animal* cell structure and for mitotic figures.

A good stain to follow is iron-haematoxylin.

| | |
|---|---|
| Mercuric chloride . . . . . . | 5 g |
| Potassium dichromate . . . . | 2.5 g |
| Distilled water . . . . . . . | 100 ml |

*Just before use,* add:

| | |
|---|---|
| Acetic acid (glacial) . . . . . . | 5 ml |

Fixation takes 10–12 h. Washing should be done in running water. After washing, transfer to alcohol (70%) to which sufficient iodine has been added to give a dark sherry colour. If the colour disappears, add more iodine to remove all traces of mercuric chloride. Iodine may be removed from sections by washing them in sodium thiosulphate soln. (i, p. 249).

*Note:* The original formula included sodium sulphate (cf. 'Muller's Fluid', p. 236) but this substance does not appear to serve any useful purpose.

**Zinc Chloride**

*For cellulose test with iodine.*

| | |
|---|---|
| Zinc chloride . . . . . . . . | 50 g |
| Distilled water . . . . . . . | 25 ml |

**Zirkle's Fluid**

*For fixation of plant tissue for mitochondria.*

| | |
|---|---|
| Ammonium dichromate . . . | 1.25 g |
| Copper sulphate . . . . . . . | 81 g |
| Potassium dichromate . . . . | 1.25 g |
| Distilled water . . . . . . . | 100 ml |

**Zwemer's Medium ('Glychrogel')**

*For mounting gelatine-embedded sections.*

| | |
|---|---|
| Gelatine (powdered) . . . . | 3 g |
| Distilled water . . . . . . . | 50 ml |

Allow to stand for 2 h in the cold.

Then warm to not more than 60°C.

When the gelatine has dissolved and the liquid is still hot,

*Add:*

| | |
|---|---|
| Glycerol . . . . . . . . . . | 20 ml |

Stir and while it is still hot,

*Add:*

| | |
|---|---|
| Chrome alum . . . . . . . . . | 0.2 g |
| Distilled water . . . . . . . | 30 ml |

Heat to dissolve.

*Add:*

| | |
|---|---|
| Camphor (as preservative) . . | A small piece |

*Note:* For use, melt by warming the container (which, otherwise, should be kept well-stoppered) to 37°C.

**Normal Solutions**

Quantities of certain substances required to make a final volume of one litre of a Normal solution in distilled water

*N.B. Figures are approximate and standardization should be carried out for volumetric work.

| Substance | Formula | No.* of g or ml per litre of Normal solution | Molarity of solution | Comments |
|---|---|---|---|---|
| Acetic acid | $CH_3COOH$ | 58.0 ml | M | Glacial |
| Ammonium chloride | $NH_4Cl$ | 53.5 g | M | |
| Ammonium hydroxide | $NH_4OH$ | 54.0 ml | M | Liquor amm, fort |
| Arsenious oxide | $As_2O_3$ | 49.5 g | M/4 | As reducing agent |
| Barium chloride | $BaCl_2.2H_2O$ | 122.0 g | M/2 | Crystalline salt |
| Citric acid | $C_3H_5O(COOH)_3.H_2O$ | 70.0 g | M/3 | |
| Cupric sulphate | $CuSO_4.5H_2O$ | 249.7 g | M | Eq. wt. for liberation of iodine from KI |
| Ferrous ammonium sulphate | $FeSO_4(NH_4)_2SO_4.6H_2O$ | 392.0 g | M | |
| Hydrochloric acid | $HCl$ | 99.5 ml | M | Conc. acid |
| Iodine | $I_2$ | 126.9 g | M/2 | |
| Lead acetate | $Pb(OCO.CH_3)_2.2H_2O$ | 189.6 g | M/2 | |
| Magnesium sulphate | $MgSO_4.7H_2O$ | 123.0 g | M/2 | Crystalline salt |
| Nitric acid | $HNO_3$ | 63.5 ml | M | Conc. acid |
| Oxalic acid | $H_2C_2O_4.2H_2O$ | 63.0 g | M/2 | |
| Potassium binoxalate | $KHC_2O_4$ | 128.1 g | M | Eq. wt. for acid-alkali reaction |
| Potassium bromate | $KBrO_3$ | 27.83 g | M/6 | Eq. wt. for oxidation-reduction |
| Potassium bromide | $KBr$ | 119.0 g | M | |
| Potassium chlorate | $KClO_3$ | 20.44 g | M/6 | Eq. wt. for oxidation-reduction |
| Potassium dichromate | $K_2Cr_2O_7$ | 49.0 g | M/6 | Eq. wt. for oxidation-reduction |
| Potassium iodate | $KIO_3$ | 35.66 g | M/6 | |
| Potassium iodide | $KI$ | 166.0 g | M | |
| Potassium permanganate | $KMnO_4$ | 31.6 g | M/5 | Used in N/10 or more dil. solns. |
| Potassium persulphate | $K_2S_2O_8$ | 135.2 g | M/2 | Dissolves with difficulty in cold water |
| Potassium tetroxalate | $KHC_2O_4.H_2C_2O_4.2H_2O$ | 84.7 g | M/3 | Eq. wt. for acid-alkali reaction |
| Silver nitrate | $AgNO_3$ | 170.0 g | M | |
| Sodium bicarbonate | $NaHCO_3$ | 84.0 g | M | |
| Sodium borate | $Na_2B_4O_7.10H_2O$ | 190.6 g | M/2 | |
| Sodium carbonate (anhydrous) | $Na_2CO_3$ | 53.0 g | M/2 | |
| Sodium carbonate (crystalline) | $Na_2CO_3.10H_2O$ | 143.0 g | M/2 | Crystalline salt |
| Sodium chloride | $NaCl$ | 58.5 g | M | |
| Sodium hydroxide | $NaOH$ | 40.0 g | M | |
| Sodium oxalate | $Na_2C_2O_4$ | 67.0 g | M/2 | |
| Sodium thiosulphate | $Na_2S_2O_3.5H_2O$ | 248.0 g | M | |
| Succinic acid | $(CH_3)_2(COOH)_2$ | 59.0 g | M/2 | |
| Sulphuric acid | $H_2SO_4$ | 28.0 ml | M/2 | Conc. acid |
| Tartaric acid | $CH(OH)_2(COOH)_2$ | 75.0 g | M/2 | |

## Refractive Indices

*Note:* (i) *To enhance transparency:* Employ mounting media of refractive index *higher* than that of Canada balsam or D.P.X. in xylene.
(ii) *To enhance visibility:* Employ mounting media of refractive index *lower* than that of Canada balsam or D.P.X. in xylene.

| In alphabetical order of substances | | Refractive Indices | | In ascending order of refractive index |
|---|---|---|---|---|
| Air | | 1.000 | 1.000 | Air |
| Albumen (egg) | | 1.350 | 1.323 | Methyl Alcohol |
| Alcohol, *n*-Butyl | | 1.399 | 1.333 | Water, distilled |
| Alcohol, Ethyl | | 1.367 | 1.335 | Sodium Chloride (0.9% aq.) |
| Alcohol, *iso*-Propyl | | 1.377 | 1.343 | Water, sea |
| Alcohol, Methyl | | 1.323 | 1.345 | Eau de Javelle (approx.) |
| Alcohol, Polyvinyl* | | 1.50 | 1.350 | Albumen (egg) |
| Amann's Medium (lacto-phenol)† | | 1.440 | 1.353 | Cytoplasm (living) (approx.) |
| Anilin Oil | | 1.58 | 1.367 | Ethyl Alcohol |
| Apáthy's Gum Syrup | | 1.52 | 1.377 | *iso*-Propyl Alcohol |
| Benzene | | 1.504 | 1.397 | Glycerol (50% aq.) |
| Bergamot Oil | | 1.464 | 1.399 | *n*-Butyl Alcohol |
| α-Bromonaphthalene | | 1.66 | 1.405 | 2 ethoxy ethanol |
| Canada Balsam (solid) | | 1.535 | 1.414 | Lactic Acid |
| Canada Balsam (in xylene) | | 1.524 | 1.415 | Gum Chloral (Faure's) |
| Castor Oil | | 1.49 | 1.420 | Farrants' Medium |
| Cedar Wood Oil (not thickened) | | 1.510 | 1.440 | Amann's Medium (Lacto-phenol)† |
| Cedar Wood Oil (thickened) | | 1.520 | 1.458 | Origanum Oil |
| Cell Constituents (fixed and cleared) | | 1.54 | 1.458 | Polyvinyl Alcohol – Lacto-Phenol*† |
| Chloral Hydrate (solid) | | 1.567 | 1.464 | Bergamot Oil |
| α-Chloronaphthalene | | 1.63 | 1.470 | Turpentine |
| 'Clarite X' | | 1.567 | 1.47 | Glycerol-Jelly |
| Clove Oil | | 1.533 | 1.471 | Liquid Paraffin |
| Creosote (beechwood) | | 1.538 | 1.473 | Olive Oil |
| Cytoplasm (living) | (approx.) | 1.353 | 1.473 | Glycerol (100%) |
| D.P.X. in xylene | | 1.532 | 1.483 | Terpineol |
| Eau de Javelle | (approx.) | 1.345 | 1.484 | 'Euparal' |
| 2 ethoxy ethanol | | 1.405 | 1.49 | Castor Oil |
| 'Euparal' | | 1.484 | 1.497 | Xylene and Toluene |
| Farrants' Medium | | 1.420 | 1.50 | Polyvinyl Alcohol* |
| Faure's Gum Chloral | | 1.415 | 1.504 | Benzene |
| Glass (crown) | | 1.518 | 1.510 | Cedar Wood Oil (not thickened) |
| Glycerol (100%) | | 1.473 | 1.510 | 'Lenzol' (Gurr's) |
| Glycerol (50% aq.) | | 1.397 | 1.510 | Neutral Mountant (Gurr's) |
| Glycerol-Jelly | | 1.47 | 1.511 | 'Mersol' (Flatters and Garnett's) |
| Gum Chloral (Faure's) | | 1.415 | 1.515 | Neutral Mountant (Flatters and Garnett's) |
| Gum Damar | | 1.542 | 1.517 | Methyl Benzoate |
| Gum Syrup (Apáthy's) | | 1.52 | 1.518 | Glass (crown) |
| 'Hyrax' (Hanna) | | 1.822 | 1.520 | Cedar Wood Oil (thickened) |
| Lactic acid | | 1.414 | 1.52 | Gum Syrup (Apáthy's) |
| Lacto-phenol (Amann's Medium)† | | 1.440 | 1.524 | Canada Balsam (in xylene) |
| 'Lenzol' (Gurr's) | | 1.510 | 1.525 | 'Micrex' (in xylene) (Gerrard's) |
| Liquid Paraffin | | 1.471 | 1.53 | Methyl salicylate (Oil of Wintergreen) |
| 'Mersol' (Flatters and Garnett's) | | 1.511 | 1.532 | D.P.X. in xylene |
| Methyl Benzoate | | 1.517 | 1.533 | Clove Oil |
| Methyl salicylate (Oil of Wintergreen) | | 1.53 | 1.535 | Canada Balsam (solid) |
| 'Micrex' (dry) (Gerrard's) | | 1.585 | 1.538 | Creosote (beechwood) |
| 'Micrex' (in xylene) (Gerrard's) | | 1.525 | 1.540 | Tolu Balsam |
| 'Mikrops 163' (Flatters and Garnett's) | | 1.633 | 1.54 | Cell Constituents (fixed and cleared) |
| Neutral Mountant (Flatters and Garnett's) | | 1.515 | 1.54 | Protein (dry) (approx.) |
| Neutral Mountant (Gurr's) | | 1.510 | 1.542 | Gum Damar |
| Olive Oil | | 1.473 | 1.567 | Chloral Hydrate (solid) |
| Origanum Oil | | 1.458 | 1.567 | 'Clarite X' |

| | | |
|---|---|---|
| Paraffin, Liquid | | 1.471 |
| Phenol | | 1.593 |
| Polyvinyl Alcohol — Lacto-phenol*† | | 1.458 |
| Protein (dry) | (approx.) | 1.54 |
| 'Sirax' (dry) | | 1.810 |
| Sodium Chloride (0.9% aq.) | | 1.335 |
| Terpineol | | 1.483 |
| Tolu Balsam | | 1.540 |
| Turpentine | | 1.470 |
| Water, distilled | | 1.333 |
| Water, sea | | 1.343 |
| Wintergreen, Oil of (Methyl salicylate) | | 1.53 |
| Xylene and Toluene | | 1.497 |

| | |
|---|---|
| 1.58 | Anilin Oil |
| 1.585 | 'Micrex' (dry) (Gerrard's) |
| 1.593 | Phenol |
| 1.63 | α-Chloronaphthalene |
| 1.633 | 'Mikrops 163' (Flatters and Garnett's) |
| 1.66 | α-Bromonaphthalene |
| 1.810 | 'Sirax' (dry) |
| 1.822 | 'Hyrax' (Hanna) |

* Refractive Index varies between 1.49 and 1.53 according to the degree of polymerization of the sample of polyvinyl alcohol.

† Refractive Index varies slightly according to the precise composition of the mixture.

# Bibliography


### Algae

CHAPMAN, V. J. (1962). *The Algae*. London: McMillan.
FRITSCH, F. E. (1935; 1945). *The Structure and Reproduction of the Algae*, vol. I; vol. II. Cambridge: University Press.
PRINGSHEIM, E. G. (1964). *Pure Cultures of Algae.* New York & London: Hafner.
WEST, G. S. and FRITSCH, F. E. (1927). *Treatise on the British Freshwater Algae.* Cambridge: University Press.

### Bacteriology

BAKER, F. J. (1967). *Handbook of Bacteriological Technique.* 2nd edn. London: Butterworths.
HAWKER, L. E., and LINTON, A. H. (1971). *Microrganisms, Function Form and Environment.* London: Arnold.
SIROCKIN, G. and CULLIMORE, S. (1969). *Practical Microbiology.* London: McGraw Hill.
STANIER, R.,DOUDOROFF, M. and ADELBERG, E. A. (1971). *General Microbiology.* 3rd edn. London: McMillan.

### Biochemistry

BONNER, J. and VARNER, J. E. (Eds.) (1965). *Plant Biochemistry.* New York and London: Academic Press.
FRUTON, J. S. and SIMMONDS, S. (1958). *General Biochemistry*, 2nd edn. New York and London: Wiley.
MAHLER, H. R. and LORDES, E. H. (1966). *Biological Chemistry.* Harper International.
WALSH, E. O'F. (1968). *Introduction to Biochemistry*, 2nd edn. English Universities Press.
STEELE, C. (1949). *Introduction to Plant Biochemistry*, 2nd edn. London: Bell.
TRACEY, M. V. (1948). *Proteins and Life.* London: Chapman & Hall.

### Botany

CLOWES, F. A. L. and JUNIPER, B. E. (1968). *Plant Cells.* Oxford: Blackwell Scientific Publications.
EAMES, A. J. and McDANIELS, L. H. (1951). *Introduction to Plant Anatomy*, 2nd edn. New York & Maidenhead: McGraw-Hill.
ESAU, K. (1965). *Plant Anatomy.* London: Wiley.
HOWARTH, W. O. and WARNE, L. G. G. (1963). *Practical Botany*, 4th edn. London: University Tutorial Press.
PRIESTLEY, J. H. and SCOTT, L. I. (1964). *Introduction to Botany*, 4th edn. London: Longmans Green.

ROBARDS, A. W. (1970). *Electron microscopy and plant ultrastructure.* London: McGraw-Hill.
WHITE, D. J. B. (1955). Study of plant anatomy. *School Science Review,* **36**, 129, 272.
WIGHT, F. G. (1955). *Practical Botany.* London: Edward Arnold.

**Culture methods**

BERKELEY, C. J. A. (1947). *Practical Plant Anatomy*, rev. edn. London: University Press.
DYBALL, R. H., ed. (1952). *Science Masters' Book.* Series III; Part 3, Biology. London: Murray.
GALTSOFF, P. S. *et al.* (1937). *Culture Methods for Invertebrate Animals.* Ithaca, N.Y.: Comstock.
GROSS, F. (1937). Diatom cultures for rearing marine larvae. *J. Mar. Biol. Ass. U.K.,* **21**, 753.
*Medical Research Council Memorandum* 35 (1958) *National Collection of Type Cultures: Catalogue of Species.* London: H.M.S.O.
*Oxoid Manual of Culture Media* (1962). London: Oxoid Divn. of Oxo Ltd.
PRINGSHEIM, E. G. (1964). *Pure Cultures of Algae.* New York & London: Hafner.
TAYLOR, M. (1952). Recent advances in *Amoeba* lore. *School Science Review,* XXXIV, 122, 106.
TAYLOR, M. (1957). Recent advances in *Amoeba* lore. *School Science Review*, XXXVIII, 136, 184.

**Cytology**

BOURNE, G. H., ed. (1964). *Cytology and Cell Physiology*, 3rd edn. New York & London: Academic Press.
BROWN, W. V. and BERTKE, E. M. (1969). *Textbook of Cytology*. Saint Louis. C.V. Mosby.
DEMEREC, M. and KAUFMAN, B. P. (1961). *Drosophila Guide.* 7th edn. Washington: Carnegie Institution.
De ROBERTIS, E. D. P., NOWINSKI, W. W. and SAEZ, F. A. (1970). *Cell Biology*, 5th edn. Philadelphia. W. B. Saunders.
FAWCETT, D. W. (1966). *The Cell. An atlas of Fine Structure.* Philadelphia: W. B. Saunders.
GILLIE, O. (1971). *The Living Cell.* London: Thames and Hudson.

**Haemocytology**

DARMADY, E. M. and DAVENPORT, S. G. T. (1963). *Haematological Technique,* 3rd edn. London: Churchill.

**Identification, nomenclature, etc.**

*Bibliography of Key Works for the Identification of the British Fauna and Flora* (1942). Association for the Study of Systematics in Relation to Biology. No. 1.

**Microscopy**

BARER, R. (1956). *Lecture Notes on the Use of the Microscope,* 2nd edn. Oxford: Blackwell.
BIRCHON, D. (1961). *Optical Microscope Technique*. London: Newnes.
CASARTELLI, J. D. (1970). *Microscopy for Students*. 2nd edn. London: McGraw-Hill.
DUDDINGTON, C. L. (1960). *Practical Microscopy.* London: Pitman.
HALL, C. A. and LINSSEN, E. F. (1961). *How to Use the Microscope*, 5th edn. London: Black.
McCLUNG, C. E. (1961). *Handbook of Microscopical Techniques,* 3rd edn. rev. by R. McCLUNG JONES. New York & London: Hafner.
MALIES, H. M. (1959). *Applied Microscopy and Photomicrography.* London: Fountain Press.
MARTIN, L. C. and JOHNSON, B. K. (1958). *Practical Microscopy,* 3rd edn. London: Blackie.
MEEK, G. A. (1970). *Practical Electron Microscopy for Biologists.* London: Wiley Inter-Science.
ROSS, K. F. A. (1967). *Phase Contrast and Interference Microscopy for Cell Biologists.* London: Edward Arnold.
SCHENK, R. and KISTLER, G. (1962). *Photomicrography.* Translated by F. BRADLEY. London: Chapman & Hall.
WHITE, G. W. (1966). *Introduction to Microscopy.* London: Butterworths.

**Microtechnique**

ADLAM, G. H. J., ed. (1931). *Science Masters' Book.* Series I; Part 2. London: Murray.
ADLAM, G. H. J., ed. (1936). *Science Masters' Book.* Series II; Part 2. London: Murray.
BAKER, F. J., SILVERTON, R. E. and LUCKCOCK, E. D. (1966). *Introduction to Medical Laboratory Technology.* London: Butterworths.
BAKER, J. R. (1958). *Principles of Biological Microtechnique.* London: Methuen.
BAKER, J. R. (1966). *Cytological Technique,* 5th edn. London: Science Paperbacks and Methuen.
*Biological Stains and Staining Methods*, 2nd edn. (1958). Poole: British Drug Houses.
CASSELMAN, W. G. B. (1959). *Histochemical Technique.* London: Methuen.
CHAMBERLAIN, C. J. (1932). *Methods in Plant Histology.* 5th edn. Chicago: University Press.
CHAYEN, J. and DENBY, E. F. (1968). *Biophysical Technique*. London: Methuen.
CONN, H. J. (1969). *Biological Stains,* 8th edn. rev. R. D. Lillie. Baltimore: Williams and Wilkins.
COWDRY, E. V. (1953). *Laboratory Technique in Biology and Medicine,* 3rd edn. London: Baillière.
CRAMP, A. C. (1947). Elementary algal techniques. *School Science Review,* XXVIII, 105, 224.
DARLINGTON, C. D. and LA COUR, L. F. (1969). *The Handling of Chromosomes.* 5th edn. London: Allen & Unwin.
DYBALL, R. H., ed. (1952). *Science Masters' Book.* Series III; Part 3. London: Murray.
FOWELL, R. R. (1959). *Biology Staining Schedules for First Year Students,* 6th edn. London: Lewis.
GRAY, P. (1955). *Microtomist's Formulary and Guide.* London: Constable.
GRAY, P. (1964). *Handbook of Basic Microtechnique.* New York & Maidenhead: McGraw-Hill.
GURR, E. (1956). *A Practical Manual of Medical and Biological Staining Techniques*, 2nd edn. London: L. Hill.
GURR, G. T. (1952). *Biological Staining Methods.* London: George T. Gurr Ltd.
HASKELL, G. (1961). *Practical Heredity with Drosophila.* Edinburgh: Oliver & Boyd.
HOPWOOD, D. (1969). Fixatives and Fixation. *Histoch. Jnl.* **1**, 323–360.
LEE, A. B. (1950). *Microtomist's Vade-Mecum*, 11th edn., ed. by J. W. GATENBY and H. W. BEAMS. London: Churchill.
LILLIE, R. D. (1965). *Histopathological Technique*. 3rd edn. New York & Maidenhead: McGraw-Hill.
McCLUNG, C. E. (1961). *Handbook of Microscopical Technique*, 3rd edn. rev. by R. McCLUNG JONES. New York & London: Hafner.
MATHER, K. (1953). *Genetics for Schools*. London: Murray.
PANTIN, C. F. A. (1959). *Notes on Microscopical Technique for Zoology.* Cambridge: University Press.
PEARSE, A. G. E. (1968). *Histochemistry*. Vol. 1. 3rd edn. London: Churchill.
RUTHMANN, A. (1970). *Methods in Cell Research*. London: Bell and Sons.
SHAW, G. W. (1959). Modern cytological techniques. *School Science Review*, XLI, 143, 88.
SHAW, G. W. (1960). *Modern Cytological Techniques.* London: Murray.
SHILLITO, J. F. (1948). Some experiments in microbiology. *School Science Review*, XXIX, 108, 213.
SPENCE, T. F. (1967). *Teaching and display techniques in Anatomy and Zoology*. Oxford: Pergamon.
STEEDMAN, H. F. (1960). *Section Cutting in Microscopy*. Oxford: Blackwell.
The 'Teachers Guides' in Biological Science & Chemistry, published for the Nuffield Foundation by Penguin Books are also valuable sources of information.

**Mycology**

AGRIOS, G. N. (1969). *Plant Pathology*. London: Academic Press.
BURNETT, J. H. (1968). *Fundamentals of Mycology*. London: Arnold.
BUTLER, E. J. and JONES, S. G. (1949). *Plant Pathology*, rev. edn. London: Macmillan.
SMITH, G. (1960). *An Introduction to Industrial Mycology*. London: Edward Arnold.

**Preservation of specimens and museum technique**

DOLLMAN, G. (1936). Preservation of museum specimens. *School Science Review*, XVIII, 69, 91.
TOMPSETT, D. H. (1970). *Anatomical Techniques.* 2nd edn. Edinburgh: Livingstone.
WAGSTAFFE, R. and FIDLER, J. H. (1955). *Preservation of Natural History Specimens;* vol. I – *Invertebrates.* London: Witherby.

**Protozoa**

JEPPS, M. W. (1956). *The Protozoa Sarcodina.* Edinburgh: Oliver & Boyd.
KUDO, R. R. (1954). *Protozoology,* 4th edn. Oxford: Blackwell.
MACKINNON, D. L. and HAWES, R. S. J. (1961). *An introduction to the study of Protozoa.* Oxford.

# Index

The index is divided into two sections. The first lists organisms, techniques and the names of substances of interest in microtechnique; the second part is an index of chemicals, dyes and their chief synonyms.

## Index of organisms and techniques

The generic names of organisms are printed in italics.

## Index of chemicals, dyes and synonyms

Synonyms are given in *italic* type.
Page number of chief references are given in **bold** type.
Preferred designations are given in **bold** type.
The abbreviation *'c/s t'* following the name of a stain indicates that the first named dye is used as a counterstain to the primary stain whose name is given immediately after the abbreviation; *'c/s w'*, on the other hand, signifies that the first named dye is the primary stain and that the dye named *after* the abbreviation is the counterstain.